A GUIDE TO **FORTRAN IV** PROGRAMMING

McCracken (D. D.)—

A Guide to FORTRAN Programming

A Guide to IBM 1401 Programming

A Guide to ALGOL Programming

A Guide to COBOL Programming

A Guide to FORTRAN IV Programming

Digital Computer Programming

McCracken (D. D.), Weiss (H.) and Lee (T. H.)—

Programming Business Computers

Gruenberger (Fred) and McCracken (D. D.)

Introduction to Electronic Computers: Problem

Solving with the IBM 1620

McCracken (D. D.) and Dorn (W. S.)—

Numerical Methods and Fortran Programming

DANIEL D. McCRACKEN
McCRACKEN ASSOCIATES, INC.

a guide to
FORTRAN IV
programming

JOHN WILEY & SONS, INC., NEW YORK · LONDON · SYDNEY

PREFACE

This book is written for the person who wants to get a rapid grasp of the use of a computer in the solution of problems in science and engineering. The essentials of FORTRAN IV are presented here in a form that can be mastered in a few hours of careful reading and practice.

It is anticipated that the book will be helpful in a variety of situations.

1. It can be used as the text for a course in engineering, science, or mathematics. One semester hour would be more than adequate to cover the material and allow the students time to run several practice problems and a sizable term problem.

2. It can be used as the text for a supplement to some other course. Covering the fundamentals of FORTRAN will take only a few hours and this "lost" time will in many cases be more than recovered by improved learning of the primary subject matter.

3. Students in an industrial course in FORTRAN programming will find the book useful as an elaboration of the necessarily rather terse descriptions contained in most FORTRAN manuals and as a guide to the many ways in which FORTRAN can be applied to the solution of realistic problems.

4. The book is suitable for individual study in school or industry.

In all cases the value of the book is enhanced by the inclusion of a large number of graded exercises, with answers to a selected set. These exercises induce thorough mastery of the fundamentals and provide an insight into methods and applications that often go considerably beyond those presented in the text.

Of particular importance are the 15 case studies, which show the application of FORTRAN in the context of meaningful applications; they demonstrate how to go about setting up a program; they show how the program actually works by reproducing real computer output from test runs. One case study is the medium for a discussion of program checkout.

The FORTRAN IV language described here is intended to be in compliance with the FORTRAN language proposed as a standard by the American Standards Association X3.4.3 FORTRAN Working Group, although for clarity no attempt has been made to discuss every feature of the proposed standard. Appendix 1 provides a comparison of ASA FORTRAN and various actual languages, which make it possible to use this book in conjunction with any actual language.

It is a pleasure to acknowledge the many and varied contributions of Mary Anne K. Angell of the International Business Machines Corporation, Fred Gruenberger of The RAND Corporation, George Armerding of Scientific Data Systems, William J. Eccles of the University of South Carolina, Evan Confrey of the Hartford State Technical Institute, Allan Collister of San Jose State College, Henry Mullish of the Courant Institute of Mathematical Sciences at New York University, and Barbara Lesser of the Computer Usage Company. Bob Matsil of the Service Bureau Corporation assisted in the testing and running of the programs in the text.

DANIEL D. McCRACKEN
Ossining, New York
August 1965

CONTENTS

1. FUNDAMENTALS OF FORTRAN COMPUTATION

1.1 The Application of Computers

Electronic computers are widely used in the solution of the problems of science, engineering, and business. This use is based on their ability to operate at great speed, to produce accurate results, to store large quantities of information, and to carry out long and complex sequences of operations without human intervention.

In this book we shall concentrate on the scientific and engineering applications of computers, typified by work of the following sorts. The design of a new airplane consumes thousands of hours of computer time in the investigation of the interrelated requirements of structures, aerodynamics, powerplants, and control systems, as they would operate under numerous flight conditions. The design of a chemical plant depends on calculations of capacities, operating conditions, and yields, under a variety of circumstances. The design of an electric transmission line calls for a study of the electrical loads that would be imposed on different sections of the line as the consumption changed and as unusual conditions developed.

It may be noted in this sampling that the computer does not solve the problem. Instead, it helps to explore alternatives. We do not ask the computer, "How shall we build this new device?" but rather, "How would the device work under this set of conditions if we built it this way?" There are many ways in which the equipment could be built; there are vari-ous operating conditions to consider, and there are several different and even conflicting goals to be balanced. The computer *cannot* enumerate the design considerations, specify the operating conditions to be investigated, or determine the goals or the tradeoffs among the conflicting goals. It *can* usually offer us great assistance in predicting the consequences of *our* choices in these matters.

1.2 The Steps in Solving a Problem with a Computer

There is much more to solving a problem with a computer than the work the computer does. It will be instructive to outline the complete process of setting up a typical scientific or engineering problem for computer solution to see just what the human does and what the computer does.

Problem identification and goal definition. This is a question of choosing a general approach, deciding what combinations of goals the system must satisfy, and specifying the conditions under which it will be required to operate. In some applications this is simple; in others it may take months. In any case, the step clearly demands a full knowledge of the problem; there is generally little the computer can do to help us.

Mathematical description. There are, as a rule, several ways to describe a process mathematically; one must be chosen or a new one developed if no standard method applies. This step requires full knowledge of the problem and the relevant fields of mathematics.

Numerical analysis. The mathematical formulation of the problem may not be directly translatable to the language of the computer, since the computer can only do arithmetic and make simple quantitative decisions. Trigonometric functions, differential equations, integrals, square roots, and logarithms, to name a few common examples, must be expressed in terms of arithmetic operations. Furthermore, it must be established that any errors inherent in the data or introduced by the computations do not invalidate the results.

This entire branch of modern mathematics is outside the scope of this book. We shall assume that the reader will approach the computer with his problem expressed in terms that are suitable for computer solution.

Computer programming. The numerical procedure must now be stated as a precisely defined set of computer operations. There are usually two steps to this part. In the first the sequence of operations is written in graphical form in a *flowchart*. The procedure must then be stated in a "language" that can be "understood" by the computer or that can be understood after a preliminary translation stage. FORTRAN is such a language.

In other words, we ordinarily draw a flowchart of the method of solution; this diagram is valuable to *us* as a clear outline of what we want to do, but it cannot be understood by the computer. Then, using the flowchart as a guide, we write a FORTRAN program, which will be understandable to the machine after completion of the preliminary translation phase that is discussed later.

The objective of this book is to teach the reader how to write procedures in the FORTRAN language.

Program checkout. There are so many chances to make mistakes in programming that most programs do not work correctly when first tried. The mistakes must be located and the program thoroughly tested to establish that it will perform as intended. The computer is used during this step.

Production. Now, finally, the program can be combined with problem data and run. In a typical situation many sets of data are entered into the computer in one "run," and answers are produced without human intervention between sets. This step

may take a few seconds to many hours, depending on the problem and the computer.

Interpretation. As we have noted, the results printed by the computer do not always constitute a final answer to the problem. The user of the computer must interpret the results to see what they mean in terms of the combinations of goals that the proposed system must satisfy. It is often necessary to repeat some or all of the preceding steps before the problem is really solved.

Several conclusions may be drawn from this discussion. First, the computer does not, by itself, solve problems; it only follows carefully defined computational procedures. Second, a computer does not relieve the user of the responsibility of planning the work carefully; in fact, the computer demands much more careful planning. The computer is faster and more accurate than a human, but it cannot decide how to proceed or what to do with the results. Third, a computer does not in any way reduce the need for a full and detailed understanding of the problem area or for a thorough knowledge of the related mathematics.

As we have already suggested, the emphasis in this book is on one of the middle steps: programming. Problem identification, goal definition, and mathematical formulation are in the province of the technical area under consideration, whatever it may be: electrical engineering, physics, statistics, or operations research. Numerical analysis is a branch of modern mathematics in its own right. Program checkout is discussed briefly; production is a relatively simple matter of running the computer; and interpretation of results is once again back into the problem area.

We take it, then, that the reader will approach the subject of this book with a full understanding of his problem and its mathematical formulation. We assume further that he has translated the mathematical statement into a series of arithmetic steps, that is, that the numerical analysis has been done. We shall show the reader how to translate the numerical procedure into a correct computer program and then leave him to make intelligent use of the results.

The summary of the steps in using a computer has been presented in terms of problems in engineering and science to make the description simpler. Of course, a wide variety of computer applications exists in other fields, ranging from business-data processing and automatic control of satellites to medical diagnosis and language translation. In other fields some of the steps we have outlined would naturally be different, but the general pattern is similar.

1.3 A FORTRAN Program

A procedure for solving a problem with FORTRAN consists of a series of *statements*, which are of several types. One specifies the arithmetic operations that are the heart of the procedure. A second calls for input or output, such as reading a data card, printing a line of results, or punching a card of results. Statements of these first two types are executed in the order in which they are written; a third type of statement alters the *flow of control* of statement execution, so that groups of statements can be executed repeatedly or the sequence otherwise changed. The fourth type of statement provides certain information *about* the procedure without itself requiring any computation.

Taken together, all the statements that specify the problem-solving procedure constitute a *source program*. When the source program has been written and punched onto cards, it is converted by a FORTRAN *compiler* into an *object program*. This is a set of elementary instructions that the computer can "understand": add two numbers, compare two numbers for equality, or print a line, for example. The translation from the source program to the object program is required because the language of FORTRAN is much more sophisticated than the language of the machine's instructions. It is the object program that is actually executed by the computer to obtain results.

The word FORTRAN thus refers both to a language for expressing problem-solving procedures and to a compiler. The FORTRAN compiler, which is also called a *processor* or *translator*, is itself a large program of computer instructions; the compiler is usually supplied by the computer manufacturer. It was this translation aspect that led to the original meaning of the word FORTRAN: FORmula TRANslation.

FORTRAN has gone through a steady process of evolution since its introduction in the mid-fifties. In this book we deal exclusively with what is now called FORTRAN-IV (FORTRAN-FOUR). We shall not, however, write the word with the identifying number, nor shall we point out the differences between FORTRAN-IV and other versions.

We turn now to a study of the elements of which statements are composed: constants, variables, operations, expressions, and functions. After a study of these basic language units, we shall learn how to combine them into statements, and we shall then be able to write some simple programs.

1.4 Constants

We begin by considering two of the kinds of numbers that can be used in FORTRAN: *integer* and *real*.

A FORTRAN integer is just what it says: a whole number. It may be zero or any positive or negative number of less than about ten decimal digits. The limits on the size of an integer vary from computer to computer. Appendix 1 provides this information for a number of versions of FORTRAN. Because integers are restricted to integral values, they are ordinarily used only in special situations, as we shall see later.

Most numbers used in FORTRAN computations are real. Inside the computer FORTRAN real numbers are represented in *floating point* form. This is similar to scientific notation, in which a number is treated as a fraction between 0.1 and 1.0 times a power of 10. The *magnitude* (sign not considered) of the number so represented must be zero or lie between limits in the range of approximately 10^{-40} to 10^{+40}. Again, the exact limits vary; see Appendix 1 for various versions of FORTRAN.

A FORTRAN integer is always an integer in the mathematical sense, whereas a FORTRAN real number may be an integer or have a fractional part. Furthermore, FORTRAN carries out computations on real numbers in such a way that we do not have to be concerned with the location of decimal points. All questions of lining up decimal points before addition or subtraction, etc., are automatically taken care of by the computer.

A FORTRAN real number is a rational real number in the mathematical sense. Irrational numbers are not permitted; they can only be approximated to some degree of precision. Indeed, not all rational numbers can be represented exactly in FORTRAN; the simple fraction $\frac{1}{3}$, for instance, can only be approximated as a decimal fraction.

(FORTRAN provides another kind of number, called *double precision*, to improve the accuracy of approximation. We shall postpone consideration of this type of number, however, so that we may write a complete program as quickly as possible. For the same reason we postpone discussion of the other two FORTRAN quantities: complex and logical. These additional types will be taken up in Chapter 3.)

Any number that appears in a statement in explicit form is called a *constant*, whereas a quantity that is given a name and is allowed to vary is a *variable*. For instance, we shall see a little later that the following are arithmetic assignment statements:

$$I = 2$$

$$X = A + 12.7$$

Here 2 and 12.7 are constants; *I*, *X*, and *A* are variables.

FORTRAN distinguishes between real and integer constants by the presence or absence of a decimal point, respectively. Thus 3 is an integer constant, but 3.0 (3., 3.0000, etc.) is a real constant. The two forms are *not* interchangeable because they are ordinarily stored and processed within the computer in entirely different ways.

If a constant is positive, it may or may not be preceded by a plus sign, as desired. If it is negative, it must be preceded by a minus sign. The following are acceptable integer constants:

0	−1234
6	10000
+400	−20000

The following are not acceptable integer constants:

12.78 (decimal point not allowed in integer)
−10,000 (comma not allowed)
123456789000 (too large in most versions)

The decimal point that characterizes a real constant may appear at the beginning of a number, at the end, or between any two digits. A real constant is permitted to have any number of digits, but only about eight digits of significance are retained by the computer. In other words, although there is no restriction on the number of digits in a real constant, it makes little sense to use more than the eight or nine significant digits that will be retained in most versions of FORTRAN.

It is possible to follow a real constant by the letter E and a one- or two-digit positive or negative integer power of 10 by which the number is to be multiplied. The power of 10 is then called the *exponent* of the constant. This simplifies the writing of very large or very small numbers. The following are acceptable real constants:

0.0	+15.016	
6.0	5.0E + 6	$(= 5.0 \times 10^6)$
6.	−7.E − 12	$(= -7.0 \times 10^{-12})$
−20000.	6.205E12	$(= 6.205 \times 10^{12})$
−.0002784	−.1E7	$(= 0.1 \times 10^7)$

The following are not acceptable real constants:

12,345.6	(comma not allowed)
+234	(no decimal point)
1.6E81	(too large in most versions)
1E − 7	(no decimal point)
5.863E2.5	(exponent part must be an integer)
E + 5	(exponent alone not permitted)

EXERCISES

***1.** Write the following numbers as FORTRAN real constants.

256 2.56 −43,000 10^{12} 0.000000492 −10 -10^{-16}

2. Write the following as FORTRAN real constants.

16 4.59016 −10,000 10^{17} 0.000006 −1 -10^{-10}

***3.** All of the following are unacceptable as real constants. Why?

87,654.3   +987   9.2E + 87   7E − 9

4. All of the following are unacceptable as real constants. Why?

−100,000   1E − 55   2.379427 − E12   2E + 5.1

***5.** Do the following pairs of real constants represent the same number in each case?

a. 16.9   +16.9
b. 23000.   2.3E4
c. 0.000007 .7E − 5
d. 1.0   1.
e. .906E5   +906.0E + 2

***6.** Some of the following are unacceptable as integer constants. Identify the errors.

+234 −234. 23,400 1E12 +1000000000000 +10000

7. Some of the following are unacceptable as integer constants. Identify the errors.

−16.5   16000   16,000.   2.E12.5   0.01

1.5 Variables and the Names of Variables

The term *variable* is used in FORTRAN to denote any quantity that is referred to by name rather than by explicit appearance. A variable is able to take on many values during the execution of a program, whereas a constant is restricted to just one value.

* Answers to starred exercises are given at the back of the book.

Variables may be integer or real. An integer variable is one that may take on any of the values permitted for an integer constant, namely, zero or any positive or negative integer in the range permitted for a particular version of FORTRAN.

The *name* of an integer variable has one to six letters or digits, the first of which is I, J, K, L, M, or N. (The limit of six letters or digits is typical but may be different in some versions.) Examples of acceptable names of integer variables: I, KLM, MATRIX, L123, I6M2K, KAPPA. Examples of unacceptable names of integer variables: J123456 (too many characters), ABC (does not begin with the correct letter), 5M (does not begin with a letter), $J78 (contains a character other than a letter or digit), J34.5 (contains a character other than a letter or digit).

A real variable is represented inside the computer in the same form as a real constant, that is, as a fraction times a power of 10. The *name* of a real variable has one to six letters or digits, the first of which is a letter but *not* I, J, K, L, M, or N. As might be suspected, the FORTRAN compiler uses the first letter of a variable name to determine whether the variable is integer or real. This convention can be overridden, however, with the type-statements REAL and INTEGER that we shall consider in Chapter 3. For now, and in any case in the absence of type-statements, the distinction between integer and real variable names is made on the basis of the first letter.

Examples of acceptable names of real variables: AVAR, R51TX, FRONT, G, F0009, SVECT, AMATRX. Examples of unacceptable names of real variables: A123456 (contains too many characters), 8BOX (does not begin with a letter), KJL1 (does not begin with the correct letter), *BCD (contains a character other than a letter or a digit), A + B (contains a character other than a letter or a digit).

The assignment of names to the variables appearing in a program is entirely under the control of the programmer. Care must be taken to observe the rule for distinguishing between the names of integer and real variables, but most people learn fairly readily to avoid this pitfall. If the rule is violated, the FORTRAN compiler will generally signal the error and not compile the source program into an object program; in a few cases the error cannot be positively identified as an error, and the program will give incorrect results.

It should be noted that the compiler places no significance on names beyond inspecting the first letter to establish whether the variable is integer or real (and not even that, if type-statements are used). A name such as B7 specifically does *not* mean B times 7, B to the seventh power, or B_7. Most programmers assign variable names that simplify recall of the meaning of the variable, but no such meaning is attached by the FORTRAN system. It should also be noted that every combination of letters and digits is a separate name. Thus the name ABC is not the same as BAC, and A, AB, and AB8 are all distinct.

EXERCISES

*1. Which of the following are acceptable names for integer variables (in the absence of a type statement), which are acceptable names for real variables (in the absence of a type statement), and which are unacceptable names for *any* variable? G, GAMMA, GAMMA421, I, IJK, IJK*, J79–12, LARGE, R(2)19, BTO7TH, ZSQUARED, ZCUBED, 12AT7, 2N173, CDC160, DELTA, KAPPA, EPSILON, A1.4, A1P4, FORTRAN, ALGOL.

2. Same as Exercise 1. K, I12G, CAT, X + 2, XP2, NEXT, 42G, LAST, MU, A*B, X1.4, (X61), GAMMA-81, AI, IA, X12, 1X2, GAMMA, KAPPA, XSQUARED, IBM7094, IBM360, COBOL.

1.6 Operations and Expressions

FORTRAN provides five basic arithmetic operations: addition, subtraction, multiplication, division, and exponentiation. Each of these operations is represented by a distinct symbol:

Addition	+
Subtraction	—
Multiplication	*
Division	/
Exponentiation	**

Note that the combination ** is considered to be one symbol; there is no confusion between ** and *, because, as we shall see, it is never correct to write two operation symbols side by side. These are the only mathematical operations allowed; any others must be built up from the basic five or computed by using the functions that are discussed later.

A FORTRAN expression is a rule for computing a numerical value. In many cases an expression consists of a single constant, a single variable, or a single function reference (as described in Section 1.7). Two or more of these elements may be combined, by using operation symbols and parentheses, to build up more complex expressions. Some ex-

TABLE 1.1

Expression	Meaning
K	The value of the integer variable K
3.14159	The value of the real constant 3.14159
A + 2.1828	The sum of the value of A and 2.1828
RHO − SIGMA	The difference in the values of RHO and SIGMA
X*Y	The product of the values of X and Y
OMEGA/6.2832	The quotient of the value of OMEGA and 6.2832
C**2	The value of C raised to the second power (C^2)
(A + F)/(X + 2.0)	The sum of the values of A and F divided by the sum of the value of X and 2.0
1./(X**2 + Y**3)	The reciprocal of $(X^2 + Y^3)$

amples of expressions and their meanings are given in Table 1.1.

In writing expressions, the programmer must observe certain rules to convey his intentions correctly.

1. Two operation symbols must never appear next to each other. Thus A* − B is not a valid expression, although A*(−B) is.

2. Parentheses must be used to indicate groupings just as in ordinary mathematical notation. Thus $(X + Y)^3$ must be written (X + Y)**3 to convey the correct meaning; X + Y**3 would be a valid expression, but, of course, the meaning is not the same. Again, $A − B + C$ and $A − (B + C)$ are both legitimate expressions, but the meanings are different. Parentheses force the *inner* operation to be done first as in ordinary mathematical notation.

3. The ambiguous expression A^{B^C} must be written as A**(B**C) or (A**B)**C, whichever is intended, but never as A**B**C. (And there *is* a difference. For instance, $(2^2)^3 = 4^3 = 64$, but $2^{(2^3)} = 2^8 = 256$.)

4. When the hierarchy of operations in an expression is not completely specified by the use of parentheses, the sequence is as follows: all exponentiations are performed first, then all multiplications and divisions, and finally all additions and subtractions. Thus these two expressions are equivalent:

a. A*B + C/D − E**F
b. (A*B) + (C/D) − (E**F)

5. Within a sequence of consecutive multiplications and/or divisions or additions and/or subtractions, in which the order of the operations is not completely specified by parentheses, the meaning is that of a left-to-right evaluation. Thus the expression A/B*C would be taken to mean $\dfrac{A}{B} \cdot C$ not

$\dfrac{A}{B \cdot C}$ and I − J + K means $(I − J) + K$, not $I − (J + K)$.

6. Any expression may be raised to a power that is a positive- or negative-integer quantity, but only a real expression may be raised to a real power. An exponent may itself be any expression of real or integer type. Thus X**(I + 2) is perfectly acceptable. In no case, however, is it permissible to raise a negative value to a real power or to raise zero to the zero power.

7. Integer and real quantities must not be *mixed* in the same expression, except that a real quantity may be raised to an integer power.

8. Parentheses in an expression indicate grouping. (They also have other uses for entirely different purposes, as we shall see later.) Specifically, they do not imply multiplication. Thus the expression (A + B)(C + D) is incorrect; it should be written (A + B)*(C + D).

Table 1.2 lists some examples of correct and incorrect ways of forming FORTRAN expressions.

These rules are important for a number of reasons. For one, it is necessary to convey the programmer's intentions correctly. Just as in ordinary mathematical notation, the expression A*(B + C) *must* be written with parentheses. For a second reason, some things are impossible because of the way the computer and the compiler operate. An integer cannot be raised to a real power because, in general, the result would have a fractional part which cannot be expressed in integer form. Integer and real quantities cannot be mixed in most versions of FORTRAN because arithmetic on the two types of numbers is often done in quite different ways.

The third reason for following these rules is less

TABLE 1.2

Mathematical Notation	Correct Expression	Incorrect Expression
$a \cdot b$	A*B	AB (no operation)
$a \cdot (-b)$	A*(−B) or −A*B	A* − B (two operations side by side)
$a + 2$	A + 2.0	A + 2 (mixed integer and real)
$-(a + b)$	−(A + B) or −A − B	−A + B or −+A + B
a^{i+2}	A**(I + 2)	A**I + 2 (= a^i + 2, and is mixed integer and real)
$a^{b+2} \cdot c$	A**(B + 2.0)*C	A**B + 2.0*C (= a^b + 2·c)
$\dfrac{a \cdot b}{c \cdot d}$	A*B/(C*D) or A/C*B/D	A*B/C*D $\left(= \dfrac{a \cdot b}{c} \cdot d \right)$
$\left(\dfrac{a + b}{c} \right)^{2.5}$	((A + B)/C)**2.5	(A + B)/C**2.5 $\left(= \dfrac{a + b}{c^{2.5}} \right)$
$a[x + b(x + c)]$	A*(X + B*(X + C))	A(X + B(X + C)) (missing operators)
$\dfrac{a}{1 + \dfrac{b}{(2.7 + c)}}$	A/(1.0 + B/(2.7 + C))	A/(1.0 + B/2.7 + C)

obvious: arithmetic operations with fractions of finite length do not obey all the normal rules of arithmetic exactly. For an example of what can happen, assume that we are working with an eight-digit system and consider this expression:

$$0.40000000 + 12345678. − 12345677.$$

If this is evaluated from left to right, the result of the addition, to eight figures, is just 12345678.; the 0.4 has been lost entirely. Then, when the 12345677. is subtracted, the final result is 1.0000000.

Suppose, on the other hand, that the expression had been written

$$0.40000000 + (12345678. − 12345677.)$$

The parentheses force the subtraction to be done first, giving 1.0000000. Now when the 0.40000000 is added, the result is 1.4000000. In other words, in the original form the addition of a small and a large number caused a complete loss of significance in the small number.

The order of arithmetic operations can lead not only to loss of significance but also to a failure to get any answer, as the following example shows. Suppose we wanted to evaluate the expression A*B/C, in which the values of A, B, and C are all in the neighborhood of 10^{30}. The multiplication is done first, as the expression has been written, giving 10^{60}. This is too large for a real variable in most versions of FORTRAN. The final result after the division, 10^{30}, would be within allowable limits, but the intermediate result is not. Since the computer cannot represent the intermediate result, it

would either stop executing the program or give a completely erroneous answer, depending on how the particular computer is built to operate.

The simple solution is to use parentheses to force the division to be done first: A*(B/C). The result of the division is a number within the allowable range, and so is the final result.*

Integer division raises a special problem of its own. When two integers are divided, the quotient is not usually an integer. Integer division is arranged to *truncate* a quotient having a fractional part to the next smaller integer, which means simply to ignore any fractional part. Thus the result of the integer division 5/3 is 1, not 2.

As it happens, most calculations do not require integer division, but it might be well to point out the precautions that should be observed if it is needed. Consider the integer expression 5/3*6. Rule 5 says that the division will be done first; thus the truncated result is 1; this is multiplied by 6 to give 6 as the final answer. The result is *not* 10, which we would get from multiplying 5 by 6 first and then dividing by 3, or 12, which we would get if the quotient were rounded instead of truncated. On the other hand, if the expression is written as 5*6/3, 6*5/3, 5*(6/3), or (6/3)*5, the result is 10.

* This discussion assumes that rule 5 on page 6 is universally followed, which unfortunately is not quite true. Some compilers instead take advantage of the associative and commutative rules. In this case we cannot really say what the sequence of operations will be in an expression like $A + B + C$; it might be as in $(A + B) + C$, as specified by rule 5, or it might be as in $A + (B + C)$. *When in doubt, parenthesize.*

All of this applies only to integer arithmetic. Any of the forms in the preceding paragraph, if written with real constants, would give 10.000000 (with perhaps one incorrect digit in the last place; see the next paragraph).

Even in real arithmetic, however, things can happen that might not be expected. Suppose we were to form this sum:

$$1.0/3.0 + 1.0/3.0 + 1.0/3.0$$

The real representation of 1.0/3.0, using floating point decimal fractions, is 0.33333333, to eight digits. The result of the additions, then, is 0.99999999. If we were to write a program that compared this actual sum with the expected result of 1.0000000, the answer, of course, would be "not equal." This might come as something of a shock to the unsuspecting programmer.

These problems are not insuperable, and some of them are not actually so different from things that can happen when working with paper and pencil or desk calculator. With a computer, however, we sometimes have to take special measures to *anticipate* such difficulties, for by the time the computer has begun to run the program we have become bystanders.

EXERCISES

1. Write FORTRAN expressions corresponding to each of the following mathematical expressions.

*a. $x + y^3$

b. $(x + y)^3$

c. x^4

*d. $a + \dfrac{b}{c}$

e. $\dfrac{a + b}{c}$

*f. $a + \dfrac{b}{c + d}$

g. $\dfrac{a + b}{c + d}$

*h. $\left(\dfrac{a + b}{c + d}\right)^2 + x^2$

i. $\dfrac{a + b}{c + \dfrac{d}{e + f}}$

*j. $1 + x + \dfrac{x^2}{2!} + \dfrac{x^3}{3!}$

*k. $\left(\dfrac{x}{y}\right)^{g-1}$

l. $\dfrac{\dfrac{a}{b} - 1}{g\left(\dfrac{g}{d} - 1\right)}$

2. Following are a number of mathematical expressions and corresponding FORTRAN expressions, each of which contains at least one error. Point out the errors and write the correct expressions.

a. $(x + y)^4$ X + Y**4

*b. $\dfrac{x + 2}{y + 4}$ X + 2.0/Y + 4.0

c. $\dfrac{a \cdot b}{c + 2}$ AB/(C + 2.)

d. $-\dfrac{(-x + y - 16)}{y^3}$ −(−X + Y − 16)/ Y**3

*e. $\left(\dfrac{x + a + \pi}{2z}\right)^2$ (X + A + 3.1415927)/ (2.0*Z)**2

f. $\left(\dfrac{x}{y}\right)^{n-1}$ (X/Y)**N − 1

*g. $\left(\dfrac{x}{y}\right)^{r-1}$ (X/Y)**(R − 1)

h. $\dfrac{a}{b} + \dfrac{c \cdot d}{f \cdot g \cdot h}$ A/B + CD/FGH

i. $(a + b)(c + d)$ A + B*C + D

j. $a + bx + cx^2 + dx^3$ which can be rewritten $a + x[b + x(c + dx)]$ A + X(B + X (C + DX)

k. $\dfrac{1{,}600{,}042X + 10^5}{4{,}309{,}992X + 10^5}$ (1,600,042X + 1E5)/ (4,309,992X + 1E5)

l. $\dfrac{1}{a^2}\left(\dfrac{r}{10}\right)^a$ 1/A**2*(R/10)**A

1.7 Mathematical Functions

FORTRAN provides for the use of certain common mathematical functions, such as square root, logarithm, exponential, sine, cosine, arctangent, and absolute value. The exact list of functions available depends on the version of FORTRAN being used and to a certain extent on the particular computer installation. All FORTRAN systems have the functions named.

Every function has a preassigned name. These we shall use and their names are given in Table 1.3.

In order to make use of a mathematical function,

it is necessary only to write its name and follow it with an expression enclosed in parentheses. This directs FORTRAN to compute the named function of the value represented by the expression in parentheses.

TABLE 1.3

Mathematical Function	FORTRAN NAME
Exponential	EXP
Natural logarithm	ALOG
Common logarithm	ALOG10
Sine of an angle in radians	SIN
Cosine of an angle in radians	COS
Hyperbolic tangent	TANH
Square root	SQRT
Arctangent; angle computed in radians	ATAN
Absolute value	ABS

As an example, suppose it is necessary to compute the cosine of an angle named X. This angle must be expressed in radians. Writing COS(X) in a statement will result in the computation of the cosine of the angle. In this example the *argument* of the function is the single variable X. The argument is not limited to a single variable but may in fact be *any* expression, subject to the restriction that in all the mathematical functions in Table 1.3 the argument must be a real quantity and the functional value is computed in real form. If, for example, we wanted the square root of $b^2 - 4ac$, we could simply write SQRT(B**2 − 4.0*A*C).

Appendix 3 contains a complete list of the functions that are ordinarily supplied with any FORTRAN compiler, including functions that have arguments and/or function values of other types than real. We shall see examples of functions involving double precision and complex values in later chapters.

1.8   Arithmetic Assignment Statements

The basic FORTRAN language elements we have discussed so far have many applications in writing source programs. The most important is computing a new value of a variable, which is done with an *arithmetic assignment statement*. Its general form is $a = b$, in which a is a variable name, written without a sign, and b is any expression, as already described. An arithmetic assignment statement is an order to FORTRAN to compute the value of the expression on the right and to give that value to the variable named on the left.

The equal sign in an arithmetic assignment statement is not used as it is in ordinary mathematical notation. We are not allowed to write statements such as $Z − RHO = ALPHA + BETA$, in which Z is unknown and the others are known. The only legitimate form of arithmetic assignment statement is one in which the left side of the statement is the name of a single variable. The precise meaning of the equal sign is then: *replace the value of the variable named on the left with the value of the expression on the right*. Thus the statement $A = B + C$ is an order to form the sum of the values of the variables B and C and to replace the value of the variable A with the sum. The preceding value of A is lost, but the values of the variables B and C are unchanged. It could well be that other parts of the program change the values of B and C during the execution of the program; when we say "the value of the variable B," we always mean *the value most recently assigned to the variable named B*.

Another example of an arithmetic assignment statement brings out very forcefully the special meaning of the equal sign. A statement such as $N = N + 1$ has the meaning: *replace the value of the variable N with its old value plus 1*. This sort of statement, which is clearly not an equation, finds frequent use.

Although mixed arithmetic is not permitted in an expression, it is possible to convert between integer and real forms by writing an expression of one type on the right and a variable of the other type on the left. If we write an integer expression on the right and a real variable on the left, for instance, all the arithmetic will be done in integers, but the result will be converted to floating point (real) form before giving the computed value to the variable on the left.

A few examples may help to clarify the uses of arithmetic assignment statements. Suppose the values of A, B, C, D, and X have already been established by preceding statements and that we need to compute a new value of R from

$$R = \frac{A + BX}{C + DX}$$

This statement will do what is required:

$$R = (A + B*X)/(C + D*X)$$

None of the variables on the right will be changed by the statement; the previous value of R will be lost.

Suppose we need to compute one of the roots of the quadratic equation $AX^2 + BX + C = 0$. Once again, A, B, and C would have to have been given values by previous assignment statements or by having had values read by using the READ statement described in the next section. This statement would call for the required calculation and would assign the computed value to the variable ROOT1:

ROOT1 = (−B + SQRT(B**2−4.0*A*C))/(2.0*A)

It might be well to review the purposes of the parentheses here. Those enclosing B**2 − 4.0*A*C are required to enclose the argument of the square-root function. The parentheses around the numerator in the expression indicate that everything before the slash is to be divided by what follows. The parentheses enclosing the 2.0*A indicate that the A is in the denominator; without this final set the action would be to divide the numerator by 2 and then multiply the entire fraction by A.

A final example shows how the argument of a function can be another function, if desired. Suppose we need to compute the value of V from

$$V = \frac{1}{\cos X} + \log \left| \tan \frac{X}{2} \right|$$

Since we have no function to compute a tangent, we must use a trignometric identity:

$$\tan \theta = \frac{\sin \theta}{\cos \theta}$$

The statement to compute V could then be as follows:

V = 1.0/COS(X)
    + ALOG(ABS(SIN(X/2.0)/COS(X/2.0)))

It would be perfectly permissible to use intermediate variables here, perhaps making the computation easier to follow in reading the source program:

    Y = X/2.0
    TAN = SIN(Y)/COS(Y)
    ABSVAL = ABS(TAN)
    V = 1.0/COS(X) + ALOG(ABSVAL)

In a group of statements like this the computer carries out the statements in the order in which they appear. This sequential execution is always followed, unless we explicitly order the computer to follow some other sequence, which we can do with the GO TO and IF statements discussed in Chapter 2 on transfer of control.

The examples in Table 1.4 show acceptable arithmetic assignment statements with equivalent mathematical forms. Variable names have been chosen arbitrarily; any other legitimate names would have been just as good. We are assuming, of course, that previous statements have established values of all variables on the right-hand side.

The examples in Table 1.5 are presented to emphasize the importance of writing expressions and statements in the exact prescribed format, because FORTRAN demands exact adherence to the rules. Each of the statements in Table 1.5 contains at least one error.

TABLE 1.4

Arithmetic Assignment Statement	Original Formula
BETA = −1./(2.*X) + A**2/(4.*X**2)	$\beta = \frac{-1}{2x} + \frac{a^2}{4x^2}$
C = 1.112*D*R1*R2/(R1 − R2)	$C = 1.112D \frac{r_1 r_2}{r_1 - r_2}$
FY = X*(X**2 − Y**2)/(X**2 + Y**2)	$F_y = x \cdot \frac{x^2 - y^2}{x^2 + y^2}$
Y = (1.E − 6 + A*X**3)**(2.0/3.0)	$y = (10^{-6} + ax^3)^{2/3}$
J = 4*K − 6*K1*K2	$j = 4K - 6k_1k_2$
I = I + 1	$i_{new} = i_{old} + 1$
K = 12	$k = 12$
PI = 3.1415927	$\pi = 3.1415927$
M = 2*M + 10*J	$m_{new} = 2m_{old} + 10j$
R = COS(X) + X*SIN(X)	$r = \cos x + x \sin x$
S = −COS(X)**4/4.0	$s = - \frac{\cos^4 x}{4}$
T = ATAN(1.41421356*SIN(X)/COS(X))	$t = \tan^{-1}(\sqrt{2} \tan x)$

TABLE 1.5

Incorrect Statement	Error
Y = 2.X + A	*missing
3.14 = X − A	Left side must be a variable name
A = ((X + Y)A**2	Not the same number of right and left parentheses; *missing
X = 1,624,009.*DELTA	Commas not permitted in constants
−J = I**2.	Integer quantities may not be raised to real powers; variable on left must not be written with a sign
BX6 = 1./−2.*A**6	Two operation symbols side-by-side not permitted, even though the minus sign here is not intended to indicate subtraction
DERIV = N*X**(N − 1)	Mixed integer and real values in the multiplication
A*X + B = Q	Left side must be a single variable; should be Q = A*X + B
FNC = CUBRT(X + Y)	No such function supplied; write FNC = (X + Y)**0.33333333
SQRT(Z) = Z**0.5	A function name cannot be used as a variable name; left side must be a variable name

EXERCISES

1. State the value of A or I stored as the result of each of the following arithmetic assignment statements and show whether the result is in integer or real form.

*a. A = 2*6 + 1
*b. A = 2/3
 c. A = 2.*6./4.
 d. I = 2*10/4
e. I = 2(10/4)
f. A = 2(10/4)
 g. A = 2.*(10./4.)
 h. A = 2.0*(1.0E1/4.0)
 i. A = 6.0*1.0/6.0
 j. A = 6.0*(1.0/6.0)
*k. A = 1./3. + 1./3. + 1./3. + 1./3.
 l. A = (4.0)**(3/2)
 m. A = (4.0)**3./2.
*n. A = (4.0)**(3./2.)
*o. I = 19/4 + 5/4
 p. A = 19/4 + 5/4
 q. I = 100*(99/100)

2. Each of the following arithmetic assignment statements contains at least one error. Identify them.

 a. −V = A + B
 b. 4 = I
 c. V − 3.96 = X**1.67
 d. X = (A + 6)**2
 e. A*X**2 + B*X + C
 f. K6 = I**A
 g. Z2 = A* − B + C**4
 h. X = Y + 2.0 = Z + 9.0
 i. R = 16.9X + AB

3. Write arithmetic assignment statements to do the following:

*a. Add 2 to the current value of the variable named BETA; make the sum the new value of a variable named DELTA.

 b. Subtract the value of a variable named B from the value of a variable named A, square the difference, and assign it as the new value of W.

*c. Square A, add to the square of B, and make the new value of C the square root of the sum.

*d. A variable named R is to have its present value replaced by the square root of 2.

 e. Multiply THETA by π and store the cosine of the product as the new value of RHO.

 f. Add the values of F and G, divide by the sum of the values of R and S, and square the quotient; assign this result to P.

*g. Multiply the cosine of two times X by the square root of one half of X; set Y equal to the result.

*h. Increase the present value of G by 2 and replace the present value of G with the sum.

 i. Multiply the present value of A by −1.0 and replace the present value of A with the product.

 j. Assign to OMEGA the value of 2π.

 k. Assign to the variable named D a value 1.1 times as great as the present value of the variable named D.

4. Write arithmetic assignment statements to compute the values of the following formulas. Use the letters and names shown for variable names.

*a. $AREA = 2 \cdot P \cdot R \cdot \sin\left(\dfrac{\pi}{P}\right)$

 b. $CHORD = 2R \sin \dfrac{A}{2}$

*c. $ARC = 2\sqrt{Y^2 + \dfrac{4X^2}{3}}$

 d. $s = \dfrac{-\cos^4 x}{x}$

*e. $s = \dfrac{-\cos^{p+1} x}{p + 1}$

*f. $g = \dfrac{1}{2}\log\dfrac{1 + \sin x}{1 - \sin x}$

 g. $R = \dfrac{\sin^3 x \cos^2 x}{5} + \dfrac{2}{15}\sin^3 x$

 h. $D = \log|\sec x + \tan x|$

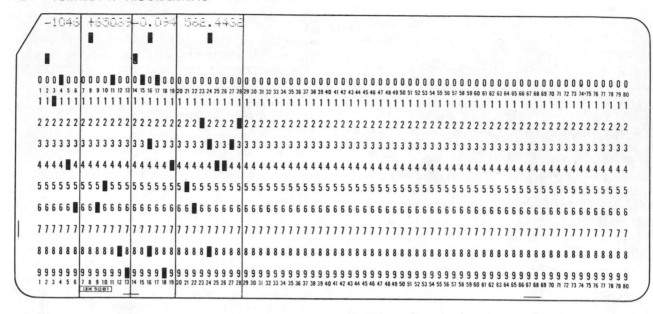

Figure 1.1.   An example of a data card.

*i.
$$e = x \arctan \frac{x}{a} - \frac{a}{2} \log (a^2 + x^2)$$

j.
$$f = -\frac{\pi}{2} \log |x| + \frac{a}{x} - \frac{a^3}{9x^3}$$

k.
$$Z = -\frac{1}{\sqrt{x^2 - a^2}} - \frac{2a^2}{3(\sqrt{x^2 - a^2})^3}$$

*l.
$$Q = \left(\frac{2}{\pi x}\right)^{\frac{1}{2}} \sin x$$

m.
$$B = \frac{e^{x/\sqrt{2}} \cos (\sqrt{x/2} + \pi/8)}{\sqrt{2\pi x}}$$

*n.
$$Y = (2\pi)^{\frac{1}{2}} x^{x+1} e^{-x}$$

o.
$$t = a \cdot e^{-\sqrt{w/2p \cdot x}}$$

1.9   Input and Output

If a problem is to be done only once, all data can be entered with the program in the form of constants in statements. This is seldom done, however; programs are usually set up to read problem data from cards at the time the program is executed, and constants are used only for quantities that really are constant. The same program can then carry out the computation on as many sets of data as desired.

FORTRAN provides a great deal of power and flexibility in the reading of data and the printing of results. And for the experienced programmer this power and flexibility is needed, for a heavy part of the total programming task revolves around input and output. For our purposes now we need only the minimum that will permit us to write complete programs. We present here accordingly a small subset of the total FORTRAN input/output capability. Various other facets of the subject are introduced in subsequent chapters, and in Chapter 6 we present a complete summary; Chapter 6 is organized to be suitable for reference.

What we need to know about input and output now can be presented with a simple example. Consider the data card in Figure 1.1. The punches on this card represent four numbers. The first is punched in columns 1–6; it is to be read into the computer and will become the value of an integer variable named J. The next number is punched in columns 7–13; it is to become the value of an integer variable named K. The third number, in columns 14–19, is to become the value of a real variable named X. The last number, columns 20–28, is to become the value of a real variable named Y.

We note that a plus sign may be punched or not, as desired.

The vertical lines drawn on the card are, of course, only for our convenience in studying the card; the computer "sees" only punches.

In order to read this card in FORTRAN, we execute a READ statement that names the four variables that are to receive values in the same order as the values are punched on the card, and we also reference a FORMAT statement that describes to the program how the data values are punched. The READ-FORMAT combination might be as follows:

READ (5, 123) J, K, X, Y
123 FORMAT (I6, I7, F6.0, F9.0)

In the READ statement the 5 is the designation of the input unit that reads the data card. In some installations a number other than 5 may be the standard for data input; the reader must determine this for himself.

The 123 refers to the *statement number* written in front of the FORMAT statement. A statement number is simply a cross-referencing device that allows one statement to refer to another; we shall encounter several other examples of the usefulness of statement numbers in later chapters.

The four variable names are listed in the same order as the corresponding values are punched on the data card.

This order also applies to the *field specifications* within parentheses in the FORMAT statement, which tell the program how the data values are punched on the card and whether the variables are integer or real. In "I6" the *I* means that the value on the card is an integer; the 6 means that the card field contains six columns. The correspondence between the *first* card field, the *first* variable name, and the *first* field specification is basic; this kind of correspondence is assumed in all input and output statements. The I7 describes a value that is an integer, which is punched in seven columns. The pattern holds: the *second* value goes with the *second* variable name and the *second* field specification.

The F6.0 goes with the third field and the third variable name, *X*. The *F* means that the number on the card is the value of a real variable; the 6 means that the card field occupies six columns; the zero has no meaning in this case, although it must still be there. The F9.0 field specification describes a card field of nine columns containing a value of a real variable.

For input of values for real variables, we usually punch a decimal point in the card field. If this is done, the corresponding field specification should be of the form Fw.0, where w is a number giving the width of the field in card columns.

To summarize: the READ statement calls for

the reading of the card. The READ statement designates the input unit, a FORMAT statement number, and the names of the variables that are to be read. The FORMAT statement contains field specifications that describe the data card and distinguish between integer and real variables.

This READ statement would in most cases be executed many times, to read many data cards. The values on the different data cards would not, of course, be all the same, but the arrangement of the fields on the cards would have to be the same: for instance, in every data card read by this READ statement and described by this FORMAT statement the first field must always occupy columns 1 to 6 and contain an integer.

These basic ideas carry over very directly to output. Suppose that we have read this data card and now want to print the four values. Consider these two statements:

WRITE (6, 67) J, K, X, Y
67 FORMAT (I10, I10, F10.4, F12.4)

The 6 in the WRITE statement designates the output unit onto which the variable values are to be written. The 67 is once again the statement number of a FORMAT statement, although of a different one this time. In this FORMAT statement we have specified that *J* and *K* are each to be printed with a total of ten printing positions. This is more space than is required for the values we read; the numbers are printed at the right of the assigned spaces. In F10.4 we ask for ten printing positions and specify that there shall be four digits to the right of the decimal point. F12.4 asks for 12 printing positions and also four decimals. The result of executing this WRITE statement, assuming the values on the card in Figure 1.1, would be as shown in the first line of Figure 1.2.

The F field specification is quite suitable when we know the maximum and minimum sizes of the numbers to be printed. When we cannot anticipate sizes, we turn to the E field specification, which puts the number into exponent form, similar to the way we are permitted to write very large or very small real constants. Consider these statements:

WRITE (6, 1672) J, K, X, Y
1672 FORMAT (I10, I10, E16.7, E16.7)

```
-1046     65089    -0.0940      562.4432
-1046     65089    -0.9400000E-01   0.5624432E 03
-1046     65089    -9.400000E-02    5.624432E 02
```

Figure 1.2. Three ways the values on the sample data card of Figure 1.1 might be printed.

The line printed this time would be as shown in the second line of Figure 1.2. The two integers are printed in the same form as before. In E16.7, the 16 specifies a total of 16 printing positions; the 7 dictates seven decimal places. We see in the printed output there are exponents giving the powers of 10 by which the fractional parts are to be multiplied.

It may be noted that the E field specification calls for a form of output in which the fraction is a number between 0.1 and 1.0, times a power of 10. Many people prefer numbers of this sort to be written as a multiplier between 1.0 and 10.0, times a power of 10. This we can call for by writing 1P in front of the field specification. The 1P is called a *scale factor*; it says that the fractional part should be multiplied by 10 and the exponent correspondingly decreased by one. We might write

WRITE (6, 9) J, K, X, Y
9 FORMAT (I10, I10, 1PE16.6, 1PE16.6)

The output would be as shown in the third line of Figure 1.2.

Whenever several consecutive field specifications are the same, we are permitted to write a *repetition number* in front of a single field specification. We might have written, for instance,

WRITE (6, 1672) J, K, X, Y
1672 FORMAT (2I10, 2E16.7)

or

WRITE (6, 9) J, K, X, Y
9 FORMAT (2I10, 1P2E16.6)

The printed results would be exactly the same as before.

EXERCISES

In each of the following exercises data values are to be read, the values used in a computation, and the results printed. The data values are to be printed with the results for easy reference. Assume that each data value is punched in 10 columns; use an F10.0 field specification for all input and an E20.8 field specification for all output.

*1. READ: a, b, c
PRINT: a, b, c, F
Evaluate:

$$F = \frac{1 + a}{1 + \dfrac{b}{c + 6}}$$

2. READ: s, x
PRINT: s, x, g
Evaluate:

$$g = (12.7 - x)^{s+2}$$

3. READ: x, y
PRINT: x, y, h
Evaluate:

$$h = \frac{x \cos^4 x}{2y}$$

*4. READ: a, b, c
PRINT: $a, b, c, X1, X2$
Evaluate:

$$X1 = \frac{-b + \sqrt{b^2 - 4ac}}{2a}$$

$$X2 = \frac{-b - \sqrt{b^2 - 4ac}}{2a}$$

5. READ: a, b, c, x
PRINT: a, b, c, x, r
Evaluate:

$$r = \frac{b \cdot c}{12}\left[6x^2\left(1 - \frac{x}{a}\right) + b^2\left(1 - \frac{x}{a}\right)^3\right]$$

*6. READ: a, e, h, p
PRINT: a, e, h, p, x
Evaluate:

$$x = \frac{e \cdot h \cdot p}{(\sin a)\left(\dfrac{h^4}{16} + h^2 p^2\right)}$$

7. READ: HO, HF, HR, HI, ZG
PRINT: HO, HF, HR, HI, ZG, ADMTNC
Evaluate:

$$ADMTNC = HO - \frac{HF \cdot HR}{HI + ZG}$$

*8. READ: a, x, s
PRINT: a, x, s, y, z
Evaluate:

$$y = \sqrt{x^2 - a^2}$$

$$z = \frac{x \cdot s}{2} - \frac{a^2}{2}\log|x + s|$$

9. READ: ET, ES, RG, ROPT, RIN
PRINT: ET, ES, RG, ROPT, RIN, F
Evaluate:

$$F = \cfrac{1}{1 - \cfrac{1 + \left(\dfrac{RG}{ROPT}\right)^2}{\left(\dfrac{ET}{ES}\right)^2\left(1 + \dfrac{RG}{RIN}\right)^2}}$$

1.10 The PAUSE, STOP, and END Statements

The PAUSE or STOP statement may be written whenever it is necessary to stop executing statements in a program. There is normally a STOP (or something equivalent) at the end of every program, when the computation is finished, but there are also other useful applications of the statements. A program is often set up to do a certain amount of checking of the input data to make sure that it is consistent and that all data values are within reasonable limits. If anything is wrong, some indication can be given to the operator by either of these statements.

The two statements are similar. Both stop the execution of the object program. Both take effect *only* when the object program is *executed;* that is, they do not cause termination of the compilation.

The difference between the two statements is this: after a STOP statement the computer cannot conveniently be made to continue with the program, whereas the PAUSE statement allows the operator to press a button on the computer console and to resume execution of the program, beginning with the statement after the PAUSE.

There are major differences in local application of the STOP and PAUSE statements. The users of large computing systems, in particular, try to avoid the wasted machine time by stopping if there is any other way out. STOP and PAUSE are sometimes actually forbidden by modifying the compiler so that they are not acceptable statements.

Users of the large computers should also be aware that FORTRAN is usually run under control of a *monitor* program, which handles "bookkeeping" operations and runs the machine between jobs. A FORTRAN program to be run with a monitor should *not* have a STOP when the program reaches the normal completion point but rather should return control to the monitor. Methods vary on how this is done. One frequent way is to write in the FORTRAN program the statement CALL EXIT. Alternatively, the compiler may be designed so that a STOP has exactly the same effect as CALL EXIT, without actually stopping.

So far we have been talking about the termination of the *object* program. Now we turn to the question of informing the compiler that the physical end of the *source* program has been reached and that no more program statements follow. This need is answered by the END statement, which must be the last statement of every program. By "last," in this case, we mean *physically* or *geographically* last, as distinguished from the statement that is *executed* last when the compiled program is run.

To put it another way, a STOP statement may appear anywhere in the program; there may be more than one, and it is not required that the last statement executed be the last statement on the last page of the program. The END statement, on the other hand, *must* be the very last card when the program is punched on cards. There must be only one END card in a program.

1.11 Writing, Punching, and Running a Program

A FORTRAN program is ordinarily written on a form similar to that shown in Figure 1.5 in Section 1.12, with one or more lines for each statement. The information on each line is then punched into a card similar to that shown in Figure 1.6. The complete set of cards constitutes the *source program deck,* which is compiled into an object program of machine instructions by a process that we shall outline shortly.

In order to be able to show sample programs on a standard form, it is necessary to describe the purpose of each of its parts.

The numbers shown above the first line of the coding form stand for the card columns into which the information on the form will be punched. The first field on the form, columns 1 to 5, contains the *statement number,* if any. We have seen one application of the statement number in connection with the FORMAT statement, and in the next chapter we shall see other applications.

Column 1 has another function, that of indicating a *comment line.* If column 1 contains a *C*, FORTRAN does not process the information on the card but prints it on a "listing" of the program (a printed version produced during compilation). Free use of comments is encouraged to make the program more easily understandable by other programmers. For that matter, the original programmer will be helped by comments when he returns to a program after he has forgotten its details.

Column 6 is used to indicate a *continuation* card. If a statement can be punched entirely on one card, column 6 may be left blank or punched with a zero. If more than one card is required for a statement, each card after the first (up to a maximum of 19 continuation cards) must be punched with some nonzero character in column 6. The first card of a continued statement must still have a zero or blank in column 6.

The statement itself is punched in columns 7 to

72. *Blanks in this field are ignored.* Blanks may thus be used freely to improve readability. The statement need not begin in column 7. Some programmers, for instance, indent the continuation of a long statement to make it a little clearer that the statement is continued; others like to leave a space on both sides of each operation symbol for readability. All such conventions are at the discretion of the programmer.

Nevertheless, it is still necessary to indicate clearly to the person who will punch the cards exactly how many spaces are desired at each point. It is for this reason that most FORTRAN coding forms have a box for each character or a short vertical line to indicate the character divisions.

Columns 73 to 80 are not processed by FORTRAN and may be used for any desired card or program identification.

It is essential that the coding forms be filled out with great care and attention to detail. The statements must always be written in the format specified; if a comma is misplaced or omitted, the program will not be compiled or it will be compiled incorrectly. At most installations it is required that only capital letters be used and that great care be taken to write certain easily confused characters in

Zero	0	The letter O	Ø
One	1	The letter I	I
Two	2	The letter Z	Ƶ

Figure 1.3. One acceptable way of distinguishing between easily confused pairs of characters.

a distinctive manner. Various conventions are available for distinguishing between such characters as the letter "O" and zero. One acceptable way to write these characters is shown in Figure 1.3.

1.12 Case Study 1: The Area of a Triangle

To illustrate the application of some of the ideas presented in this chapter, let us take a very simple program and see how a complete FORTRAN program to solve it could be worked out.

If the lengths of the sides of a triangle are given by the values of the variables A, B, and C, then the area of the triangle can be computed from

$$\text{AREA} = \sqrt{S(S - A)\,(S - B)\,(S - C)}$$

where

$$S = \frac{A + B + C}{2}$$

We are to read the values of A, B, and C from a card. The value of A is punched in columns 1 to 10, with a decimal point but without an exponent. The value of B is punched in columns 11 to 20 in the same form, and the value of C is punched in columns 21 to 30. Figure 1.4 shows a typical data card on which the values of A, B, and C are 300, 400, and 500, respectively.

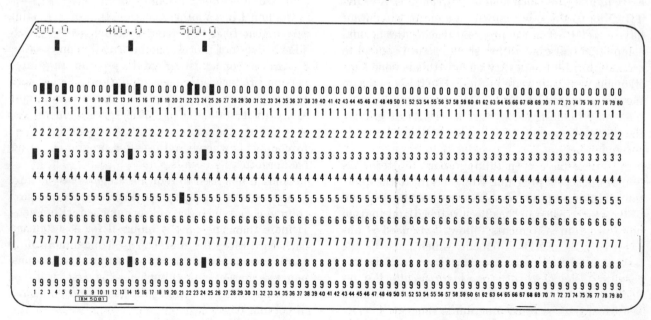

Figure 1.4. An illustrative data card for the program of Figure 1.5. (Case Study 1.)

FORTRAN CODING FORM

Program Area of a triangle		Punching Instructions							Page 1 of 1
		Graphic					Card Form #	*	Identification TRIANGLE
Programmer D. D. McCracken	Date	Punch							73 80

```
C CASE STUDY 1 - AREA OF A TRIANGLE
C
      READ (5, 23) A, B, C
   23 FORMAT (3F10.0)
      S = (A + B + C) / 2.0
      AREA = SQRT(S * (S - A) * (S - B) * (S - C))
      WRITE (6, 17) A, B, C, AREA
   17 FORMAT (1P4E16.7)
      STOP
      END
```

Figure 1.5. A program to find the area of a triangle given the lengths of its sides. (Case Study 1.)

After the area has been computed, the area and the lengths of the sides are printed, with the area last. Each of the four numbers occupies 16 printing positions and has seven decimal places and an exponent.

A program that will do the required computing is shown in Figure 1.5. We note that the statement number of the first FORMAT statement has been written in columns 4 and 5, whereas that of the second FORMAT statement has been written in columns 2 and 3. This shows that statement numbers may be written anywhere in columns 1 to 5 if they are less than five digits long. We see repetition numbers used in both FORMAT statements, for in this example the three numbers to be read all have the same format and all four numbers to be printed also have the same format. The FORMAT statements have been written immediately after their associated input and output statements; this is conventional but not required: a FORMAT statement may, in fact, be written anywhere in the program. The statement number identifies it even if it does not immediately follow the statement that refers to it.

In the first FORMAT statement the field specification is F10.0. We recall that F means that the input data will be stored inside the computer in real form, that is, as a fraction and an exponent. The 10 tells FORTRAN that 10 columns are allocated to each number. The zero means that if no decimal points were punched in the data field in the card the numbers in that field would be taken to have zero decimal places. If decimal points are punched the zero has no effect. In the second FORMAT statement the 1P means that the decimal point will be shifted one place to the right and the exponent adjusted accordingly, and the E means that the numbers will be printed with an exponent, indicating the power of 10 by which the fractional part is multiplied. The 16 means that 16 printing positions are allocated to each number; the 7 means that seven decimal places will be printed.

We see that all equal signs and operation symbols have been written with spaces on both sides and that commas in the READ and WRITE statements have been followed by spaces. This was done for readability; it is not required.

Figure 1.6 shows the source program card that is punched from the line for computing the area.

When all the cards are punched, the source-program deck is placed in the reader of the computer, with the machine under control of the FORTRAN compiler program. (An intermediate card-to-tape operation, in which the computer actually reads a magnetic tape, is often employed, although it requires no additional attention from us.) The compiler reads the deck (or tape prepared from the deck) and produces from it an object program deck

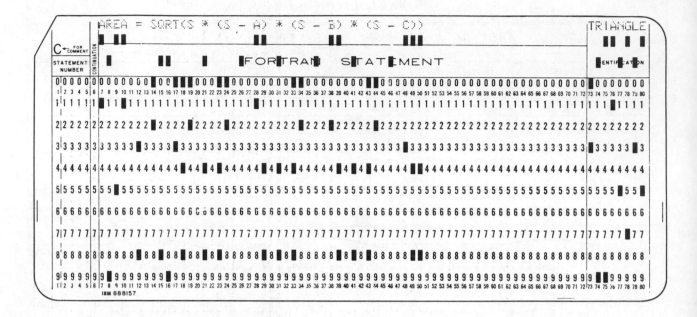

Figure 1.6.   A source program card from the program of Figure 1.5. (Case Study 1.)

```
C CASE STUDY 1 - AREA OF A TRIANGLE
C
      READ (5, 23) A, B, C
   23 FORMAT (3F10.0)
      S = (A + B + C) / 2.0
      AREA = SQRT(S * (S - A) * (S - B) * (S - C))
      WRITE (6, 17) A, B, C, AREA
   17 FORMAT (1P4E16.7)
      STOP
      END
```

Figure 1.7.   The listing produced by the computer as one output of the compilation of the program of Figure 1.5. (Case Study 1.)

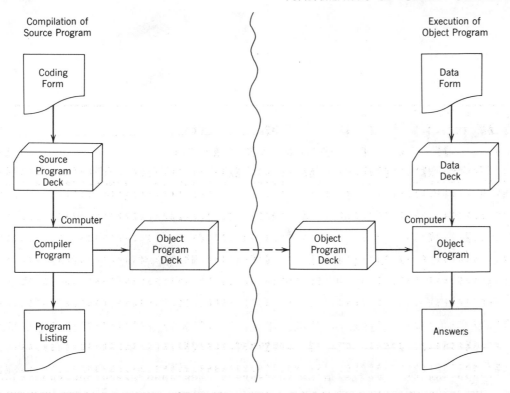

Figure 1.8. Schematic representation of the complete process of compiling and executing a FORTRAN program.

of machine instructions (or a tape for punching such a deck). The data card is *not* read during this operation.

One output of the compilation process is the *listing* of the source program. This shows in readable form exactly what went into the computer; it becomes the primary documentation of the program. Figure 1.7 is the source program listing corresponding to Figure 1.5.

The actions described so far are represented on the left side of Figure 1.8, which is a schematic picture of the process of compiling and executing a FORTRAN program.

In some FORTRAN compiler systems the object program is punched out on cards and must then be loaded into the computer. In other systems the object program is left in the computer after compilation, and control can be immediately transferred to the object program. The second method is known in the trade as a "load and go" operation.

Either way, the object program now takes control of the machine. It reads the data card, carries out the processing specified by the machine instructions created from the source program, prints the results (or writes a tape for printing), and stops (or returns control to the monitor).

Figure 1.9 shows the line of printing produced by the program for the data in Figure 1.4.

3.0000000E 02   4.0000000E 02   5.0000000E 02   6.0000000E 04

Figure 1.9. A line of output from the program in Figure 1.5, using the input in Figure 1.4. (Case Study 1.)

2. TRANSFER OF CONTROL

2.1 Introduction

In the brief programming examples in Chapter 1 it was tacitly assumed that FORTRAN statements are executed sequentially, in the order written. However, we shall often want to execute statements in some order other than the normal one-after-the-other sequence. Sometimes we shall return to the beginning of a program to execute it again with different data, or we may branch around a section of the program, depending on the values of computed intermediate results.

In this chapter we shall explore the FORTRAN language elements available for making transfers of control, and we shall also look into a number of examples that illustrate the use of these language elements and of computers generally.

2.2 The GO TO Statement

The GO TO statement provides a means of *transferring control* to some statement other than the next one in sequence. The statement takes the form

GO TO n

where *n* is the statement number of another statement in the program. When such a statement is encountered, the next statement executed will be the one having the specified statement number *n*. This other statement is allowed to be any executable statement in the program, either before or after the GO TO statement itself.

We have already had brief contact with statement numbers in connection with the FORMAT statement. We saw there that a statement number is merely an identification of a statement, so that statements elsewhere in the program may refer to it.

A statement number is a positive number of five decimal digits or less; it is written in columns 1 to 5 of the FORTRAN coding form and punched in columns 1 to 5 of the statement card. No two statements may have the same number, but there is no requirement that every statement be numbered. Furthermore, there is no sequencing implied by the statement numbers. The first numbered statement need not bear the number 1, and statement numbers need not be assigned in an unbroken sequence or even in an ascending sequence. To emphasize this point, an acceptable sequence of statement numbers would be 500, 7, 9936, 9935, 9937, 201, and 258. Interspersed between the statements having these numbers could be others having no statement numbers. In short, statement numbers provide a cross reference when one statement must refer to another. They serve no other purpose.

2.3 The Arithmetic IF Statement

The simple GO TO statement causes an *unconditional* transfer of control to the statement having the statement number written after the GO TO. That is, execution of the transfer does not depend on any condition of the data, status of the machine, or anything else. The unconditional GO TO is important and heavily used, as we shall see, but by itself it would permit little work to be done. We must also be able to transfer *if* some condition is met during program execution. This is the function of the arithmetic IF statement.

The arithmetic IF statement has the form

$$IF\ (e)n_1, n_2, n_3$$

in which *e* stands for any expression and n_1, n_2, and n_3 are statement numbers. The operation of the statement is as follows: if the value of the expression within parentheses is negative, the statement having the statement number n_1 is executed next; if the value of the expression is zero, statement n_2 is executed next; and if the expression is positive n_3 is executed next.

For a simple example of the use of the arithmetic IF statement, consider the following formula:

$$Q = \begin{cases} -\dfrac{\pi}{2} & \text{if } a < 0 \\ 0 & \text{if } a = 0 \\ \dfrac{\pi}{2} & \text{if } a > 0 \end{cases}$$

Suppose now that we are doing a problem in which it is necessary to select the appropriate value for *Q*, assuming that *a* has already been given a value by a previous statement (not shown). The program segment of Figure 2.1 will do this.

The arithmetic IF statement calls for an examination of the value of the variable *A*. If the value of this variable at the time the IF is executed is negative, statement 4 will be executed next. This calls for *Q* to be set equal to -1.5707963, which is $-\pi/2$. After that we find the statement GO TO 3; statement 3 is the next statement after this program segment, whatever it might be. If the GO TO 3 were not there, the program would automatically go on in sequence to statement 5, in which *Q* would be set equal to zero; this, of course, would not be what we want. In other words, the GO TO 3 statement skips around the other parts of the program to statement 3, in which the value of *Q* would presumably be

```
    IF (A) 4, 5, 6
4   Q = -1.5707963
    GO TO 3
5   Q = 0.0
    GO TO 3
6   Q = 1.5707963
3
```

Figure 2.1. Program segment illustrating the use of the arithmetic IF statement to make a three-way transfer of control. Other statements would precede and follow this segment.

```
    IF (X - 2.1) 40, 40, 30
40  Y = 0.5 * X + 0.95
    GO TO 45
30  Y = 0.7 * X + 0.53
45
```

Figure 2.2. Another illustration of the use of the arithmetic IF statement, this time to make a two-way transfer of control.

used. If the value of *a* is found to be zero, the IF statement causes a transfer to statement 5, in which *Q* is set equal to zero and once again we transfer to the continuation of the program. If the value of *a* is found to be positive, the IF statement causes a transfer of control to statement 6 in which *Q* is set equal to $\pi/2$, and we then go on immediately to the next statement.

Most programs are run many times with different sets of data. As this arithmetic IF statement is encountered in different runs, the paths taken would vary as the value of *a* varied. In other words, the "decision" here is made each time the IF statement is executed in the object program.

For another example of the use of the arithmetic IF statement, suppose we are required to compute *y* as a function of *x* by one of two formulas:

$$y = 0.5x + 0.95 \quad \text{if } x \leq 2.1$$

$$y = 0.7x + 0.53 \quad \text{if } x > 2.1$$

This computation may be carried out by the program segment shown in Figure 2.2. The branch of the IF statement taken depends on the value of the expression $x - 2.1$. If $x - 2.1$ is negative, *x* is obviously less than 2.1 and we transfer to statement 40, which computes *y* according to the appropriate formula for that case. If *x* is equal to 2.1, we also reach the same formula, as required in the problem statement. If $x - 2.1$ is positive, then *x* is greater than 2.1 and we go to statement 30, which computes *y* according to the appropriate formula. Whatever appears at 45 could use the value of *y* which has now been computed—by either method.

2.4   The Computed GO TO Statement

The arithmetic IF statement provides us with a three-way test on the value of an arithmetic expression. The computed GO TO extends the range of the FORTRAN language by providing an *n*-way branch based on the value of an integer variable.

The statement has the general form

$$GO\ TO\ (n_1, n_2, \ldots, n_m), i$$

In this statement i must be an integer variable written without a sign, and $n_1, n_2, \ldots, n_m$ must be statement numbers of statements elsewhere in the program. If the value of the variable i at the time this statement is executed is j, then control is transferred to the statement with the statement number n_j. For instance, suppose we have written the statement

$$\text{GO TO } (4, 600, 13, 9, 526), \text{IAC}$$

If the value of the variable IAC is 1, then control will be transferred to statement number 4; if it is 2, to statement 600; if it is 3, to statement 13; and so on. The value of the integer variable must be in the range of 1 to m, where m denotes how many statement numbers there are in parentheses. If it is not in this range, the results are not predictable; in other words, we do not know in general what the program will do.

As an example of one kind of calculation that can be done with the computed GO TO statement, consider another problem. We are required at a certain point in a program to compute the value of one of the first five Legendre polynomials, which are defined as follows:

$$P_0(x) = 1$$
$$P_1(x) = x$$
$$P_2(x) = \tfrac{3}{2}x^2 - \tfrac{1}{2}$$
$$P_3(x) = \tfrac{5}{2}x^3 - \tfrac{3}{2}x$$
$$P_4(x) = \tfrac{35}{8}x^4 - \tfrac{15}{4}x^2 + \tfrac{3}{8}$$

We assume that x has previously been computed and that a value between zero and four has been given to an integer variable named LEG. It is the value of LEG that determines which of the five Legendre polynomials must be computed: if LEG = 0, we are to compute $P_0(x)$; if LEG = 1, we are to compute

```
      LEG1 = LEG + 1
      GO TO (68, 69, 70, 71, 72), LEG1
   68 P = 1.0
      GO TO 65
   69 P = X
      GO TO 65
   70 P = 1.5*X**2 - 0.5
      GO TO 65
   71 P = 2.5*X**3 - 1.5*X
      GO TO 65
   72 P = 4.375*X**4 - 3.75*X**2 + 0.375
   65
```

Figure 2.3. Program segment using the computed GO TO to select one of five formulas, depending on the value of an integer variable.

$P_1(x)$, and so on. We cannot use the computed GO TO directly because of the restriction that the value of the integer variable must not be less than 1. Therefore we shall first add 1 to LEG to make it fall in the range of 1 to 5 instead of 0 to 4. A program for carrying out this computation is shown in Figure 2.3. P is the value of whichever Legendre polynomial is computed.

2.5 The Logical IF Statement

The final tool for transfer of control that we shall consider is the logical IF statement, which has the general form

$$\text{IF (e) S}$$

where e is a *logical expression* and S is any other statement except another logical IF or a DO (discussed in Chapter 5). The simplest form of logical expression is one that asks a question about two arithmetic expressions. Is x greater than or equal to 12? Is I equal to $N - 1$? We write such *relational expressions* by using any of the following six *relational operators:*

Relational Operator	Meaning
.LT.	Less than
.LE.	Less than or equal to
.EQ.	Equal to
.NE.	Not equal to
.GT.	Greater than
.GE.	Greater than or equal to

The periods in these relational operators are required to distinguish them from variable names that the programmer may invent.

The action of the logical IF is as follows: if the logical expression is true, statement S is executed; if the logical expression is false, statement S is not executed. Either way, the next statement executed is the one following the logical IF, unless S was a GO TO and the expression was true.

To see a simple example of the use of logical IF, let us return to an earlier example:

$$y = 0.5x + 0.95 \quad \text{if } x \le 2.1$$
$$y = 0.7x + 0.53 \quad \text{if } x > 2.1$$

This calculation can be done with two logical IF statements:

$$\text{IF (X .LE. 2.1) Y} = 0.5 * \text{X} + 0.95$$
$$\text{IF (X .GT. 2.1) Y} = 0.7 * \text{X} + 0.53$$

If x is less than or equal to (.LE.) 2.1, the statement $Y = 0.5*X + 0.95$ will be executed, which is the correct formula for computing y in that case. If x is greater than 2.1, the statement in the first IF will not be executed, but the statement in the second IF will be.

It may occur to some readers to wonder why a condition is needed on the second statement: if x is not less than or equal to 2.1, it surely must be greater—there are no other possibilities. Why not write

$$IF (X .LE. 2.1) \ Y = 0.5*X + 0.95$$

$$Y = 0.7*X + 0.53$$

The difficulty, of course, is that the second statement would *always* be executed, even when the answer on the first IF had been "yes." Thus y would first be computed from the first formula and then recomputed from the second. The second result would destroy the first, and we would not have the correct value for y.

The power of the logical IF is considerably increased by the combination of several relational expressions with the *logical operators* .AND., .OR., and .NOT. . We can write, for instance,

IF (X .GE. EPS .AND. NUMBER .LT. 10)
$$GO \ TO \ 789$$

This says that if *both* conditions are met, the GO TO should be executed, but if either of the conditions is not satisfied the GO TO will not be executed, and the next statement in sequence will be taken.

The .OR. operator is "satisfied" if *either or both* of the expressions it joins are true. The .NOT. operator reverses the truth value of the expression it modifies. For instance, the logical IF statement

$$IF (.NOT.(X .LT. 12.0)) \ R = X + 31.0$$

has the same effect as

$$IF (X .GE. 12.0) \ R = X + 31.0$$

because "not less than" means the same thing as "greater than or equal to."

In the expression .NOT. (X .LT. 12.0) the parentheses are required to inform the compiler that the .NOT. modifies the entire relational expression. Under certain circumstances the meaning would otherwise be ambiguous.

We shall see several examples of the use of the various forms of the logical IF in the case studies at the end of this chapter. The use of the logical operators .AND., .OR., and .NOT. will be studied more thoroughly in the next chapter in the discussion of logical variables.

2.6 Flowcharts

An important tool of programming is the *flowchart*, or *block diagram*, which allows the programmer to plan the sequence of operations in a program before writing it. In any problem that is even moderately complex the interrelationships within it are difficult to keep clearly in mind without some visual representation. A flowchart provides this visual assistance. It also greatly facilitates communication between programmers and is a valuable part of the documentation of a program.

A flowchart is made up of a set of boxes, the shapes of which indicate the nature of the operations described in the boxes, along with connecting lines and arrows that show the "flow of control" between the various operations.

For our purposes here the notation, which is quite simple, contains the following symbols:

A rectangle indicates any processing operation except a decision.

A diamond indicates a decision. The lines leaving the box are labeled with the decision results that cause each path to be followed.

A trapezoid indicates an input or output operation.

An oval indicates the beginning or ending point of the program.

A small circle indicates a connection between two points in a flowchart, where a connecting line would be too clumsy.

Arrows indicate the direction of flow through the flowchart; every line should have an arrow on it.

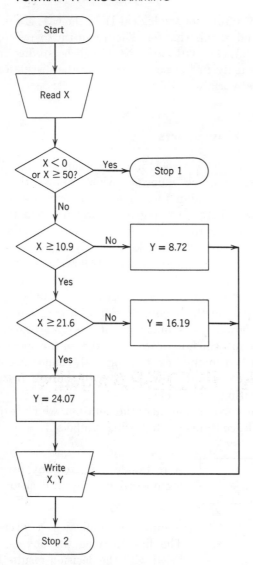

Figure 2.4. Flowchart of a method of evaluating a step function. The corresponding program is shown in Figure 2.5.

To illustrate how a flowchart may be used, we shall work out another problem involving IF statements. Suppose we are required to read a value of x, perform certain checking on x, and compute a value of y according to the following step function:

$$y = \begin{cases} 8.72 & \text{if } 0.0 \leq x < 10.9 \\ 16.19 & \text{if } 10.9 \leq x < 21.6 \\ 24.07 & \text{if } 21.6 \leq x < 50.0 \end{cases}$$

The values of x and y are then to be printed. If $x < 0.0$ or $x \geq 50.0$, we are to stop without computing y or printing x and y.

A flowchart of a procedure for doing this job is shown in Figure 2.4. This flowchart has been drawn with some attention to its implementation in FORTRAN terms. For instance, the first decision box actually will require two comparisons, which we shall do with a logical IF containing an .OR.. If we did not have the logical IF available, it would be necessary to combine two arithmetic IF statements to accomplish the same thing, which is entirely possible, of course. The Stops are seen to be numbered, which is done to indicate whether the error stop or the normal stop occurred.

A program corresponding to the flowchart of Figure 2.4 is shown in Figure 2.5. We begin by reading the value of x, after which comes the FORMAT statement. A FORMAT statement is said to be nonexecutable, and it is allowed to appear almost anywhere in the program. Next is a logical IF to test for an out-of-range x value. Another logical IF branches to the second test if x is greater than or equal to 10.9; if this branch is not taken, then x must be less than 10.9, so we set y equal to 8.72 as required and transfer to the WRITE statement. Another IF checks x against 21.6, after which we set y equal to 16.19 or 24.07, whichever is correct.

There is never just one way to write a program, and seldom is it even true that one way is better than all other possibilities. Figure 2.6. presents another program than does the same processing as the program in Figure 2.5. The new version uses no GO TO statements at all, but instead arranges logical IF's in such a manner that exactly one of them will be satisfied. The net result is a program containing fewer statements but which may take a little longer to run, for if x is found between 0.0 and 10.9 we will carry out the two following logical IF's even though we already know that the answer will be "no."

Additional flowcharts will be found in the case studies.

```
      READ (5, 18) X
   18 FORMAT (F10.0)
      IF (X .LT. 0.0 .OR. X .GE. 50.0) STOP 1
      IF (X .GE. 10.9) GO TO 24
      Y = 8.72
      GO TO 30
   24 IF (X .GE. 21.6) GO TO 26
      Y = 16.19
      GO TO 30
   26 Y = 24.07
   30 WRITE (6, 19) X, Y
   19 FORMAT (1P2E15.7)
      STOP 2
      END
```

Figure 2.5. Program of the step function evaluation flowcharted in Figure 2.4.

```
        READ (5, 18) X
   18 FORMAT (F10.0)
      IF (X .LT. 0.0 .OR. X .GE. 50.0) STOP 1
      IF (X .LT. 10.9) Y = 8.72
      IF (X .GE. 10.9 .AND. X .LT. 21.6) Y = 16.19
      IF (X .GE. 21.6) Y = 24.07
      WRITE (6, 19) X, Y
   19 FORMAT (1P2E15.7)
      STOP 2
      END
```

Figure 2.6. An alternative method of programming the step function evaluation problem.

2.7 Case Study 2: Current in an AC Circuit

This case study is a realistic application of the GO TO and IF statements in carrying out the same basic computations on several different sets of data values.

Suppose that we are required to compute the current flowing in an ac circuit that contains resistance, capacitance, and inductance in series.* The current in the circuit is given by

$$I = \frac{E}{\sqrt{R^2 + (2\pi f L - 1/2\pi f C)^2}}$$

where I = current, amperes
E = voltage, volts
R = resistance, ohms
L = inductance, henrys
C = capacitance, farads
f = frequency, cycles per second

We shall assume that the purpose of the computation is to provide the data for drawing a graph of the relation between current and frequency. Therefore we shall arrange to read in fixed values of voltage, resistance, inductance, and capacitance and then a series of values of frequency. We shall print each frequency with the current at that frequency.

We wish to write a program that will process any number of frequency cards without knowing in advance how many there may be in a given run. To accomplish this we shall specify that the last data card will be a *sentinel* consisting of a *negative* fre-

*The examples used in case studies and elsewhere are taken from various areas of science and engineering. As outlined at the beginning of the book, the *complete* process of problem solution requires a full understanding of the subject-matter area and of the formulation of the problem. We are assuming, however, that the preliminary steps have been completed. The reader is therefore *not* required to know how the formulas are derived or, for that matter, what they mean. The emphasis is on programming; it should not matter very much if a particular example is taken from an unfamiliar area.

quency. It could never actually be necessary to compute the current for a negative frequency, so that such a sentinel may safely be used without danger of confusion with actual data. After reading each frequency card, we need only use an IF to determine whether it is the sentinel. If it is not, we simply proceed with the computation. After printing each result we return to read another frequency card, knowing that eventually a negative number will turn up and that the IF statement will then lead to a STOP to terminate program execution.

The sequence of operations can be visualized more clearly with the help of a flowchart, as shown in Figure 2.7. We first read the values of the four

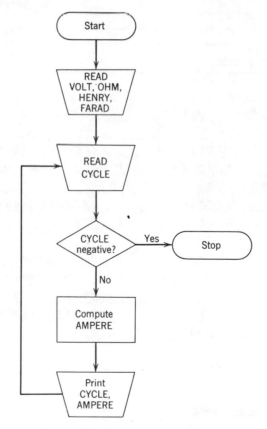

Figure 2.7. Flowchart of an ac circuit calculation. (Case Study 2.)

parameters that do not change: voltage, resistance, inductance, and capacitance. These quantities are identified in the flowchart by the symbols that will be used in the program, making it easier to compare the flowchart and the program.

This first step of reading the parameters will not be repeated; all of the following steps will be carried out for each frequency card. In order to be able to read new frequency cards as long as more remain, without reading the fixed parameters again, we make the reading of a frequency card a separate box (and a separate statement in the program). Immediately after reading a frequency card we check to see whether it is a sentinel (negative frequency) and stop the execution of the program if it is. Naturally this would not happen after reading the *first* frequency card, and it may appear pointless to test for the possibility the first time. The point to remember is that we are now in a section of the program that will be repeated an unknown number of times; there may be one frequency card or a hundred. This being the case, we *do* need to test for a sentinel every time except the first. Arranging to

avoid the test the first time would be more trouble and more time-consuming in the computer than making the test the first time also.

If the frequency card is not a sentinel, we reach the box that calls for the computation of the current (AMPERE). This will be a long statement in the program; we have not shown the formula in the box, although it would not be incorrect flowcharting practice to do so. After computing the current we print the frequency and the corresponding current and return to read another frequency card.

The program, as diagrammed here, will continue to read frequency cards, to compute and print the current, and then return to read another card, until it "gets out of the loop" by discovering a sentinel card.

With the process precisely defined by a well-understood flowchart, the program in Figure 2.8 is fairly easy to write and to understand.

In setting up the program we do run into a minor difficulty. The symbols in the formula are not acceptable as variable names, for I and L would represent integer variables, and we want all the vari-

---

FORTRAN CODING FORM

```
C CASE STUDY 2 - CURRENT IN AN A-C CIRCUIT
C
C THE FIRST READ IS EXECUTED ONLY ONCE
      READ (5, 301) VOLT, OHM, HENRY, FARAD
  301 FORMAT (4F10.0)
C THE SECOND READ IS EXECUTED ONCE FOR EACH FREQUENCY CARD
  302 READ (5, 301) CYCLE
C TEST FOR SENTINEL
      IF (CYCLE .LT. 0.0) STOP
      AMPERE = VOLT / SQRT(OHM**2 + (6.2831853 * CYCLE * HENRY
     1 - 1.0 / (6.2831853 * CYCLE * FARAD))**2)
      WRITE (6, 303) CYCLE, AMPERE
  303 FORMAT (1P2E16.6)
      GO TO 302
      END
```

Figure 2.8. Program for an ac circuit calculation. (Case Study 2.)

ables to be real. This is a problem that is often present; we must always be on guard to avoid inadvertently mixing integer and real computations. One solution to this problem is to prefix the unacceptable variable names with some letter that will make them real, which is perfectly satisfactory. Or, by using simple techniques discussed in Chapter 3, we could designate I and L as real, overriding the naming convention. We shall follow a different approach: the units in which the variables are expressed all happen to begin with the proper letters for real variables.

It will be noted that the first line of the program is a comment line, which identifies the program, and that comment lines interspersed throughout explain its various points. Heavy use of comments for these purposes is strongly recommended.

Statement numbers have been given to the FORMAT statements and to the one statement that is referred to by the GO TO. Note that the arithmetic statement has been written on two lines by use of a continuation line.

The GO TO statement specifies that after the frequency and the computed value of the current have been printed control should return to the second READ statement, which has been given the statement number 302, to repeat the whole process.

The first FORMAT statement is used with two different READ statements, even though the first reads four values and the second only one. We shall explore the precise rules for this sort of thing in Chapter 6; for now we can say that if the same field specifications are desired there is no problem so long as a READ statement never names more variables than there are field specifications in the associated FORMAT. (This is really legal, but it has a special action.) In the second FORMAT statement note the use of the scale factor (the 1P) to shift the decimal point to a position between the first and second digits. The exponent is automatically adjusted to reflect the change.

This program was run with a data card that gave the parameters as 10 volts, 1000 ohms, 0.1 henry, and 0.00000005 farad ($= 0.05$ mfd). The frequency cards ranged from 1000 to 3500 cps in steps of 100 cps. The output is shown in Figure 2.9.

Column headings have been added "by hand" to make it easier to study the output here, a practice that will be followed in most case studies. In Chapter 6 we shall learn how the computer can be instructed rather simply to print various kinds of output identification.

CYCLE	AMPERE
1.000000E 03	3.644952E-03
1.100000E 03	4.134017E-03
1.200000E 03	4.660153E-03
1.300000E 03	5.225284E-03
1.400000E 03	5.828922E-03
1.500000E 03	6.466531E-03
1.600000E 03	7.127408E-03
1.700000E 03	7.792432E-03
1.800000E 03	8.432597E-03
1.900000E 03	9.009916E-03
2.000000E 03	9.482331E-03
2.100000E 03	9.812741E-03
2.200000E 03	9.979223E-03
2.300000E 03	9.981339E-03
2.400000E 03	9.838950E-03
2.500000E 03	9.584684E-03
2.600000E 03	9.254599E-03
2.700000E 03	8.881114E-03
2.800000E 03	8.489619E-03
2.900000E 03	8.098015E-03
3.000000E 03	7.717813E-03
3.100000E 03	7.355712E-03
3.200000E 03	7.015075E-03
3.300000E 03	6.697088E-03
3.400000E 03	6.401600E-03
3.500000E 03	6.127688E-03

Figure 2.9. Output of the program of Figure 2.8, using the parameter values stated in the text. (Case Study 2.)

When $2\pi fL = 1/(2\pi fC)$, the term in parentheses in the radical is zero and the circuit is said to be *resonant*. In the printout of Figure 2.9 a broad resonance peak around the resonant frequency of about 2250 cps is evident.

2.8 Case Study 3: Column Design

An engineer wishes to obtain data for plotting a curve of the safe loading of a certain type of load-bearing column as a function of the slimness ratio of the column. He has selected from a handbook two empirical formulas that give the safe loading in two ranges of the slimness ratio.

$$S = \begin{cases} 17{,}000 - 0.485R^2 & \text{for } R < 120 \\ \dfrac{18{,}000}{1 + \dfrac{R^2}{18{,}000}} & \text{for } R \geq 120 \end{cases}$$

where S = safe loading, pounds per square inch
R = slimness ratio, dimensionless

The safe loading is to be calculated for slimness ratios of 20 to 200 in steps of 5.

Planning a program to get the desired output can be approached by breaking it down into three questions:

1. How to choose between the two formulas, given a value of R. This is fairly easy: use an IF statement to compare the size of R against 120 and branch to one of two arithmetic statements to apply the appropriate formula.

2. How to run through the required values of R. This can be handled in a number of ways. Perhaps the easiest is to start R at 20, compute S, then add 5 to R, compute a new value of S, etc., each time around testing to see whether R has reached 200. This method will not require the reading of data cards, which makes the program a bit simpler, but it does mean that to run it for any values of R other than those "built into" it would require a program change. We are buying simplicity at the cost of inflexibility — a common tradeoff.

3. How to present the results, taking into account the accuracy expected. The accuracy of the computed results is almost completely dominated by the question of the accuracy of the approximation formulas. The handbook from which they were taken is silent on accuracy (a not uncommon situation), but we can draw some conclusions from the fact that the constants are given to only two or three significant figures. Furthermore, mechanical design formulas of this kind usually include a safety factor, so that extreme precision is clearly not indicated.

We shall see, however, that there *is* an accuracy problem in getting the successive values of R for other values of the increment in R than the one stated. We shall return to this question later.

It appears that if we presented the results as integers we should be providing more significant figures than could possibly mean anything. In fact, we should probably be much closer to reality if we printed three or four significant figures, multiplied by a power of 10—which is exactly what we can do using the E field specification.

A flowchart is shown in Figure 2.10. We begin by setting R equal to 20 to get our starting value, in a step that is not repeated. Then we must test to see whether R is more or less than 120—which seems pointless, since we just made it 20. The point, as in Case Study 2, is that we are now in a part of the program that will be repeated many times as R increases. There is no way to say to a computer, "Be sensible: use the first formula until R reaches

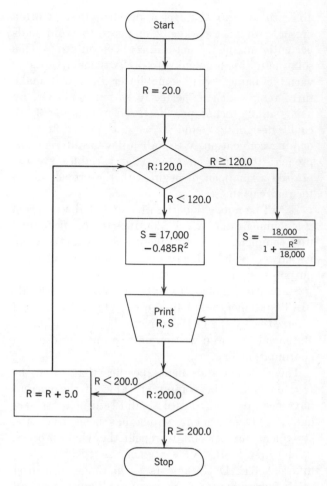

Figure 2.10.   Flowchart of a column design calculation. (Case Study 3.)

120." *We* must provide an *explicit* test on the value of R *every time.*

The decision box takes us to one of the two formulas to compute S, after either of which we print the values of R and S. (It is a good idea, incidentally, to print both the computed function value *and* the argument. If we were to print only the computed result, anyone using the output would have to figure out for himself the R value corresponding to each value of X.)

Now we ask whether R is greater than or equal to 200. If it is, we have just computed the last line of the output and we stop accordingly. If not, we add five to it and go around again. One would think that R could never be greater than 200 at this point; if it were, we should already have left the loop the time before. This is indeed true *with the numbers used here*. We shall return to this point shortly.

The FORTRAN program is shown in Figure 2.11. If the flowchart has been clearly understood, it should not be too much trouble to follow the pro-

```
C CASE STUDY 3 - COLUMN DESIGN
C
C INITIAL VALUE FOR R - NOT REPEATED
      R=20.
C CHOOSE BETWEEN THE TWO FORMULAS
   10 IF(R.GE.120.)GOTO30
      S=1.7E4-.485*R*R
      GOTO40
   30 S=1.8E4/(1.+R*R/1.8E4)
   40 WRITE(6,101)R,S
  101 FORMAT(F10.0,1PE15.3)
C TEST FOR COMPLETION
      IF(R.GE.200.)STOP
C INCREMENT R
      R=R+5.
      GOTO10
      END
```

Figure 2.11.   Program for a column design calculation. (Case Study 3.)

gram. The FORMAT statement provides a review of two of the most common field specifications. In F10.0 the *F* means that the number will be printed

in fixed format (without an exponent), the 10 means that 10 printing positions will be allotted to the number, and the zero means that there will be no digits after the decimal point. In 1PE15.3 the 1P means shifting the decimal point to the more familiar position between the first and second digits, the E means floating point form (with an exponent), the 15 means 15 printing positions, and the 3 means three decimal places.

This program has been written in a more compact style than will ordinarily be used, to demonstrate

R	*S*
20.	1.681E 04
25.	1.670E 04
30.	1.656E 04
35.	1.641E 04
40.	1.622E 04
45.	1.602E 04
50.	1.579E 04
55.	1.553E 04
60.	1.525E 04
65.	1.495E 04
70.	1.462E 04
75.	1.427E 04
80.	1.390E 04
85.	1.350E 04
90.	1.307E 04
95.	1.262E 04
100.	1.215E 04
105.	1.165E 04
110.	1.113E 04
115.	1.059E 04
120.	1.000E 04
125.	9.636E 03
130.	9.284E 03
135.	8.944E 03
140.	8.617E 03
145.	8.302E 03
150.	8.000E 03
155.	7.710E 03
160.	7.431E 03
165.	7.164E 03
170.	6.908E 03
175.	6.663E 03
180.	6.429E 03
185.	6.204E 03
190.	5.989E 03
195.	5.783E 03
200.	5.586E 03

Figure 2.12.   Output of the program of Figure 2.11. (Case Study 3.)

R	*S*
195.5986	5.759E 03
195.6986	5.755E 03
195.7986	5.751E 03
195.8986	5.747E 03
195.9986	5.743E 03
196.0986	5.739E 03
196.1986	5.735E 03
196.2985	5.731E 03
196.3985	5.727E 03
196.4985	5.723E 03
196.5985	5.719E 03
196.6985	5.715E 03
196.7985	5.711E 03
196.8985	5.707E 03
196.9985	5.703E 03
197.0985	5.699E 03
197.1985	5.695E 03
197.2985	5.692E 03
197.3985	5.688E 03
197.4985	5.684E 03
197.5985	5.680E 03
197.6985	5.676E 03
197.7985	5.672E 03
197.8985	5.668E 03
197.9985	5.664E 03
198.0985	5.660E 03
198.1985	5.656E 03
198.2985	5.652E 03
198.3985	5.648E 03
198.4985	5.644E 03
198.5985	5.641E 03
198.6985	5.637E 03
198.7985	5.633E 03
198.8985	5.629E 03
198.9985	5.625E 03
199.0985	5.621E 03
199.1985	5.617E 03
199.2985	5.613E 03
199.3985	5.609E 03
199.4985	5.606E 03
199.5985	5.602E 03
199.6985	5.598E 03
199.7985	5.594E 03
199.8985	5.590E 03
199.9985	5.586E 03
200.0985	5.582E 03

Figure 2.13.   Output of the program of Figure 2.11, modified to use an interval of 0.1 and print more decimals. (Case Study 3.)

```
C  TENR IS ALWAYS A WHOLE NUMBER IN THIS VERSION, AND WHOLE NUMBERS
C  ARE REPRESENTED EXACTLY IN THE COMPUTER USED.  THEREFORE, ERRORS
C  DO NOT ACCUMULATE.  TENR IS DIVIDED BY 10 TO GET THE VALUE OF R.
C
       TENR = 200.0
   10  R = TENR / 10.0
       IF ( R .GE. 120.0) GO TO 30
       S = 1.7E4 - 0.485 * R * R
       GO TO 40
   30  S = 1.8E4 / ( 1.0 + R * R / 1.8E4)
   40  WRITE (6, 101) R, S
  101  FORMAT (F10.4, 1PE15.3)
       IF ( R .GE. 200.0) STOP
       TENR = TENR + 1.0
       GO TO 10
       END
```

Figure 2.14. The program of Figure 2.11 revised to use an interval of 0.1 and with a modified method of incrementing R. (Case Study 3.)

that matters of spacing in writing programs are at the discretion of the programmer.

The output is shown in Figure 2.12.

Let us now return to the question of the accuracy in the method of incrementing R. Suppose we ask that S be printed for all values of R from 20 to 200 in steps of 0.1. To do this we simply change the constant in $R = R + 5$. to make it read $R = R + 0.1$. While we are changing the program, let us also change the FORMAT statement so that we can get seven digits in R. These will be needed to see what is happening. The last few lines of the output this time are shown in Figure 2.13.

What has happened? Why is the last value not 200? The answer is that the program was run on a binary computer, and there is no exact binary representation of the decimal fraction 0.1. In the computer used, the IBM 7094, the floating binary approximation of decimal 0.1 differs from the true value by about 2^{-33}. This small error builds up when it is added to R hundreds of times, as this version of the program requires.

If we had required R to be *exactly* 200 in order to get out of the loop, we would naturally never have achieved the equality.

This particular problem would not arise in a decimal computer, since decimal 0.1 obviously has an exact representation in such a machine. The problem is nevertheless fairly common.

The best solution is to make the addition of the increment either in integers, which are exact, or in some real number that has an exact representation. As it happens, the floating point (FORTRAN real) representation of a mathematical integer is exact. What we can do, therefore, is to work with a variable called, say, TENR, which is ten times the value of R. To this we add one each time, getting an exact sum. Then before going into the computa-

R	S
195.6000	5.759E 03
195.7000	5.755E 03
195.8000	5.751E 03
195.9000	5.747E 03
196.0000	5.743E 03
196.1000	5.739E 03
196.2000	5.735E 03
196.3000	5.731E 03
196.4000	5.727E 03
196.5000	5.723E 03
196.6000	5.719E 03
196.7000	5.715E 03
196.8000	5.711E 03
196.9000	5.707E 03
197.0000	5.703E 03
197.1000	5.699E 03
197.2000	5.695E 03
197.3000	5.691E 03
197.4000	5.688E 03
197.5000	5.684E 03
197.6000	5.680E 03
197.7000	5.676E 03
197.8000	5.672E 03
197.9000	5.668E 03
198.0000	5.664E 03
198.1000	5.660E 03
198.2000	5.656E 03
198.3000	5.652E 03
198.4000	5.648E 03
198.5000	5.644E 03
198.6000	5.640E 03
198.7000	5.637E 03
198.8000	5.633E 03
198.9000	5.629E 03
199.0000	5.625E 03
199.1000	5.621E 03
199.2000	5.617E 03
199.3000	5.613E 03
199.4000	5.609E 03
199.5000	5.606E 03
199.6000	5.602E 03
199.7000	5.598E 03
199.8000	5.594E 03
199.9000	5.590E 03
200.0000	5.586E 03

Figure 2.15. Output of the program of Figure 2.14. (Case Study 3.)

30

tion we divide TENR by 10 to get R. This division will give a result that is not always exactly correct, *but this error does not accumulate.*

The revised program is shown in Figure 2.14. The last few lines of output this time are given in Figure 2.15.

2.9 Case Study 4: Newton-Raphson Method, Program Checkout

In this case study we shall use the Newton-Raphson method, one of the most common numerical techniques, for finding a root of an equation as the vehicle for an introduction to methods of "checking out" a program to remove its errors and to ensure accuracy.

Given a function of x, $F(x) = 0$, the Newton-Raphson method says that, subject to certain conditions, if x_i is an approximation to a root, a better approximation is given by

$$x_{i+1} = x_i - \frac{F(x_i)}{F'(x_i)}$$

where the prime denotes the derivative.

For instance, suppose we have the function $F(x) = x^2 - 25$. As a first approximation to the root, take $x_0 = 2$. Since $F'(x) = 2x$, a better approximation can be found from

$$x_1 = x_0 - \frac{x_0^2 - 25}{2x_0} = 2 - \frac{4 - 25}{4} = 7.25$$

This is called an *iteration* formula. Continuing in the same way, now substituting 7.25 into the same formula, and so on, we get a succession of approximations:

$$x_0 = 2$$

$$x_1 = 7.25$$

$$x_2 = 5.35$$

$$x_3 = 5.0114$$

$$x_4 = 5.00001$$

$$x_5 = 5.0000000$$

The approximation can be made as accurate as we please by continuing the process. One root of the original equation is indeed 5, the square root of the constant term.

The Newton-Raphson method is readily adapted to computer use. In fact, some variation of the scheme just sketched is actually used for finding square roots. Let us try it on a more interesting equation:

$$F(x) = \cosh x + \cos x - 3 = 0$$

We find readily that

$$F'(x) = \sinh x - \sin x$$

so the iteration formula is

$$x_{i+1} = x_i - \frac{\cosh x_i + \cos x_i - 3}{\sinh x_i - \sin x_i}$$

We shall have to compute the hyperbolic sine and cosine from exponentials, since we have no built-in functions for evaluating them:

$$\cosh x = \frac{e^x + e^{-x}}{2}$$

$$\sinh x = \frac{e^x - e^{-x}}{2}$$

Figure 2.16 is a flowchart of the basic computational scheme. We begin by assigning a value to X, which becomes our "previous" approximation. In the iteration formula we wrote x_i. The subscript is not needed; all that is necessary is to have two

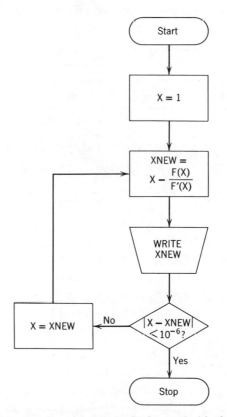

Figure 2.16. Flowchart of the Newton-Raphson method for finding the root of an equation F(x) = 0. (Case Study 4.)

different variables, one for the "old" value of X and another for the "new" value. We write XNEW for the new and compute it from the iteration formula. Because it will be interesting to see the succession of approximations, we now write out the value of XNEW. Ordinarily we would do this only at the conclusion, when the root had been found.

Next comes the test for convergence: are the last two approximations the same, to within 10^{-6}? This question has to be asked in terms of the absolute value of the difference between X and XNEW, because we do not know, in general, whether the convergence will be from above or below. If the process has not converged, we set $X = $ XNEW, which makes the just-computed value the "old" value the next time around, and return to compute another XNEW.

The program shown in Figure 2.17 contains quite a number of deliberate errors. After noting a few features of the program, we shall trace through the steps we might follow in discovering and correcting the various kinds of error. To simplify this discussion, all statements have been given statement numbers.

Statement 2 assigns the value of e^x to the variable EX. This will be used twice in the formula, and it

is wasteful of time to go through the function evaluation twice. Statement 3 assigns the value of e^{-x} to EMX, since e^x and e^{-x} are reciprocals. Division is also faster than function evaluation. (Naturally, *in this program* the time savings could not be detected with a stopwatch, but the principles are valid.) The iteration formula in statement 4 is routine, as is the WRITE statement.

The IF statement uses the absolute value function ABS to eliminate the sign of the difference between X and XNEW. Statements 8 and 9 are unexceptional.

There are a great many ways to make mistakes in a program. One of the easiest is in punching the program cards. If the programmer punches them himself, he may make mistakes because he is not experienced at operating the card punch. If they are punched by a cardpunch operator, there is the danger of misreading handwriting. Either way, much time can be saved in the long run by checking the deck carefully before trying to compile it.

One common way to prove the accuracy of punching is to *verify* the deck with a *verifier*. This machine has the same general appearance as a card punch but examines only the punching. A second operator strikes the same keys, but all that happens

FORTRAN CODING FORM

Program				Punching Instructions				Page of
			Graphic				Card Form # *	Identification
Programmer		Date	Punch					73 80

```
C CASE STUDY 4 - NEWTON-RAPHSON METHOD - PROGRAM CHECKOUT
C THIS PROGRAM CONTAINS MANY DELIBERATE ERRORS
C
   1  X = 1.0
   2  EX = EXP(X)
   3  EMX = 1.0 / EX
   4  XNEW = X + ((EX+EMX)/2. + COSF(X) - 3.)/((EX-EMX)/2 - SIN(X)
   5  WRITE (6,6), XNEW
   6  FORMAT (F10.6)
   7  IF (ABS(X - XNEW) .LT. 1.E-6), STOP
   8  XNEW = X
   9  GO TO 2
  10  END
```

Figure 2.17. Program for the Newton-Raphson method of finding the root of an equation. (Case Study 4.) ***This program contains deliberate errors.***

```
C CASE STUDY 4 - NEWTON-RAPHSON METHOD - PROGRAM CHECKOUT
C THIS PROGRAM CONTAINS MANY DELIBERATE ERRORS
C
   1 X = 1.0
   2 EX = EXP(X)
   3 EMX = 1.0 / EX
   4 XNEW = X + ((EX+EMX)/2. P COSF(X) - 3.)/((EX-EMX)/2  - SIN(X)
   5 WR1TE (6,6), XNEW
   L FORMAT (F10.6)
   7 IF (ABS(X - XNEW) .LT. 1.E-6) STOP
   8 XNEW = X
   9 GO TO 2
  10 END
```

Figure 2.18. Tabulator listing of the deck punched from the program of Figure 2.17. (Case Study 4.)

is that the holes in the cards are matched to see if they correspond to the keys struck by the verifier operator. If not, a red light signals the discrepancy.

A second way to check the accuracy of the punching of the program deck is to *list* it with a *tabulator*. Figure 2.18 shows the listing of the deck in Figure 2.17. Study discloses three errors in punching. In statement 4 there is a P where there should be a plus sign; this happens to be easy to do because of the way the cardpunch works. The same explanation applies to the L where statement number 6 should be. In statement 5 WRITE has been punched as WR1TE; this would prevent the program from being compiled. We correct these errors, checking the corrected cards most carefully to see that no new errors were made in repunching.

A study of this listing of the program will no doubt reveal to the careful reader many of the deliberate errors also. This is generally true. *Deskchecking* of the program listing before compiling is usually a good investment of the programmer's time as well as a saving of some wasted computer time. Let us pretend that we have not seen these other errors, so that we may learn how they can be detected later in the process.

Now we shall try to compile. All FORTRAN compilers include some degree of diagnostic checking for statements that are *syntactically* illegal; that is, statements that do not follow the rules for forming a statement, no matter what they might mean. FORTRAN cannot determine whether we wrote what we meant to, in general, but it can sometimes establish without question that a statement is illegal. The degree of checking in the various FORTRAN systems varies widely.

In our case the compiler detected two errors the first time compiling was attempted, as shown in Figure 2.19. The comment "parentheses do not balance" refers, we discover after a little searching, to a missing right parenthesis at the end of the statement. In the second line of the first error comment we note "assembly suppressed." Assembly is part of the compilation process, and its deletion means that the program was not translated into an object program. This is a disabling error. Still, the error scan was continued, looking for other possibilities. We see that statement 5 contained an error of a different kind: we inserted an unnecessary comma, but the meaning was still clear. A warning message was issued but the compilation was not deleted because of this error.

The compiler used for this program consists of a number of phases or passes. If a disabling error is detected in the first phase, that phase is completed but no others are initiated. After we have corrected the two errors noted in the first phase, we try again. This time the error scan continues to a second phase, in which another error is detected. This time the compilation is again disabled, with the error message (not reproduced) on statement 4: "types combined illegally by an arithmetic operator." A search discloses a missing decimal point in the 2 near the end of the statement.

Correcting this, we try once more. The message (again not reproduced) this time is "undefined virtual control section 'COSF'." What a virtual control section might be need not concern us, for we see immediately that COSF was written where it should have been COS. As it happens, earlier versions of FORTRAN required the name of every function to end in F; forgetfulness can be blamed for this one.

With these corrections made, the program compiles. There may still be errors! (And there are.) There is a limit to the amount of checking that can economically be designed into a compiler, and there are certain types of error that cannot be detected in any case.

```
C CASE STUDY 4 - NEWTON-RAPHSON METHOD - PROGRAM CHECKOUT
C THIS PROGRAM CONTAINS MANY DELIBERATE ERRORS
C
  1 X = 1.0
  2 EX = EXP(X)
  3 EMX = 1.0 / EX
  4 XNEW = X + ((EX+EMX)/2. + COSF(X) - 3.)/((EX-EMX)/2  - SIN(X)
```

PARENTHESES DO NOT BALANCE.

SOURCE ERROR 31, LEVEL 3.   ASSEMBLY SUPPRESSED.

```
  5 WRITE (6,6), XNEW
```

THE CORRECT FORM IS (...) LIST- NOT (...),LIST -
SUPERFLUOUS COMMA IGNORED.

SOURCE ERROR 267, LEVEL 1.   WARNING ONLY.

```
  6 FORMAT (F10.6)
  7 IF (ABS(X - XNEW) .LT. 1.E-6) STOP
  8 XNEW = X
  9 GO TO 2
 10 END
```
ASSEMBLY DELETED.

Figure 2.19. The first error listing produced by the compiler from the program of Figure 2.17. (Case Study 4.)

When the corrected program was run, the computer wrote out several hundred feet of magnetic tape output before the operator decided that something probably was wrong and interrupted the program at the computer console. When the tape was printed, it was found that the value −1.746581 had been written out continuously; the tape contained the one value approximately 50,000 times.

What happened? Somehow the iteration system was not iterating correctly; the suspicion is that it never got a new value to work with. This was indeed the case: in statement 8 the variables are reversed from what we want.

With this statement corrected, we go back to the computer. This time the answers are different, but the process never converges. The first 20 approximations are shown in Figure 2.20. Now we have to wonder if the iteration formula itself is correct. We accordingly carefully inspect the method of computing sinh x and cosh x, the formula for the derivative, and anything else we can think of to check. An excellent idea is to calculate what the first value of XNEW should be, using a book of tables

XNEW

```
-1.746581
-1.623947
-1.333526
-0.405951
44.334846
45.334846
46.334846
47.334846
48.334846
49.334846
50.334846
51.334846
52.334846
53.334846
54.334846
55.334846
56.334846
57.334846
58.334846
59.334846
```

Figure 2.20. The first 20 approximations to the root of an equation produced by the program of Figure 2.17, after correcting some of the errors. (Case Study 4.)

```
C CASE STUDY 4 - NEWTON-RAPHSON METHOD - PROGRAM CHECKOUT
C REVISED VERSION - ERRORS REMOVED AND AN ITERATION COUNTER INCLUDED
C
    1 X = 1.0
C N IS A COUNT OF THE NUMBER OF ITERATIONS
      N = 1
    2 EX = EXP(X)
    3 EMX = 1.0 / EX
    4 XNEW = X - ((EX+EMX)/2. + COS(X) - 3.)/((EX-EMX)/2. - SIN(X))
    5 WRITE (6,6) XNEW
    6 FORMAT (F10.6)
C THE IF STATEMENT NOW INCLUDES A TEST OF THE ITERATION COUNTER
    7 IF (ABS(X - XNEW) .LT. 1.E-6 .OR. N .GT. 20) STOP
      N = N +1
    8 X = XNEW
    9 GO TO 2
   10 END
```

Figure 2.21. The final correct version of the program for finding the root of an equation by the Newton-Raphson method. (Case Study 4.)

and a desk calculator. This is revealing: the value should be about 3.75, whereas we had −1.75. Sooner or later it will be noticed that in statement 4 the fraction $F(x)/F'(x)$ is being *added* to X instead of being *subtracted* from it.

This could have been discovered from the first run, of course, if an approximate value had been computed for a check. It is always a very good idea to compute a test case by desk calculator.

The chances are getting better that the next time we may get a correct answer, but while we are making this change let us insert a *counter* in the program to set a limit on the number of iterations. It is most disconcerting to leave a program to be run on the night shift and discover in the morning that it ran two hours when we thought it might take two minutes at the longest. The counter is a simple matter of setting N equal to 1 at the beginning of the program, adding one to it on each iteration, and in each iteration asking if it has yet exceeded some reasonable limit on the number of iterations. The test is readily made a part of the IF statement we already have by using the logical operator .OR. to combine it with the convergence test.

The completed program is shown in Figure 2.21.

XNEW
```
3.746581
2.947440
2.348734
1.995278
1.871750
1.858076
1.857921
1.857921
```

Figure 2.22. The sequence of approximations produced by the program of Figure 2.21. (Case Study 4.)

The output from it is given in Figure 2.22, where we see the rapid convergence to an answer that is in fact correct.

Most programs either do not compile the first time or, if they do, they produce incorrect answers. Experienced programmers expect to have to spend time on program checkout and they plan accordingly. We may conclude this brief introduction to the subject of program checkout with a few suggestions on how to go about it.

1. Checkout is usually facilitated if values of intermediate variables are available. In common practice we insert extra WRITE statements to get the values, then remove the cards and recompile when checkout is completed.

2. Time spent in desk-checking a program will shorten the total time the programmer must spend on checkout and will also save computer time. This should be done both before and after the program cards are punched.

3. Never assume that a program is correct just because the compiler detects no errors.

4. Accomplish as much as you can with each computer run. Resist the almost overwhelming temptation to rush back to the machine after finding each error.

5. The final test of a program is comparison with hand calculations wherever possible. In choosing test cases, try to select values that bring all parts of the program into operation.

EXERCISES

1. In each of the following you are to draw a flowchart of the decisions required and to write statements to carry out the actions. You may regard these actions as

a small part of a larger program; that is, you may assume that previous statements have given values to all variables and you need not write input and output statements.

*a. If a is greater than b, set x equal to 16.9, but if a is less than or equal to b, set x equal to 56.9.

b. If rho + theta $< 10^{-6}$, transfer to the statement numbered 156; otherwise do nothing.

*c. If rho + theta $< 10^{-6}$, transfer to statement 156; otherwise transfer to statement 762.

*d. Place whichever of the variables x and y is algebraically larger in BIG.

e. Place whichever of the variables x, y, and z is algebraically largest in BIG3. (This can be done with only two IF statements. Establish which of x and y is larger, place it in a temporary location, and then compare this number with z to find the largest of the three.)

f. The variables named r and s may be positive or negative. Place the one that is larger *in absolute value* in BIGAB.

*g. An angle named THETA is known to be positive and less than 30 radians. Subtract 2π from THETA as many times as necessary to reduce it to an angle less than 2π; leave the reduced angle in THETA.

*h. If g and h are both negative, set SIGNS equal to -1; if both are positive, set SIGNS to $+1$; if they have different signs, set SIGNS to zero.

i. Y1, Y2, and Y3 are the ordinates of three points on a curve. If Y2 is a *local maximum*, that is Y2 $>$ Y1 and Y2 $>$ Y3, transfer to statement 456; otherwise transfer to statement 567.

*j. If $a < 0$ and $b > 0$, or if $c = 0$, set OMEGA equal to $\cos(x + 1.2)$; otherwise do nothing.

k. If $i = 1$ and $R < S$, transfer to statement 261; if $i = 1$ and $R \geq S$, transfer to statement 275; if $i \neq 1$, transfer to statement 927.

*l. If $N = 1$, 2, or 8, transfer to statement 250; if $N = 3$ or 7, transfer to statement 251; if $N = 4$, 5, 6, transfer to statement 252. You may assume that N is not less than 1 nor greater than 8.

m. Same as l, except STOP if it is not true that $1 \leq N \leq 8$.

*n. If $0.999 \leq x \leq 1.001$, STOP; otherwise transfer to statement 639. Do this in two ways:

    1. With a logical IF having two relations combined with an .AND..

    2. With a logical IF having only one test, using the absolute value function.

*o. XREAL and XIMAG are the real and imaginary parts of a complex number. Set SQUARE equal to 1 if XREAL and XIMAG are both less than 1 in absolute value; otherwise do nothing.

p. Set CIRCLE equal to 1 if $\sqrt{\text{XREAL}^2 + \text{XIMAG}^2} \leq 1$; otherwise do nothing.

q. Set DIAMND equal to 1 if the point with coordinates XREAL and XIMAG lies within a square of side $\sqrt{2}$ with its corners on the coordinate axes.

2. In the following exercises you are to draw a flowchart and write a complete program, including input and output. You may use F10.0 field specifications for all input and 1PE20.7 for all output.

*a. Read the value of ANNERN; print ANNERN and compute and print TAX according to the following table:

ANNERN (annual earnings)	TAX
Less than $2000	Zero
$2000 or more but less than $5000	2% of the amount over $2000
$5000 or more	$60 plus 5% of the amount over $5000

b. The current United States Withholding Tax on a weekly salary can be computed as follows: 14% of the difference between a man's gross pay and $13 times the number of dependents he claims. Do not assume that there will always be a tax: a man may not have earned more than his dependency allowance. Read the values of GROSS and DEPEND; compute and print TAX, along with GROSS and DEPEND.

*c. Y is to be computed as a function of X according to

$$Y = 16.7X + 9.2X^2 - 1.02X^3$$

There will be no data to read; compute and print both X and Y for X values from 1.0 to 9.9 in steps of 0.1. You may assume for this exercise that you are working with a decimal computer, so that adding 0.1 to X repeatedly will eventually give 9.9 *exactly*.

*d. Same as (c) but your computer is binary. Since the binary representation of decimal 0.1 is a nonterminating fraction, there is no guarantee that adding the binary representation of 0.1 to X repeatedly will give 9.9 *exactly*. Therefore, if you were to start X at 1.0, add 0.1 each time around, and each time test X against 9.9, the odds are you would not get exact equality and thus go on past 9.9. In fact, you might never get out of the loop. Write a program to solve this problem by letting an integer variable run from 10 to 99; convert to real, then divide by 10. Use the result as the independent variable.

e. Y is to be computed as a function of X according to the formula

$$Y = \sqrt{1 + X} + \frac{\cos 2X}{1 + \sqrt{X}}$$

for a number of equally spaced values of X. Three numbers are to be read from a card: XINIT, XINC, and XFIN. XINIT, we assume, is less than XFIN; XINC is positive. Y is to be computed and printed initially for $X = $ XINIT. Then X is to be incremented by XINC, and Y is to be computed and printed for this new value of X, and so on, until Y has been computed for the largest value of X not exceeding XFIN. (The phrase "the largest value of X *not exceeding* XFIN" lets us ignore the problem presented in the last two exercises. However, this formulation does mean that if the data is set up with the intention of terminating the process with X exactly equal to XFIN it may not do so.)

3. In the following exercises the emphasis is on trying to devise decision processes rather than on computations. Draw a flowchart or describe your method in

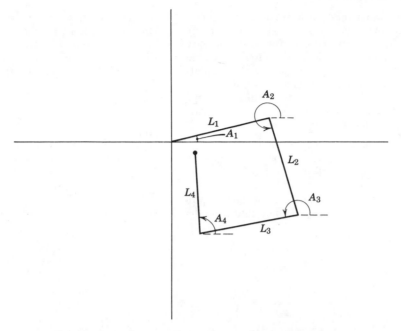

Figure 2.23.   One possible figure to be analyzed in Exercise 3a.

words. Write a program if you wish. The methods you devise must be *capable* of implementation in FORTRAN, even if you do not write programs. (Some of them are quite difficult.)

a. Given four line segments that supposedly form a square as sketched in Figure 2.23, compute the value of CLOSRE, the distance of the end of L_4 from the origin. You may not take advantage of any particular orientation of the square. If the error of closure is less than 1% of the sum of the lengths of the four sides and no side is zero, set the variable OK to 1; otherwise set OK to zero.

b. Given two times, both expressed in hours and minutes since midnight, such as 0145, 1130, or 2350, you are guaranteed that $h_1 m_1$, the first time, is earlier than $h_2 m_2$, the second time, and that they are less than 24 hours apart. You are *not* guaranteed that they are in the same day: for instance, 2350 before midnight is earlier than 0200 after midnight of the same night. Compute the difference between the two times in minutes.

c. Suppose that the squares of a tic-tac-toe game are numbered as shown in Figure 2.24 and that you are given N1, N2, and N3, the numbers of three squares. Assume that N1 < N2 < N3. If the three squares so designated lie in a line, set LINE to 1; otherwise set LINE to zero. Can you suggest a way to renumber the squares that would greatly simplify the test?

d. A certain parlor game requires the determination of the number of common letters in two five-letter words, neither of which has any duplicated letters. For instance, there are no common letters in BLACK and WHITE, one common letter in BLACK and MAUVE, and five common letters in NAILS and SNAIL. Outline a method of computing in DUPE the number of common letters.

e. You are given 10 pairs of x-y values, representing coordinate points on a bubble-chamber photograph. Devise a way to decide whether the track is circular and, if so, to compute its radius of curvature. There should be an allowance for experimental error; that is, your test must not ask that the points represent a circular arc *exactly*.

f. Devise an approximation process to find a value of x for which $\cosh x = 3 - \cos x$.

g. Devise an approximation process to find a value of x for which $\cos x + \sqrt{4.28 - x^2} = x^2 + 5.32$.

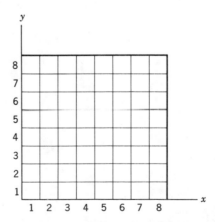

Figure 2.25.   Numbering system for a checkerboard used in Exercise 3i.

1	2	3
4	5	6
7	8	9

Figure 2.24.   Numbering scheme for tic-tac-toe used in Exercise 3c.

h. For each of two aircraft you are given the speed, altitude, direction, and position. If the altitudes vary by at least 1000 ft., do nothing else. If the altitudes vary less than 1000 ft. and the flight paths intersect within a half hour, determine whether at any time the two aircraft are within 10 minutes flying time of each other.

i. A checkerboard is placed on a coordinate system, as shown in Figure 2.25. The equations of two lines are determined by four numbers a, b, c, d in

$$y = ax + b$$

$$y = cx + d$$

If the two lines intersect anywhere on the board, produce the square number. If they do not intersect, determine whether at any point on the board they pass through adjacent squares.

j. Suppose you have discovered that your FORTRAN system contains a function named F. You know nothing about it, except that if you write a statement such as

$$Y = F(X)$$

where X has already been given a value, a value is stored for Y. Devise a test to establish whether F is a continuous function of X over the range $(0, 5)$. (You will have to arrange a suitable modification of the usual definition of continuity to allow for the fact that FORTRAN "real" numbers are only rational fractions in the mathematical sense. By *mathematical* definitions, no function of any sort in a digital computer is ever continuous.)

3. DOUBLE PRECISION, COMPLEX, AND LOGICAL VARIABLES

3.1 Introduction

So far we have dealt with real and integer quantities and have used the IJKLMN naming convention for distinguishing between them. In this chapter we shall learn first how to override the naming convention, for example, allowing ABC to be the name of an integer variable and IM the name of a real variable. We shall then spend most of the chapter studying three other types of variables, double precision, complex, and logical, all of which simplify or make possible various kinds of useful and interesting processing and which we shall investigate in three extended case studies.

3.2 Type Statements

A type statement consists of one of the declarations INTEGER, REAL, DOUBLE PRECISION, COMPLEX, LOGICAL, or EXTERNAL, followed by as many variable names as necessary, separated by commas. For instance, we might write the following TYPE statements in a program:

```
REAL J
INTEGER B
INTEGER I, ABC, ROOT8
REAL MATRIX, NUMBER, X
DOUBLE PRECISION DENOM,
  PREVX, TERM, N
COMPLEX T, N1, N2, D1
LOGICAL A1, A2, K
EXTERNAL COS, MULT
```

The type statement must precede the first use of the name in any executable statement in the program.

The variable I could have been omitted from the INTEGER statement and X from the REAL statement without effect; these names are already identified as integer and real, respectively, by their first letters. On the other hand, there is no harm in such "unnecessary" inclusions in type statements, and some programmers make a point of naming every variable in a type statement. This helps to guard against failure to give a correct type to a variable whose name does not agree with the naming convention. (An electrical engineer's habit and training is to use I for current and L for inductance, for instance. If he makes the point of putting all variable names in type statements, he will be less likely to overlook the necessity of naming I and L in a REAL statement.)

In contrast, variables that are to be considered as double precision, complex, or logical *must* be named in suitable type statements; otherwise they are taken to be real or integer, according to the naming convention.

The EXTERNAL statement is mentioned here only for completeness, for it is considered to be a type statement. However, we shall not consider it until Chapter 7 in functions and subroutines. At that time we shall also learn that the five type specifications can be applied to functions as well as to variables.

For the rest of this chapter we turn to a study of the three new types of quantity.

3.3 Double Precision Constants, Variables, and Operations

A double-precision number is one that is represented and used more or less like a real number but has more digits. Sometimes there are twice as many digits, as suggested by the name double precision, but this is not always the case. It would probably be safe to say *at least* twice as many digits; one major computer has about $2\frac{1}{3}$ times as many in a double-precision floating point number as a single-precision number.

This extra precision in the representation of numbers is most commonly needed to guard against the effect of rounding error in computations that involve long sequences of arithmetic or operations combining very large and very small numbers in addition or subtraction. We shall examine some examples later.

A double-precision constant is written in exponent form, but with a D instead of an E. The following are acceptable double-precision constants:

$$1.5D0$$
$$5.0D4 \qquad (= 5.0 \times 10^4)$$
$$5.0D-4 \qquad (= 5.0 \times 10^{-4})$$
$$1.2345678923456D0$$

In many FORTRAN systems a long number such as the last may be written without the exponent.

Arithmetic expressions are formed in double precision according to the same rules that apply to real expressions. The operation symbols ($+$, $-$, $*$, $/$, $**$) are the same.

The only question we need to investigate in this area is that of combining double-precision quantities with real (single-precision) quantities in an arithmetic expression. This is explicitly permitted and always gives a double-precision result, which means that simple constants need not be written in double-precision form. As a matter of fact, double-precision constants are needed only if they really have more digits than can be expressed with a real constant and as arguments of functions.

It is permissible to have an integer, real, or double-precision variable on the left side of an arithmetic assignment statement and an expression on the right of some other type. All arithmetic is done according to the expression on the right, and the result is converted according to the variable on the left. (Mixing of integer and real or integer and double precision in an arithmetic expression is not permitted, however.)

Appendix 2 contains tables showing the permissible combinations of integer, real, and double precision values.

The following examples are all acceptable uses of double-precision quantities, assuming that R1, R2, etc., are all real variables, D1, D2, etc., are double-precision and I1, I2, etc., are integer variables.

$$D1 = D2*D3 + (D4 - 8756.7865432D0)/D5$$

$$D1 = 4.0*D2 - D3 / 1.1D0$$

$$D1 = R1 + D1 + R2$$

$$R1 = (D1*D2 - D3*D4) / (D1*D5 - D3*D6)$$

$$D1 = R1 + 2.0$$

$$D1 = (I1 - 8)*I2$$

$$I1 = R1 + D1$$

$$D1 = D2**2$$

It may be noted that in the second example there is a point to making 1.1D0 a double-precision constant: in a binary computer 1.1 has no exact representation of any length, but the double-length constant would be a closer approximation. On the other hand, 4.0, being a whole number, is represented exactly in almost all floating point systems, so that there is no loss of accuracy in using it as a real (single-length) constant.

FORTRAN double-precision functions are provided for a number of mathematical functions. For convenience in remembering, the names of all functions with double-precision function values begin with D. Appendix 3 summarizes the most common functions involving double-precision values. Most of them, as noted, take one or more double-precision arguments and furnish a double-precision function value, but certain special purpose functions do not follow the pattern. For instance, the function SNGL ("Single") takes a double-precision argument and supplies as the function value the real representation of the most significant part of the argument.

Input and output of double-precision quantities is handled with D, a new field specification. D-conversion is the same as E-conversion, except that (1) the list variable associated with such a field specification should be double-precision, (2) there can be more digits (17 is typical), and (3) D is used for the exponent indicator rather than E.

3.4 Case Study 5: Error Analysis in a Double-Precision Sine Routine

The Taylor series for the sine

$$\sin x = x - \frac{x^3}{3!} + \frac{x^5}{5!} - \frac{x^7}{7!} + \cdots$$

is usually described as valid for any finite angle, and the truncation error committed by stopping the summation after a finite number of terms is said to be less in absolute value than the first term neglected. These statements would be true *if there were some way to keep an infinite number of digits in each arithmetic result*. In actual fact it is almost useless for large values of x.

In this case study we shall investigate why this happens, in an attempt to understand the need for double-precision quantities even when the final results are much less accurate than the number of digits carried in program variables.

We shall write a program to evaluate the series directly; that is, we shall start with the first term and continue to compute terms until one that is less in absolute value than, say, 10^{-17} is reached. The sum of the series then ought to be within 10^{-17} of the correct value of the sine.

The program requires a stratagem to avoid producing intermediate results too large to be represented in the computer. The largest angle we shall consider will be about 70 radians; if we were to try to raise 70 to the large powers that will be required, we should greatly exceed the sizes permitted of real and double-precision variables in all but a few FORTRAN systems. Therefore we shall take another approach, that of computing each term from the preceding term. The recursion relation is not complicated. Having the first term x, we can get the next term by multiplying by $-x^2$ and dividing by 2×3. Having the second term, we can get the third by multiplying by $-x^2$ and dividing by 4×5. In short, given the preceding term, we can get the next one by multiplying by $-x^2$ and dividing by the product of the next two integers.

A flowchart is shown in Figure 3.1. It is set up to read cards, each containing an angle in degrees, until it reaches a "sentinel card" with an angle of zero. The angle is first converted to radians by dividing by $180/\pi$; the result is called X. Now we need to get the recursion process started. We shall continually be adding a new term to a sum that will become the sine when enough terms have been computed. To get started we set this sum

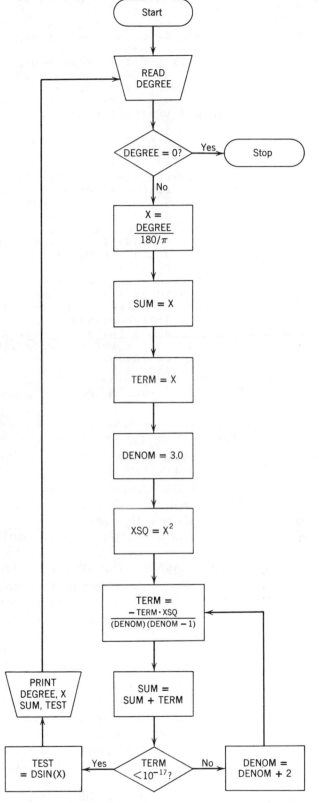

Figure 3.1. Flowchart of a method of computing a sine in double precision. (Case Study 5.)

```
C CASE STUDY 5 - DOUBLE PRECISION SINE ROUTINE
C
      DOUBLE PRECISION X, TERM, SUM, XSQ, DENOM, TEST, DEGREE
  506 READ (5, 504) DEGREE
  504 FORMAT (D23.16)
C TEST FOR ZERO END-OF-DECK SENTINEL
      IF (DEGREE .EQ. 0.0D0) STOP
C CONVERT FROM DEGREES TO RADIANS
      X = DEGREE / (180.0/3.14159265358979321)
C SET UP INITIAL VALUES
      SUM = X
      TERM = X
      DENOM = 3.0
      XSQ = X**2
C COMPUTE NEW TERM FROM PREVIOUS TERM
   25 TERM = -TERM * XSQ / (DENOM * (DENOM - 1.0))
C GET SUM OF TERMS SO FAR
      SUM = SUM + TERM
C TEST FOR CONVERGENCE
      IF (DABS(TERM) .LT. 1.0D-17) GO TO 24
      DENOM = DENOM + 2.0
      GO TO 25
C CONVERT FROM DOUBLE TO SINGLE PRECISION
   24 SDEGR = SNGL(DEGREE)
C GET VALUE FROM SUPPLIED DP SINE ROUTINE FOR COMPARISON
      TEST = DSIN(X)
      WRITE (6, 89) SDEGR, X, SUM, TEST
   89 FORMAT (F8.0, 1P3D26.16)
      GO TO 506
      END
```

Figure 3.2. Program for computing a sine in double precision. (Case Study 5.)

equal to X; the first term computed by the recursion relation will be $-x^3/3!$. Thus the preceding term is initially X. To get the successive integers (mathematical integers, not FORTRAN integers!) we start a variable named DENOM at 3.0. To save recomputing x^2 repeatedly, we compute it once before entering the loop, giving it the name XSQ.

Getting a new term is a simple matter of multiplying the preceding term by $-$XSQ and dividing by the product of DENOM and DENOM -1.0. This new term replaces the preceding term and is added to the sum. We are now ready to find out whether enough terms have been computed. We ask whether the absolute value of the term just computed is less than 10^{-17}. If it is, we are ready to print the result and go back to read another card. If not, the value of DENOM must be incremented by 2.0 before returning to compute another term.

Besides printing the value of the sine computed by this method, it might be interesting to use the double-precision sine routine supplied with the FORTRAN system to compute it also. This is done just before printing.

The program shown in Figure 3.2 illustrates many of the aspects of double-precision programming. The type statement is placed before the appearance of

any variable name, as required. In the READ statement we ask for a double-precision value, which is associated with a D field specification in the FORMAT statement. The field width of 23 allows space for a sign, one digit before the decimal, the decimal point, 16 digits after the decimal, and a four-position exponent. The IF statement that checks for a zero-degree sentinel compares DEGREE with a double-precision zero; the use of the double-precision constant is not actually required.

The statement that converts from degrees to radians shows something that we ordinarily do not see: a division of one constant by another, which should be made with a desk calculator beforehand — but desk calculators that do 17-digit arithmetic are not readily available. If this program were to be run a great many times, it might be worthwhile to make a preliminary run to get the conversion constant.*

---

* Finding tables to give constants to many places can be a problem also. This program was initially written during a visit to Chicago forced by a snowstorm. Most motels do not carry π to 16 decimals, so it was originally computed in the program by writing 4.0*DATAN(1.0D0). This statement was modified in the version displayed.

Down to statement 24 we follow the flowchart quite closely. The only point to note is the occasional mixing of real and double-precision quantities in an arithmetic expression.

At 24 we use the function SNGL to get the more significant half of DEGREE into the form for a real variable. The idea here is that we shall actually be computing the sine for angles that are a whole number of degrees. Therefore we would rather print them in single-length form than as whole numbers, but we cannot write DEGREE in the WRITE statement and then use an F field specification in the FORMAT statement: double-precision variable names in the WRITE list must be associated only with D field specifications. To use the F field specification we must convert to real form. (This is a valid example of the use of the SNGL function, but it may be noted that we could also have written SDEGR = DEGREE to get the same conversion from double to real. Other examples can be found in which the SNGL function is strictly required or is at least a significant convenience.)

The results shown in Figure 3.3 are for 30° plus multiples of 360°. The exact result in every case should therefore be ½. The entry for 30° is as close as we should reasonably expect: 15 correct digits. At 390° we still have 14 good digits; at 750° the number is down to 11; at 1110° there are only 9; at 1470 only 6; at 1830 only 3. At 2190° there are *no* correct digits, and for 2550 degrees the computer tells us that the sine is −130! Larger values likewise lead to complete nonsense.

Let us consider the first entry in which the method fails completely (2550°) to see if we can determine what happened. Using a separate program, not shown, the values of the individual terms and sums were printed. The first term is just the value of X:

44.505895925855405

The second term, to 17 digits,

−14,692.692643741607

When these two terms are added, only 17 digits can be kept. The result is

−14,648.186747815750

The three rightmost digits of the first term had to be shifted off before adding and have been permanently lost. The third term is

1,455,145.7461934667

When the sum of the first two terms is added to this term, once again we can keep only 17 digits, so that the preceding sum must be shifted right two places before adding. That means that five digits of the first term have been permanently lost in this sum:

1,440,497.5594456506

The next few terms are

−68,626,571.044772073
1,887,969,175.3547401
−33,996,742,846.947168
431,665,965,172.74578
−4,071,585,970,550.4682
29,650,348,430,733.331
−171,727,082,331,700.35

By now all but four of the original digits of the first term have been lost; they can never re-enter the computation after the terms start decreasing, when the sum should, of course, be reduced to a number less than 1. The largest term in the series is

$$1.2617630349119573 \cdot 10^{18}$$

SDEGR	X	SUM	TEST
30.	5.2359877559829884D−01	4.9999999999999987D−01	4.9999999999999982D−01
390.	6.8067840827778854D 00	4.9999999999994720D−01	4.9999999999999947D−01
750.	1.3089969389957472D 01	4.9999999990064699D−01	5.0000000000000067D−01
1110.	1.9373154697137056D 01	4.9999999951502385D−01	4.9999999999999947D−01
1470.	2.5656340004316645D 01	5.0000017361712441D−01	5.0000000000000067D−01
1830.	3.1939525311496229D 01	4.9945143207988698D−01	4.9999999999999822D−01
2190.	3.8222710618758815D 01	7.3177176570829348D−01	4.9999999999999822D−01
2550.	4.4505895925855405D 01	−1.3044427329053243D 02	4.9999999999999822D−01
2910.	5.0789081233034987D 01	7.5386000394932480D 03	4.9999999999999822D−01
3270.	5.7072266540214578D 01	1.9678711858946683D 06	4.9999999999999822D−01
3630.	6.3355451847394164D 01	2.2823679813746440D 10	4.9999999999999822D−01
3990.	6.9638637154573741D 01	1.6950649464866085D 13	4.9999999999999338D−01

Figure 3.3.   The output of the program of Figure 3.2 for a series of angles. (Case Study 5.)

After adding this to the sum of the preceding terms, *all* of the digits of the first term have left the scene, along with some of the digits of other terms.

A big part of our accuracy problem is clearly that we lose digits in the small numbers when they are added to the very much larger terms.

But this is not the only problem. This example was run on a computer in which double-precision variables are represented with the equivalent of about 17 decimal digits. Consider a term such as this one, which is the largest term in the series for sin 3270°·

$$3.2246921509364463 \cdot 10^{23}$$

Writing this out, we have

$$322,469,215,093,644,630,000,000$$

The zeros at the right, of course, are not significant; they merely locate the decimal point. In other words, this value is an approximation to some rational fraction; the zeros stand for digits that we cannot keep in the computing system. Putting it another way, this approximation could differ from the true value by as much as 5,000,000. This kind of error makes it hopeless to expect any significance at all in computing a final value that is properly never greater than 1.

We may note briefly how the sine function supplied with the system fared. In all cases there are at least 14 good digits. The slightly decreased accuracy for larger angles is caused by losses of significance in the conversion from degrees to radians and in the reduction of the argument to an angle less than $\pi/2$. The latter is the first action in a practical sine routine, after which only a relatively few terms of the series are required and the round-off problems are minor.

This case study was not intended to be a realistic illustration of the value of double precision but rather a demonstration of the problem of roundoff errors and of the problem of adding very large and very small quantities. These problems are present in almost all calculations, whether done with single or double precision. The problems are usually much less severe in double precision, of course, but even this is no automatic cure-all, as we have seen.

If it really had been necessary to use the method of this case study to compute the sines of angles in the range of 1000 to 1500°, double precision would have been an absolute necessity: the same program, but using single precision, breaks down after about 1000°. In computing sines, we have a way out in the form of a preliminary reduction of the angle. In other applications double precision is the only choice.

3.5 Complex Constants, Variables, and Expressions

A complex quantity in FORTRAN is an ordered pair of FORTRAN real quantities, the first representing the real part of the complex number and the second the imaginary part. We are able to write constants that represent complex numbers; we can specify, using a COMPLEX statement, that a variable represents the real and imaginary parts of a complex number; we can do arithmetic on complex numbers; we have functions available for carrying out various mathematical operations on complex quantities. The capability provided by FORTRAN complex operations is a great saving in programmming effort in certain problems.

A complex constant consists of a pair of real constants enclosed in parentheses and separated by a comma. The following are examples of complex constants and their meanings:

(2.0, 3.0)	2.0 + 3.0i
(2.E5, 2.5E4)	200,000 + 25,000i
(1.075, −0.653)	1.075 − 0.653i
(1.0, 0.0)	1.0 (pure real)
(0.0, 5.0)	5.0i (pure imaginary)

A FORTRAN complex variable is one that has been declared to be complex in a COMPLEX statement. The initial-letter naming convention has no application here, because a variable is never considered to be complex unless it has been so declared; there are no restrictions on the initial letter. A complex variable is stored within the computer as two real quantities.

The five familiar arithmetic operations are all defined for operations on complex quantities, although, of course, the computer must do all the manipulations necessary to separate the complex operations from actions on the real and imaginary parts. For reference, these may be reviewed:

$$(a + bi) + (c + di) = (a + c) + (b + d)i$$

$$(a + bi) - (c + di) = (a - c) + (b - d)i$$

$$(a + bi)*(c + di) = (ac - bd) + (ad + bc)i$$

$$(a + bi) / (c + di) = \frac{(ac + bd)}{c^2 + d^2} + \frac{(bc - ad)}{c^2 + d^2}i$$

$$(a + bi)**I$$

```
C ILLUSTRATIONS OF OPERATIONS ON COMPLEX NUMBERS
C
      COMPLEX A, B, Z, R
C THE DATA CARD FOR THE FOLLOWING READ CONTAINS A = 1 + 2I, B = 3 + 4I
      READ (5, 100) A, B
  100 FORMAT (4F10.0)
      Z = A + B
      WRITE (6, 101) Z
  101 FORMAT (15H1ADDITION        , 2F10.5)
C
      Z = A * B
      WRITE (6, 102) Z
  102 FORMAT (15H0MULTIPLICATION, 2F10.5)
C
      Z = CEXP(A)
      WRITE (6, 103) Z
  103 FORMAT (15H0EXPONENTIAL     , 2F10.5)
C
      Z = 2.0 * A + (10.0, 20.0)
      WRITE (6, 104) Z
  104 FORMAT (15H0SAMPLE 4        , 2F10.5)
C
      R = CMPLX(1.0, 1.0)
      Z = A - R
      WRITE (6, 105) Z
  105 FORMAT (15H0SAMPLE 5        , 2F10.5)
      STOP
      END
```

Figure 3.4. A program illustrating operations on FORTRAN complex variables.

A meaning has not been shown for exponentiation, because the method of raising a complex number to a power in the computer depends on the size of the exponent. For small powers, an actual multiplication is used. For larger powers the number may be converted to polar form and use made of De Moivre's formula.*

A complex quantity can be raised to an integer power only; it cannot be raised to a power that is a real or complex number (using the FORTRAN operator **, that is; the operations are, of course, defined mathematically and can be done in FORTRAN with functions).

---

*A complex number $a + bi$ can be converted to the form $\rho \, (\cos \theta + i \sin \theta)$ in which $\rho = \sqrt{a^2 + b^2}$ is called the absolute value and $\theta = \tan^{-1} b/a$ is called the amplitude. Then $(a + bi)^n = \rho^n \, (\cos n\theta + i \sin n\theta)$.

ADDITION	4.00000	6.00000
MULTIPLICATION	−5.00000	10.00000
EXPONENTIAL	−1.13120	2.47173
SAMPLE 4	12.00000	24.00000
SAMPLE 5	0.	1.00000

Figure 3.5. The output of the program of Figure 3.4.

FORTRAN provides functions for computing the exponential function, logarithm, sine, cosine, and square root of a complex number. The argument and functions are both complex in most cases. The absolute value function supplies a real value. The first letter of all complex-valued functions has been made C for ease in remembering. The list may be found in Appendix 3.†

The complex square root function CSQRT again applies De Moivre's formula.

Four other functions that are provided for manipulating complex variables find heavy use. REAL supplies the real part of its complex argument; AIMAG supplies the imaginary part of its complex argument, both as a FORTRAN real number. The function CMPLX takes two real argument ex-

---

† For reference, here are the definitions of these functions in terms of separate operations on their real and imaginary parts.

$$CABS(a + bi) = \sqrt{a^2 + b^2}$$

$$CEXP(a + bi) = e^a(\cos b + i \sin b)$$

$$CLOG(a + bi) = \tfrac{1}{2} \log(a^2 + b^2) + i \tan^{-1} b/a$$

$$CSIN(a + bi) = \sin a \frac{e^b + e^{-b}}{2} + i \cos a \frac{e^b - e^{-b}}{2}$$

$$CCOS(a + bi) = \cos a \frac{e^b + e^{-b}}{2} - i \sin a \frac{e^b - e^{-b}}{2}$$

pressions, separated by commas, and supplies as the function value the complex number composed of the two values. For instance, we could write

$$Z = CMPLX(A, B)$$

A and B would have to be FORTRAN real variables and Z a FORTRAN complex variable. The result of the statement would be to assign the value of A as the real part of Z, and B as its imaginary part. Since the arguments can be any real-valued expressions, we might also write

$$Z2 = CMPLX (0.0, 4.0*OMEGA + 3.56)$$

This would create in $Z2$ the pure imaginary number with the value given by the expression.

The function CONJG takes a complex argument and supplies the complex conjugate of the number as the function value:

$$CONJG(a + bi) = (a - bi)$$

Input and output of complex numbers is fairly simple. Whenever a complex variable appears in the list of a READ or WRITE statement, FORTRAN expects to transmit two real values and to find two corresponding field specifications in the FORMAT statement. For instance, if H is real and Z is complex, we could write

WRITE (6, 100) H, Z
100 FORMAT (F10.0, F10.3, F12.5)

The F10.0 would be associated with the value of H, the F10.3 with the real part of Z, and the F12.5 with the imaginary part of Z.

Complex and real FORTRAN quantities may be mixed in an expression. When this is done, the FORTRAN reals are taken to be pure real numbers, mathematically; the result is always a complex number. Thus, if Z has been declared to be complex, we may write such expressions as $4.0*Z$ or $Z - H$, where H is a FORTRAN real number. No other mixing is permitted.

Figure 3.4 is a simple illustrative program, which shows several arithmetic statements and some functions. The program reads values of two complex variables named A and B and prints various arithmetic combinations of the two and functions of A. The READ statement lists A and B, with a FORMAT statement having four field specifications. The output FORMAT statements include *Hollerith text*, which will be studied in detail in Chapter 6, to provide line identification. The values of A and B

throughout were $1.0 + 2.0i$ and $3.0 + 4.0i$. The output is shown in Figure 3.5.

3.6 Case Study 6: A Servomechanism Frequency Response Plot

The following case study uses FORTRAN complex variables in a practical engineering problem.

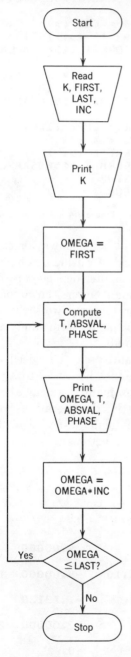

Figure 3.6. Flowchart of a servomechanism frequency response plot calculation. (Case Study 6.)

The transfer function of a certain servomechanism is given by

$$T(j\omega) = \frac{K(1 + j0.4\omega)(1 + j0.2\omega)}{j\omega(1 + j2.5\omega)(1 + j1.43\omega)(1 + j0.02\omega)^2}$$

where ω = angular frequency, radians/second
$j = \sqrt{-1}$ *
T = transfer function
K = amplification factor

Without attempting to show the complete theory, we characterize a transfer function as follows. Consider a "black box" with two input terminals and two output terminals. An input signal with a given frequency is applied to the input; the signal appears at the output, multiplied by the magnitude (absolute value, in the complex variables sense) of the transfer function, with its phase shifted by the phase angle (amplitude) of the transfer function.

---

*In mathematics the symbol for $\sqrt{-1}$ is, of course, i. In electrical engineering i is used for current; j is written for $\sqrt{-1}$.

The transfer function will in general be a complex number. If we indicate the transfer function as $T(j\omega) = a + bi$, the situation can be restated a little more clearly. The magnitude of the input signal appears at the output multiplied by $\sqrt{a^2 + b^2}$ and with its phase shifted by an angle $\theta = \arctan b/a$. Both effects depend strongly on the frequency of the input signal. We shall develop a program, therefore, to show how the servomechanism represented by the transfer function responds to different frequencies. This information is important in designing the servomechanism for stability, among other things.

The program is set up to operate as follows. We wish to read a value of K along with an initial and final value of ω and an increment by which ω should be multiplied to get successive points. For each value of ω we are to print the real and imaginary parts of the transfer function, the magnitude, and the phase angle.

A flowchart is shown in Figure 3.6. We begin by

```
C CASE STUDY 6 - SERVOMECHANISM FREQUENCY RESPONSE
C
      REAL K, FIRST, LAST, INC, OMEGA, ABSVAL, PHASE
      COMPLEX T, N1, N2, D1, D2, D3, D4
C READ PARAMETERS
      READ (5, 500) K, FIRST, LAST, INC
  500 FORMAT (4F10.0)
      WRITE (6, 600) K
  600 FORMAT (1PE14.5)
      OMEGA = FIRST
C SET UP COMPLEX FACTORS, USING THE CMPLX FUNCTION TO CONVERT FROM
C THE FORM OF TWO FORTRAN REAL NUMBERS, REPRESENTING THE REAL AND
C IMAGINARY PARTS OF THE COMPLEX NUMBER, TO THE FORM OF ONE FORTRAN
C COMPLEX NUMBER
    6 N1 = CMPLX(1.0, 0.4 * OMEGA)
      N2 = CMPLX(1.0, 0.2 * OMEGA)
      D1 = CMPLX(0.0, OMEGA)
      D2 = CMPLX(1.0, 2.5 * OMEGA)
      D3 = CMPLX(1.0, 1.43 * OMEGA)
      D4 = CMPLX(1.0, 0.02 * OMEGA)
C COMPUTE TRANSFER FUNCTION
      T = K * N1 * N2 / (D1 * D2 * D3 * D4**2)
C GET ABSOLUTE VALUE
      ABSVAL = CABS(T)
C USE TWO-ARGUMENT ARCTANGENT FUNCTION TO GET PHASE ANGLE
C ANGLE IS GIVEN IN RADIANS - MUST CONVERT TO DEGREES
      PHASE = 57.29578 * ATAN2(AIMAG(T), REAL(T))
C NOTE THAT T IS COMPLEX, REQUIRING TWO ASSOCIATED FIELD SPECIFICATIONS
      WRITE (6, 700) OMEGA, T, ABSVAL, PHASE
  700 FORMAT (1P5E14.4)
C INCREMENT OMEGA
      OMEGA = INC * OMEGA
C TEST FOR COMPLETION
      IF (OMEGA .LE. LAST ) GO TO 6
      STOP
      END
```

Figure 3.7.   Program for a servomechanism frequency response plot calculation. (Case Study 6.)

reading the data and immediately print the value of K; assuming that the program would normally be used to run through values of ω for many different values of K, it is essential that the output be identified with the parameter value. Then we set ω equal to the starting value that has been read, compute the four output numbers, and print them. After incrementing ω we ask whether the new value is greater than the specified final value of ω and stop if it is; otherwise we return to compute the new point.

In the program of Figure 3.7 we begin with the type statements. The REAL statement includes the names of four variables (FIRST, ABSVAL, OMEGA, and PHASE), which would be regarded as real by default even if they were not mentioned in the REAL.

The computation loop begins at statement 6, where we see the CMPLX function used to assemble the real and imaginary parts of N1, the first complex factor in the numerator of the transfer function. The six statements at 6 and following would, of course, make no sense if the variables had not been declared to be complex. D1 is the $j\omega$ factor

OMEGA	Treal	Timag	Absolute Value	Phase
K 9.00000E 02				
2.0000E-02	-3.0236E 03	-4.4825E 04	4.4927E 04	-9.3859E 01
2.5000E-02	-3.0183E 03	-3.5782E 04	3.5909E 04	-9.4822E 01
3.1250E-02	-3.0101E 03	-2.8528E 04	2.8687E 04	-9.6023E 01
3.9062E-02	-2.9974E 03	-2.2702E 04	2.2899E 04	-9.7522E 01
4.8828E-02	-2.9777E 03	-1.8012E 04	1.8256E 04	-9.9387E 01
6.1035E-02	-2.9474E 03	-1.4225E 04	1.4527E 04	-1.0171E 02
7.6294E-02	-2.9010E 03	-1.1155E 04	1.1526E 04	-1.0458E 02
9.5367E-02	-2.8310E 03	-8.6526E 03	9.1039E 03	-1.0812E 02
1.1921E-01	-2.7272E 03	-6.6013E 03	7.1425E 03	-1.1245E 02
1.4901E-01	-2.5775E 03	-4.9127E 03	5.5478E 03	-1.1768E 02
1.8626E-01	-2.3699E 03	-3.5246E 03	4.2473E 03	-1.2392E 02
2.3283E-01	-2.0976E 03	-2.3991E 03	3.1868E 03	-1.3116E 02
2.9104E-01	-1.7658E 03	-1.5171E 03	2.3280E 03	-1.3933E 02
3.6380E-01	-1.3975E 03	-8.6770E 02	1.6450E 03	-1.4816E 02
4.5475E-01	-1.0312E 03	-4.3270E 02	1.1183E 03	-1.5724E 02
5.6843E-01	-7.0793E 02	-1.7677E 02	7.2966E 02	-1.6598E 02
7.1054E-01	-4.5486E 02	-4.9785E 01	4.5757E 02	-1.7375E 02
8.8818E-01	-2.7736E 02	-2.7010E-01	2.7736E 02	-1.7994E 02
1.1102E 00	-1.6365E 02	1.1616E 01	1.6406E 02	1.7594E 02
1.3878E 00	-9.5371E 01	9.7045E 00	9.5863E 01	1.7419E 02
1.7347E 00	-5.5858E 01	5.0283E 00	5.6084E 01	1.7486E 02
2.1684E 00	-3.3256E 01	1.3112E 00	3.3282E 01	1.7774E 02
2.7105E 00	-2.0240E 01	-8.5931E-01	2.0258E 01	-1.7757E 02
3.3881E 00	-1.2615E 01	-1.8497E 00	1.2749E 01	-1.7166E 02
4.2352E 00	-8.0560E 00	-2.1286E 00	8.3325E 00	-1.6520E 02
5.2940E 00	-5.2776E 00	-2.0381E 00	5.6575E 00	-1.5888E 02
6.6174E 00	-3.5556E 00	-1.7839E 00	3.9780E 00	-1.5336E 02
8.2718E 00	-2.4720E 00	-1.4763E 00	2.8793E 00	-1.4915E 02
1.0340E 01	-1.7784E 00	-1.1690E 00	2.1282E 00	-1.4668E 02
1.2925E 01	-1.3232E 00	-8.8535E-01	1.5921E 00	-1.4621E 02
1.6156E 01	-1.0117E 00	-6.3441E-01	1.1941E 00	-1.4791E 02
2.0195E 01	-7.8401E-01	-4.1981E-01	8.8933E-01	-1.5183E 02
2.5244E 01	-6.0331E-01	-2.4448E-01	6.5096E-01	-1.5794E 02
3.1554E 01	-4.4978E-01	-1.1173E-01	4.6345E-01	-1.6605E 02
3.9443E 01	-3.1697E-01	-2.3324E-02	3.1783E-01	-1.7579E 02
4.9304E 01	-2.0702E-01	2.4000E-02	2.0841E-01	1.7339E 02
6.1630E 01	-1.2398E-01	3.9887E-02	1.3024E-01	1.6217E 02
7.7037E 01	-6.8087E-02	3.7407E-02	7.7686E-02	1.5122E 02
9.6296E 01	-3.4608E-02	2.7951E-02	4.4485E-02	1.4107E 02
1.2037E 02	-1.6514E-02	1.8296E-02	2.4647E-02	1.3207E 02
1.5046E 02	-7.5115E-03	1.1000E-02	1.3320E-02	1.2433E 02
1.8808E 02	-3.3008E-03	6.2538E-03	7.0714E-03	1.1783E 02

Figure 3.8. Output of the program of Figure 3.7. (Case Study 6.)

in the denominator. Pure imaginaries like this must be set up as complex numbers, whereas pure reals can simply be written as FORTRAN reals. We see this in the statement for computing T: K, which was declared to be REAL, is multiplied by N1, etc., which are complex. We are explicitly permitted to do *this* kind of mixing.

T is a complex number. We are able to print its real and imaginary parts simply by naming it in the WRITE statement and putting two field specifications in the associated FORMAT. The absolute value is found with the CABS function. The phase is a little more complicated. Mathematically, the arctangent is a many-valued function: there are infinitely many angles having the same tangent. The FORTRAN arctangent function must therefore be written under some assumption of the range of angles that will be regarded as the principle values. The function ATAN accepts a single argument and provides an angle as the result in the range of $-\pi/2$ to $+\pi/2$. The function ATAN2 accepts two arguments, separated by commas, which are assumed to be, respectively, the ordinate and abscissa of a point in any one of the four quadrants. The function provides the arctangent of the quotient of the first argument divided by the second; the result is in the range of $-\pi$ to $+\pi$. The difference between the two types of arctangent function is that the two arguments of ATAN2 carry quadrant information.

The result, in either case, is an angle in radians. We convert to degrees by multiplying by $180/\pi$.

We now write the five required numbers, increment ω, and return to compute another point if ω is less than or equal to LAST.

This program was run with suitable input values. The output is shown in Figure 3.8. We see that for frequencies out through about 20 radians/sec the input signals are amplified, but after that they are attenuated. The phase angle starts out near $-90°$, moves to nearly $-180°$, moves across the real axis to values a little less than $+180°$, then back down again, and back up again. This behavior for larger frequencies is of considerable interest to the servomechanism designer.

3.7 Logical Constants, Variables and Expressions

A FORTRAN logical quantity is one that can take on only the values "true" and "false."

A *logical constant* is either of the following:

$$.TRUE.$$

$$.FALSE.$$

A *logical variable* is a variable that has been declared in a LOGICAL type statement. As with double precision and complex variables, there is no initial-letter naming convention, since a variable is never assumed to be the logical type unless it has appeared in a LOGICAL statement. A logical variable can take on only the values .TRUE. and .FALSE..

A *logical assignment statement* has the form

$$a = b$$

in which a is a logical variable and b is a logical expression.

A logical expression, as we have already seen many times in connection with the logical IF statement, may be a relational expression, such as I .EQ. 20. Thus if L1, L2, etc., are logical variables, we may write logical assignment statements like these:

$$L1 = .TRUE.$$

$$L2 = .FALSE.$$

$$L3 = A .GT. 25.0$$

$$L4 = I .EQ. 0$$

$$L5 = L6$$

The first two are the logical equivalent of statements of the form

$$variable = constant$$

L3 would be set to .TRUE. if the value of the real variable A is greater than 25.0, and to .FALSE. if A is less than or equal to 25.0. Likewise, L4 would be set to .TRUE. if the value of I were in fact zero and to .FALSE., otherwise. L5 would be set to the same truth value as L6 currently has.

We have seen that a *relational expression* is one that compares integer, real, or double-precision values by using the relational operators .LT., .LE., .EQ., .NE., .GT., and .GE.. A *logical expression* combines logical values and/or relational expressions by using the *logical operators* .AND., .OR., and .NOT.. Thus we can write logical assignment statements like these:

$$L1 = D .LT. EPS .OR. ITER .GT. 20$$

$$L2 = D .GE. EPS .AND. ITER .LE. 20$$

$$L3 = BIG .GT. TOLER .OR. SWITCH$$

L1 would be given the value .TRUE., if *either or both* of the relations were true, and .FALSE., otherwise. L2 would be given the value .TRUE. if and only if *both* relations were true, and false, otherwise. L3 would be given the value .TRUE. if the relation were satisfied, if the logical variable SWITCH were true, or both.

The logical operator .NOT. reverses the truth value of the expression it operates on. For instance, consider this statement:

$$L = A .GT. B .AND. .NOT. SWITCH$$

If SWITCH is true, .NOT. SWITCH is false, and if SWITCH is false, .NOT. SWITCH is true. Thus *L* would be given the value .TRUE. if the value of *A* were greater than the value of *B* *and* the value of SWITCH were .FALSE..

In the absence of parentheses, the hierarchy of logical operators is .NOT., .AND., and .OR.. For instance, take this expression, in which all variables are logical:

L = A .AND. B .OR. C .AND. .NOT. D .AND. E
The .NOT. D is performed first, then the three .AND.s, then the .OR..

The .AND. .NOT. and .OR. .NOT. combinations are the only ones in which two operators may appear side by side.

Parentheses may be used to dictate a meaning other than that implied in the hierarchy of operators. For instance, we may write

$$L = A .AND. (B .OR. C) .AND. .NOT.$$
$$(D .AND. E)$$

Most FORTRAN systems provide for input and output of logical values by use of the L field specification. This is of the form Lw, where w specifies the number of columns or printing positions. On input the first letter in the card field must be *T* or *F*, which may be followed by any other characters. Thus it is possible, if we wish, to use the field specification L5 and punch TRUE or FALSE. On output a *T* or *F* is printed at the right side of the *w* printing positions.

Logical variables may be used for a variety of purposes. We shall see in Case Study 7 how they can be valuable when the problem actually does require processing of variables that are permitted to take on only two values, as in digital computer circuits. But logical variables are valuable in many other circumstances as well.

One common use of logical variables is to "save" the result of a decision to avoid having to repeat the test on which it is based. Consider the following simple example.

In Chapter 2 we defined a function of *x*

$$y = 0.5x + 0.95 \quad \text{if } x \leq 2.1$$
$$y = 0.7x + 0.53 \quad \text{if } x > 2.1$$

This computation can be written in a compact and easily-understood form:

LOGICAL FIRST

FIRST = X .LE. 2.1

IF (FIRST) Y = 0.5*X + 0.95

IF (.NOT. FIRST) Y = 0.7*X + 0.53

Obviously it can also be written in many other ways, but this way is about as easy to follow as any and about as fast. The speed is based on the fact that, as it happens, a test of a logical variable can be done very quickly by the computer.

Suppose that we have values of *X* and *Y*, which represent a point in Cartesian coordinates. We wish to set QUAD equal to the number of the quadrant in which the point lies.

LOGICAL XPOS, YPOS

INTEGER QUAD

XPOS = X .GT. 0.0

YPOS = Y .GT. 0.0

IF (XPOS .AND. YPOS) QUAD = 1

IF (.NOT. XPOS .AND. YPOS) QUAD = 2

IF (.NOT. XPOS .AND. .NOT. YPOS) QUAD = 3

IF (XPOS .AND. .NOT. YPOS) QUAD = 4

In this case the logical variables make it unnecessary either to repeat the determination of the signs of *X* and *Y* or to go into a complicated series of GO TO statements. (We have not worried here about points on the axes. With suitable agreements about the conventions needed, this aspect could easily be included.)

Another example of the usefulness of logical variables would be a calculation in which a certain factor would be included or omitted from a formula. The program could be set up to read a value of a logical variable, then used to determine the course of the calculation.

3.8 Case Study 7: Logical Design of a Binary Adder

Digital computers are built from thousands of individual logical elements, each of which is able to take on one of just two states, depending on some logical function of its inputs. In this case study we begin with four logical variables named B2, B1, A2, and A1, which are to represent two binary numbers, B and A, of two digits each. From these, using formulas representing computer logical elements, we are to produce the three digits C4, C2, and C1 of the sum. We visualize the arrangement of the digits as

$$
\begin{array}{r}
A2 \quad A1 \\
+ \ B2 \quad B1 \\
\hline
C4 \quad C2 \quad C1
\end{array}
$$

As an example,

$$
\begin{array}{r}
0 \quad 1 \\
+ \ 1 \quad 1 \\
\hline
1 \quad 0 \quad 0
\end{array}
$$

We shall be working with logical variables which have truth values only; a digit of one will be represented by .TRUE., zero by .FALSE.. We shall generate all 16 possible combinations of binary digits for a complete test of the adder circuit.

The circuit is shown in schematic form in Figure 3.9. The four digits are represented by boxes at the bottom. All the other boxes stand for logical elements, the nature of which is stated in the box. Boxes representing values to which a name is given in the program have the name shown at the top left. In the middle row, inputs are shown below the boxes; in the top row inputs are marked by arrows.

This diagram presents the logical design of the adder in graphic form. For instance, the units digit of the sum (C1) is seen to be 1 if either A1 *or* B1 is 1 *and* it is *not* true that both A1 *and* B1 are 1. The second digit (C2) is 1 if either all three of K2 (the carry from position 1), A2, and B2 are 1 or any one of them, but not two, is 1. C4 is 1 if any two or more of K2, A2, and B2 are 1.

The logical assignment statements to evaluate the various expressions here will be shown shortly. First, we should look at the flowchart of Figure 3.10, which shows how we shall work through the 16 combinations of values of B2, B1, A2, and A1. This scheme uses a nest of loops. The result is that B1 alternates between true and false, B2 is false twice, then true twice, then false twice, and so on.

The type declarations and the first four logical assignment statements in the program of Figure 3.11 present no difficulties. In the statement for C1 we see the need for parentheses. The intention, as written, is to evaluate the expression in the following sequence:

1. .NOT. K2
2. A1 .OR. B1
3. .AND. of the above.

Without the parentheses, the sequence would be

1. .NOT. K2
2. .NOT. K2 .AND. A1
3. .OR. of the above.

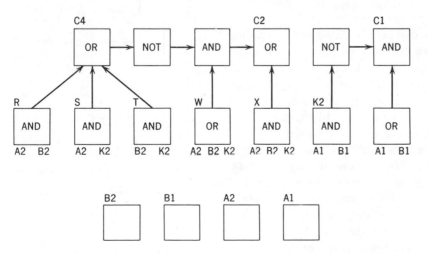

Figure 3.9. Arrangement of input binary digits (B2, B1, A2, and A1) and the logical operations leading to sum digits (C4, C2, and C1) in one "logical design" of a binary adder. (Case Study 7.)

The two expressions (with and without parentheses) do not mean the same thing, just as $-A*(B + C)$ and $-A*B + C$ do not mean the same thing.

In the next statement X will be set to .TRUE. only if all three of the variables are true.

In the statement in which C2 is computed the parentheses make the intention clear but are not actually required; the sequence of evaluation and the meaning would be the same without them.

After computing C2, we are ready to print the results. This could be done with the L field specifications, giving T's and F's. We prefer, however, to make the printout more attractive by making it look like what it represents: binary additions. To this end we convert each logical variable to an integer variable, in which zero stands for false and 1 stands for true. This translation is accomplished by first setting all seven of the output variables to zero and then setting to 1 any that correspond to logical values of .TRUE..

Three WRITE statements are used to print the augend, the addend, and the sum on three separate lines. The FORMAT statements to which the WRITE statements refer use the Hollerith field specification (H) to give the desired line and character spacing. When a line of information is transmitted to the printer, the first character is not printed, but instead is used to control paper movement:

Character	Action
blank	single space
0	double space
1	skip to top of next page
+	suppress spacing

Although it has not been pointed out, preceding programs have been arranged so that the first character in every line was a blank by allowing at least one extra space in the first field specification. Here, and in most programs from now on, we shall use a Hollerith field specification to guarantee that the desired paper spacing will be achieved.

In FORMAT statement 200 we see a Hollerith field specification 3H0bb, where the b's stand for blanks. The zero is the carriage control character, which will cause double spacing. The two blanks will be inserted into the line, with the net effect of starting the printing on that line two spaces to the right of the point at which it would otherwise start. FORMAT statement 201 begins with a Hollerith field specification 3Hbbb; the first blank specifies single spacing, and the other two blanks

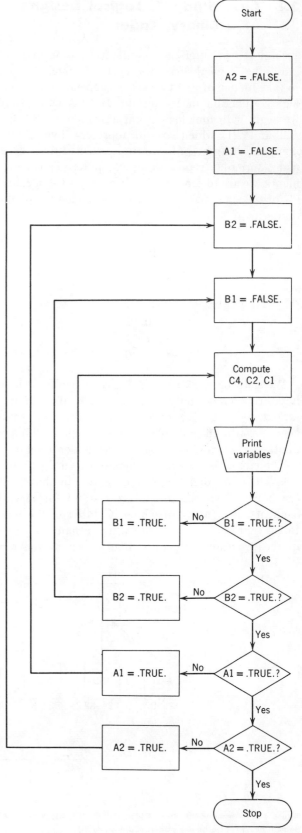

Figure 3.10. Flowchart of a method of testing the logical design of a binary adder, using FORTRAN logical variables. (Case Study 7.)

```
C CASE STUDY 7 - LOGICAL DESIGN OF A BINARY ADDER
C
      LOGICAL A1, A2, B1, B2, K2, C1, C2, C4, R, S, T, W, X
      INTEGER A1OUT, A2OUT, B1OUT, B2OUT, C1OUT, C2OUT, C4OUT
C STATEMENTS 1-4 ARE PART OF THE SCHEME FOR OBTAINING ALL
C COMBINATIONS OF VALUES FOR THE FOUR INPUT VARIABLES
1     A2 = .FALSE.
2     A1 = .FALSE.
3     B2 = .FALSE.
4     B1 = .FALSE.
C THE NEXT 9 STATEMENTS ARE ALL LOGICAL ASSIGNMENT STATEMENTS,
C COMPUTING THE VALUES OF THE SUM DIGITS
5     K2 = A1 .AND. B1
      C1 = .NOT. K2 .AND. (A1 .OR. B1)
      X = A2 .AND. B2 .AND. K2
      W = A2 .OR. B2 .OR. K2
      T = B2 .AND. K2
      S = A2 .AND. K2
      R = A2 .AND. B2
      C4 = R .OR. S .OR. T
      C2 = X .OR. (W .AND. .NOT. C4)
C THE NEXT GROUP OF STATEMENTS CONVERTS FROM LOGICAL VALUES TO
C ZEROS AND ONES, ZERO STANDING FOR FALSE AND ONE FOR TRUE
      A2OUT = 0
      A1OUT = 0
      B2OUT = 0
      B1OUT = 0
      C4OUT = 0
      C2OUT = 0
      C1OUT = 0
      IF (A2) A2OUT = 1
      IF (A1) A1OUT = 1
      IF (B2) B2OUT = 1
      IF (B1) B1OUT = 1
      IF (C4) C4OUT = 1
      IF (C2) C2OUT = 1
      IF (C1) C1OUT = 1
C THE FORMAT STATEMENTS THAT ARE REFERENCED BY THE WRITE STATEMENTS
C CONTAIN HOLLERITH FIELD SPECIFICATIONS, EXPLAINED IN THE TEXT
      WRITE (6, 200) A2OUT, A1OUT
      WRITE (6, 201) B2OUT, B1OUT
      WRITE (6, 202) C4OUT, C2OUT, C1OUT
  200 FORMAT (3H0  , 2I2)
  201 FORMAT (3H   , 2I2)
  202 FORMAT (1H , 3I2)
C THE REMAINING STATEMENTS ARE A PART OF THE SCHEME FOR OBTAINING ALL
C COMBINATIONS OF VALUES OF THE FOUR INPUT VARIABLES
      IF (B1) GO TO 6
      B1 = .TRUE.
      GO TO 5
6     IF(B2) GO TO 7
      B2 = .TRUE.
      GO TO 4
7     IF (A1) GO TO 8
      A1 = .TRUE.
      GO TO 3
8     IF(A2) STOP
      A2 =.TRUE.
      GO TO 2
      END
```

Figure 3.11.   A program for testing the logical design of a binary adder. (Case Study 7.)

```
    0 0
    0 0
  0 0 0

    0 0
    0 1
  0 0 1

    0 0
    1 0
  0 1 0

    0 0
    1 1
  0 1 1

    0 1
    0 0
  0 0 1

    0 1
    0 1
  0 1 0

    0 1
    1 0
  0 1 1

    0 1
    1 1
  1 0 0

    1 0
    0 0
  0 1 0

    1 0
    0 1
  0 1 1

    1 0
    1 0
  1 0 0

    1 0
    1 1
  1 0 1

    1 1
    0 0
  0 1 1

    1 1
    0 1
  1 0 0

    1 1
    1 0
  1 0 1

    1 1
    1 1
  1 1 0
```

Figure 3.12. The output of the program of Figure 3.11. The 16 triplets can be read as exercises in binary addition. (Case Study 7.)

are inserted in the line as before. In statement 202 we have a 1Hb for spacing, followed by the 3I2 for the three integers to be printed; we do not want the two blank spaces this time, which were used before to make the other numbers line up with this one.

The testing that comes after the output closely follows the logic of the flowchart.

The output from the program is shown in Figure 3.12. We see that, viewed as exercises in binary addition, all 16 cases give correct results, and we conclude that the adder design (and the program) is correct.

We hasten to point out that this is by no means the only way to set up a binary adder. As a matter of fact, this one is a copy of system that may be used to demonstrate to elementary school children how computers work. Seventeen children, arranged as in Figure 3.9, but spread out so that each logical element can see his inputs, and with each child holding a card defining his logical operation, will function beautifully.

EXERCISES

Note. Throughout these exercises variable names beginning with R, I, D, C, and L should be assumed to be real, integer, double-precision, complex, and logical, respectively.

1. State the value stored by each of the following assignment statements:

*a. $C1 = 2.0*(1.0, 2.0)$
 b. $C2 = (2.0, 0.0)*(1.0, 2.0)$
 c. $C3 = (2.0, 3.0)**2$
*d. $C4 = CMPLX(1.0 + 4.0, 4.0**2)$
 e. $C5 = CMPLX(REAL((1.0, 2.0)),$
    $AIMAG((3.0, 4.0)))$
 f. $R1 = CABS((3.0, 4.0))$
*g. $R2 = AIMAG((4.0, 0.0)*(1.0, 3.0))*2.0$
 h. $R3 = AIMAG((4.0, 0.0)*(1.0, 3.0)*2.0)$
 i. $C6 = CEXP((0.0, 3.1415927)) + (4.0, 4.0)$
 j. $R4 = SQRT(REAL(C6)**2 + AIMAG(C6)$
    $**2)/CABS(C6)$

2. Have the following pairs of logical expressions the same truth values?

*a. L1 .AND. L2 .OR. L3
   (L1 .AND. L2) .OR. L3
 b. L1 .AND. L2 .OR. L3
   L1 .AND. (L2 .OR. L3)
*c. L1 .AND. L2 .OR. L3 .AND. L4
   (L1 .AND. L2) .OR. (L3 .AND. L4)
 d. .NOT. L1 .AND. L2
   .NOT. (L1 .AND. L2)
*e. .NOT. (L1 .OR. L2)
   .NOT. L1 .AND. .NOT. L2
*f. L1 .AND. L2 .AND. L3 .AND. 1 .EQ. 2
   L4 .AND. .NOT. L4

g. L1 .AND. L2 .OR. A .LT. B .OR. A .GE. B
L3 .OR. .NOT. L3

3. Are the mixtures of data types in the following expressions permitted?

*a. D2 = D1*4.0
 b. D2 = D1*4
 c. D2 = D1**4
d. C1 = R1(4.0, 5.0)
 e. L1 = R1 .GE. D1 .OR. D3 .LT. 1.E-11
*f. IF (D1 .EQ. 0) R2 = I1*I2/I3
 g. L1 = R1 .GE. C1 .AND. I1 .LT. 10
*h. L1 = C1 .GT. C2
 i. L1 = C1 .EQ. C2
*j. L1 = CABS(C1) .GE. CABS(C2)
 k. L1 = ABS(REAL(C1) − AIMAG(C1)) .LT. 1.E-2
*l. L2 = 4.0*D1 .LT. 2.0 + R1 .AND. I1 .LE. 9 .AND. L1
 m. L3 = R1 .NE. R2 .OR. L1 .AND. .NOT. L2
*n. L1 = R1 .EQ. R2
 o. R1 = L1 .OR. L2
*p. R1 = I1 + 6
 q. D1 = I1 + 5
 r. I1 = R1**2
*s. I1 = D1**3
 t. D2 = 2.0/D1 + R1 − I1
 u. L1 = L1 .OR. L2

4. Consider the following system of equations:

$$140679x + 556685y = 146710$$

$$81152x + 321129y = 84631$$

Write two programs to solve this system, using Cramer's rule (see page 58, Ch. 4), in one program using real variables and in the other, double precision. (It is assumed that your computer has real numbers with about 6 to 8 decimal digits of significance.) Why should there be a difference in the results, when the data can be represented exactly with single precision (real)?

5. Write a program, using double precision throughout, to compute the values of D1 and D2 from

$$D1 = (A + \sin B − 10^9)*C$$

$$D2 = (A − 10^9 + \sin B)*C$$

The data card read by the program should enter the following values:

A: 1.0D9
B: 2.0D0
C: 1.0D7

Why the difference in the two results? Are not the two formulas equivalent, since addition is commutative?

6. Write a program, using complex variables throughout, to solve two simultaneous equations in two unknowns.

$$(2 + 3i)x + (4 − 2i)y = (5 − 3i)$$

$$(4 + i)x + (−2 + 3i)y = (2 + 13i)$$

The solution is $x = 1 + i$, $y = 2 − i$.

7. Write a program, using complex variables throughout, to solve the quadratic equation

$$ax^2 + bx + c = 0$$

where a, b, and c are complex. Use the formula

$$x = \frac{−b \pm \sqrt{b^2 − 4ac}}{2a}$$

Run the program with a data card that specifies

$$a = 1 + i$$

$$b = 2 + 3i$$

$$c = −7 + i$$

Run again, this time with a card that gives

$$a = 2$$

$$b = 3$$

$$c = −12$$

(Read them as complex numbers, i.e., as $2 + 0i$, etc., and use the program without change.)

8. Write a program, using complex variables throughout, to compute and print z and e^z for a succession of values along a vertical line through $(1, 0)$, such as $1 − 5i$, $1 − 4i$, $1 − 3i$, . . . , $1 + 4i$, $1 + 5i$. This will demonstrate how the complex exponential function maps a vertical line.

9. Write a program, using complex variables throughout, to compute and print z and e^z for a succession of values along a $45°$ line through the origin: $−5 − 5i$, $−4 − 4i$, . . . , $4 + 4i$, $5 + 5i$.

10. Write a program, using complex variables throughout, to compute and print z and e^z for 20 points equally spaced along the arc of a circle with the center at the origin and radius 1.

11. Write a program, using complex variables throughout, that reads a value of z, then computes and prints $a = \cos^2 z + \sin^2 z$. Make up a series of data cards and run the program as a demonstration that $\cos^2 z + \sin^2 z = 1$ holds with complex variables.

12. Write a program, using complex variables throughout, to read z and c, then compute and print $A = z^c = \exp(c \log z)$. Use the program to demonstrate that $(−i)^i = e^{\pi/2}$.

13. Write a program to demonstrate that $\log 3 − \pi i$, $\log 3 + \pi i$, $\log 3 + 3\pi i$, and $\log 3 + 5\pi i$ are all solutions of $e^z + 3 = 0$.

14. Modify the program of Figure 3.7 to compute the following transfer function instead of the one given:

$$T(j\omega) = \frac{100}{j\omega(1 + 0.25j\omega)(1 + 0.0625j\omega)}$$

15. Modify the program of Figure 3.7 to compute the following transfer function instead of the one given:

$$T(j\omega) = \frac{1260}{j\omega(1 + 0.25j\omega)(1 + 0.001j\omega) + \dfrac{20(j\omega)^4}{(1 + 0.5j\omega)(1 + 0.4j\omega)}}$$

16. Modify the program of Figure 3.11 so that C1, C2, and C4 can be computed without the use of intermediate variables, using the following formulas:

C1 = A1 .AND. .NOT. B1 .OR. .NOT. A1 .AND. B1

C2 = (A2 .AND. .NOT. B2 .OR. .NOT. A2 .AND. B2)
    .AND. (.NOT. A1 .OR. .NOT. B1)
    .OR. A1 .AND. B1 .AND. (.NOT. A2 .AND.
    .NOT. B2 .OR. A2 .AND. B2)

C4 = A1 .AND. B1 .AND. B2 .OR. A1 .AND. B1 .AND.
    A2 .OR. A2 .AND. B2

17. Case Study 7 can be done entirely without logical variables. Let the values of A1, A2, etc., be zero or 1 instead of false or true. Then write statements of the following sort:

IF (K2 .EQ. 0 .AND. (A1 .EQ. 1

.OR. B1 .EQ. 1)) C1 = 1

Modify the program along these lines and run it to see if it gives identical results.

4. SUBSCRIPTED VARIABLES

4.1 Introduction

The FORTRAN techniques that we have discussed so far permit a great deal of useful computing to be done, but they do not provide us with much power in dealing with certain problems that occur frequently. In particular, we need better methods of handling large arrays of related data, such as those found in simultaneous equations and many other applications. In this chapter we shall investigate the use of subscripted variables, which make it possible to refer to a complete array of data by one generic name. Subscripted variables are useful in themselves, as we shall see in a case study, and they take on added power in conjunction with the DO statement, which we shall investigate in Chapter 5.

4.2 Definitions

Subscripted variables permit us to represent many quantities with one variable name. A particular quantity is indicated by writing a subscript (or subscripts) in parentheses after the name. The complete set of quantities is called an *array*, and the individual quantities are called *elements*. A subscripted variable in FORTRAN may have one, two, or three subscripts, and it then represents a one-, two-, or three-dimensional array. (When used in this connection, one-dimensional refers to the number of *subscripts*, not to the number of *elements:* a one-dimensional array can have many elements, and it would be permissible for a three-dimensional array to have only one element.)

The first element of a one-dimensional array is element number 1, the second is element number 2, etc., up to the number of elements in the array. In mathematical notation we might write $x_1, x_2, x_3, \ldots, x_{19}, x_{20}$; in FORTRAN subscript notation we write $X(1), X(2), X(3), \ldots, X(19), X(20)$. We must always number elements consecutively, starting with 1.

A two-dimensional array is composed of horizontal rows and vertical columns. The first of the two subscripts then refers to the *row number*, running from 1 to the maximum number of rows, and the second to the *column number*, running from 1 to the maximum number of columns. For instance, an array of two rows and three columns might be shown in mathematical notation as

$$a_{1,1} \quad a_{1,2} \quad a_{1,3}$$

$$a_{2,1} \quad a_{2,2} \quad a_{2,3}$$

In FORTRAN subscript notation the elements would be written $A(1,1)$, $A(1,2)$, $A(1,3)$, $A(2,1)$, $A(2,2)$, $A(2,3)$. We note that the subscripts are separated by commas, as they are in three-dimensional variables.

A three-dimensional array may be viewed as composed of planes, each of which contains rows and columns. The interpretation, however, depends somewhat on the purpose of the computation; other interpretations are possible.

Some versions of FORTRAN allow more than three subscripts, seven being the number permitted in several systems.

$$D = SQRT((X(1)-Y(1))**2 + (X(2)-Y(2))**2 + (X(3)-Y(3))**2)$$

Figure 4.1. An example of the use of subscript notation, to compute a distance.

The name of a subscripted variable is formed in the same way as a nonsubscripted variable name. If the name is not mentioned in a type statement, the array is assumed to consist entirely of integer or entirely of real elements, depending on the initial letter. If the name is mentioned in a DOUBLE PRECISION, COMPLEX, or LOGICAL statement, the elements are assumed to be entirely of the one kind. In the case of double-precision and complex variables the extra computer storage required is automatically taken into account; no special handling of the subscripts is required. To emphasize: the elements of any given array must *all* be of one kind. An array, for instance, cannot consist partly of real and partly of integer elements.

4.3 Examples of the Subscript Notation

Suppose we have two points in space, represented in coordinate form by x_1, x_2, x_3 and y_1, y_2, y_3. We are required to compute the distance between them, which is given by

$$d = \sqrt{(x_1 - y_1)^2 + (x_2 - y_2)^2 + (x_3 - y_3)^2}$$

Now suppose that we have set up an array called X, the three elements of which are the coordinates of the point X, and another similarly for Y. The computation of the distance between the points can be called for by the statement in Figure 4.1.

For another example of the subscript notation consider the problem of solving two simultaneous equations in two unknowns. To emphasize the similarity of subscripted variables with mathematical notation we may write the system of equations completely in mathematical subscript form.

$$c_{1,1}x_1 + c_{1,2}x_2 = b_1$$

$$c_{2,1}x_1 + c_{2,2}x_2 = b_2$$

This problem can conveniently be set up with a one-dimensional array of two elements for the constant terms b_1 and b_2 and another for the unknowns x_1 and x_2, which we shall compute. The coefficients (c's) are the four elements of a two-dimensional array of two rows and two columns.

The solution of such a small system of equations can be done conveniently by Cramer's rule, according to which

$$x_1 = \frac{b_1c_{2,2} - b_2c_{1,2}}{c_{1,1}c_{2,2} - c_{2,1}c_{1,2}}$$

$$x_2 = \frac{b_2c_{1,1} - b_1c_{2,1}}{c_{1,1}c_{2,2} - c_{2,1}c_{1,2}}$$

A program to evaluate these formulas is shown in Figure 4.2. The computation of the denominator is done in a preliminary statement to avoid repeating the arithmetic. After that we make a test on the size of the denominator to determine whether it is close to zero. If it is exactly zero, there is either no solution or an infinity of solutions, depending on the constant terms. Either way, this formulation does not apply, and if we tried to use it we would be dividing by zero. This would give an error indication in most computers and would stop some. We have tested for a small divisor rather than specifically for zero, because rounding errors could give a nonzero denominator even when there is a possibility of trouble.

The test we have used here would not be suitable if the value of the denominator could properly be very large or very small. If the variables were such that the correct values of the numerator and denominator were both in the range of 10^{-8}, the test we have used would clearly not give a proper indication of the course of the calculation. On the other hand, if the values were properly in the 10^6 range, our test would also tell us very little.

The solution in such a case would be to use a test of the size of the denominator *in relation* to the numerator. We might decide, for instance, that if the numerator is more than 10^6 times larger than the denominator in absolute value we should stop. The program could be appropriately rewritten. A

```
DENOM = C(1,1) * C(2,2) - C(2,1) * C(1,2)
   IF (ABS(DENOM) .LT. 1.E-5) STOP
   X(1) = (B(1) * C(2,2) - B(2) * C(1,2)) / DENOM
   X(2) = (B(2) * C(1,1) - B(1) * C(2,1)) / DENOM
```

Figure 4.2. A program segment using subscripted variables to solve two simultaneous equations.

similar observation applies to several programs in other chapters.

4.4 Motivations for the Use of Subscripted Variables

The foregoing examples show the fundamental ideas of the subscript notation, but they do not really indicate the power of the technique. After all, there is nothing in the examples that could not be done just as conveniently by giving each element a separate name. Why then are subscripted variables such an important feature of FORTRAN?

The reason is that the subscripts themselves may be variables or certain types of expressions, which means that we can set up a program to perform a basic computation and then make the same computation on many different values by changing the value of the subscripting variable.

Suppose, for example, that we need to compute the sum of squares of 20 numbers, x_1 to x_{20}, stored in the computer. We could, of course, give them 20 different names and set up a long arithmetic statement to compute the sum of their squares, but this would be tedious, cumbersome, and inflexible. Instead, we set up the 20 numbers as the elements of a one-dimensional array which we shall call X. Now, any of the 20 numbers can be referenced by the name $X(I)$, and we arrange for I to take on all the values from 1 to 20.

In the usual mathematical notation

$$SUMSQ = \sum_{i=1}^{20} x_i{}^2$$

The computation can be done with the program shown in Figure 4.3. We first set SUMSQ equal to zero so that we may use a single expression to compute each of the intermediate sums. Then I is made 1 so that when statement 180 is first executed we get the first element from the array of values. Then 1 is added to I and a test is made to determine whether all of the values have been processed. Note

```
      SUMSQ = 0.0
      I = 1
180   SUMSQ = SUMSQ + X(I)**2
      I = I + 1
      IF (I .LE. 20) GO TO 180
      STOP
```

Figure 4.3. A program segment using subscripted variables and the IF statement to compute the sum of the squares of 20 numbers.

that when the IF shows that $I = 20$ we must still go back once more because I is incremented *before the test.*

Statement 180 and the two following it are executed exactly 20 times to give the sum of the squares of the 20 elements of the array. We shall see in Chapter 5 that this program can be made even simpler by use of a DO statement.

4.5 The DIMENSION Statement and Other Information

When subscripted variables are used in a program, certain information about them must be supplied to the FORTRAN compiler:

1. Which variables are subscripted?
2. How many subscripts are there for each subscripted variable?
3. What is the maximum size of each subscript?

These questions are answered by the DIMENSION statement. Every subscripted variable in a program must be mentioned in a DIMENSION statement,* and this statement must appear before the first occurrence of the variable in the program. A common practice is to give the dimension information for all subscripted variables in DIMENSION statements at the beginning of the program. One DIMENSION statement may mention any number of variables, and there may be any number of DIMENSION statements.

The DIMENSION statement takes the form
DIMENSION V, V, V, . . .

where the V's stand for variable names followed by parentheses enclosing one, two, or three unsigned integer constants that give the maximum size of each subscript. When FORTRAN processes a DIMENSION statement, it sets aside enough storage locations to contain arrays of the sizes specified by the information in the statement. Thus if a program contains the statement

DIMENSION X(20), A(3,10), K(2,2,5)

the FORTRAN compiler will assign 20 storage locations to the one-dimensional array named X; 30 (3×10) to the two-dimensional array A; and

---

* Or in a COMMON statement that includes dimension information, as we shall see in Chapter 7, or in a type statement.

20 $(2 \times 2 \times 5)$ to the three-dimensional array K. If any of these variables had been named in a DOUBLE-PRECISION or COMPLEX statement, twice as much storage would have been assigned to each. The extra storage is automatically taken into account in all usage of the subscripts; the programmer need give no thought to the extra storage.

It is the programmer's responsibility to write the program so that no subscript is ever larger than the maximum size he has specified in the DIMENSION statement. Furthermore, subscripts must never be smaller than 1; zero and negative subscripts are not permitted. If these restrictions are violated, the source program will in some cases be rejected by the compiler. In other cases, in which the illegal subscripts are developed only at execution time, the program will be compiled but will in all probability give incorrect results.

The DIMENSION statement is said to be *non-executable;* that is, it provides information only to the FORTRAN compiler and does not result in the creation of any instructions in the object program. The FORMAT statement is also non-executable, as are the type statements and several others. A nonexecutable statement may appear almost anywhere in the source program, even between two assignment statements. As already noted, however, the dimension information for each subscripted variable must be given before the first appearance of that variable in the program. Furthermore, a DIMENSION statement must not be the first statement in the range of a DO statement (see Section 5.4).

Subscripted variables, with a few exceptions noted later, may appear in any place in which a nonsubscripted variable may be written. For a simple example consider the READ statement that might be used to read in the data for the simultaneous equations example in Section 4.3. The DIMENSION, READ, and FORMAT statements for that problem could be

```
    DIMENSION B(2), C(2,2), X(2)
    READ (5, 16) C(1,1), C(2,1), C(1,2),
        C(2,2), B(1), B(2)
16 FORMAT (6F10.0)
```

When a READ statement is written with the elements indicated in this explicit form, the elements may be entered in any sequence desired. The programmer may choose, for instance, to write

```
READ  (5, 16)  C(1,1), C(1,2), B(1), C(2,1),
        C(2,2), B(2)
```

The data naturally would have to be punched on the data card in the corresponding order.

We may occasionally want to deal with the elements of an array *without* explicitly naming them all. It is permissible to use an input or output statement in which the name of the array is written without any subscripts; this will cause reading or writing of the entire array. Thus we could follow the DIMENSION statement in the example above with

```
READ  (5, 16)  C, B
```

to read all the elements of the two arrays.

It is necessary, of course, in such a case to have a convention regarding the sequence of the elements, since we are not specifying the sequence we require. The sequence in which the elements must appear on a card read by an input statement without subscripts, or the order in which they will be printed by an output statement without subscripts, is as follows. For one-dimensional arrays the elements are taken in sequence, starting with the element corresponding to the subscript 1 and proceeding to the largest subscript as defined in the DIMENSION statement. For two-dimensional arrays the elements are taken in such a manner that the first subscript varies most rapidly. Thus the statements

```
DIMENSION  R(2,3)
```

```
READ  (5, 16)  R
```

would require that the elements be punched in the sequence R(1,1), R(2,1), R(1,2), R(2,2), R(1,3), R(2,3). This can be summarized by saying that the elements of a two-dimensional array are taken in *column-order.* For three-dimensional arrays the elements are taken in such a manner that the first subscript varies most rapidly and the last varies least rapidly.

4.6   Allowable Forms of Subscripts

So far we have seen that subscripts may be integer constants or integer variables. Three other forms of subscript are permitted. If I stands for a nonsubscripted integer variable and L and L' are integer constants, all of the allowable subscript forms are as follows:

General Form	Example
I	J12
L	3
$I \pm L$	$K + 29$
$L*I$	$2*LIMIT$
$L*I \pm L'$	$3*LAST - 7$

The value of a subscript expression is determined each time the subscripted variable is used in the program. The value must never be less than 1 nor greater than the maximum specified in a DIMENSION statement, and a variable in a subscript expression must not itself be subscripted.

There are many situations in which the last three forms of subscripts find application. We may illustrate the use of these forms in an example that can be done in three different but equivalent ways.

Suppose that at a certain point in a program the following computation is required:

$$y = \begin{cases} a + bx + cx^2 & \text{if } k = 1 \\ d + ex + fx^2 & \text{if } k = 2 \\ g + hx + ix^2 & \text{if } k = 3 \end{cases}$$

The values of k and x have already been established. We know how to write three statements with the different coefficients and then to use an IF statement to pick the appropriate statement. The procedure, however, is made much simpler with subscripting.

Suppose we make the nine coefficients the elements of a one-dimensional array, which we may call C:

$$\begin{array}{ccccccccc} a & b & c & d & e & f & g & h & i \\ 1 & 2 & 3 & 4 & 5 & 6 & 7 & 8 & 9 \end{array}$$

If $k = 1$, the numbers of the desired elements are

$$1 = 3k - 2$$
$$2 = 3k - 1$$
$$3 = 3k$$

If $k = 2$, the numbers of the desired elements are

$$4 = 3k - 2$$
$$5 = 3k - 1$$
$$6 = 3k$$

If $k = 3$, the numbers are

$$7 = 3k - 2$$
$$8 = 3k - 1$$
$$9 = 3k$$

Thus for any value of k the proper coefficients will be used if we write

$$Y = C(3*K - 2) + C(3*K - 1)*X + C(3*K)*X**2$$

If the coefficients had been arranged thus

$$\begin{array}{ccccccccc} a & d & g & b & e & h & c & f & i \\ 1 & 2 & 3 & 4 & 5 & 6 & 7 & 8 & 9 \end{array}$$

the statement would have been

$$Y = C(K) + C(K + 3)*X + C(K + 6)*X**2$$

Another approach, which also gives the same results, is to make the coefficients the elements of a two-dimensional array:

$$\begin{array}{ccc} a & b & c \\ d & e & f \\ g & h & i \end{array}$$

In this array K can be used to select the proper row (first subscript) and 1, 2, or 3 can be used to select the proper column (second subscript). The arithmetic statement now becomes

$$Y = C(K, 1) + C(K, 2)*X + C(K, 3)*X**2$$

Thus we see that subscripted variables facilitate the selection of one set of data from a larger set. We also see that the elements of an array, in contrast to ordinary mathematical usage, are not required to have any particular relation to one another. (But, again, they all have to be of the same type: real, integer, double-precision, complex, or logical.)

The most common use of subscripted variables is in carrying out the same basic computation on a set of related values. We shall see an example in the following study.

4.7 Case Study 8: Linear Interpolation

To illustrate the use of subscripted variables in a practical application, we shall consider linear interpolation in an array of data. Such a computation would ordinarily be a part of a larger program, but here we shall simply read the x and y values, then read a series of x values for which the corresponding y values should be found by interpolation and printed.

We assume that the x and y values of a curve are punched in a deck of cards, each card containing one x and one y value. The deck is assumed to be in ascending sequence on the x values, and there may be no more than 200 of them. We do not assume that the x values are equally spaced. The x and y values are punched in 10 columns each, in a form suitable for reading with F10.0 field specifications. The last card in this part of the deck will contain a nonzero punch in column 21.

Figure 4.4 is a flowchart of the work of the program of Figure 4.5. Let us examine the flowchart and the program together.

The DIMENSION statement in the program says that X and Y are one-dimensional subscripted variables, each with a maximum of 200 elements. I is set to 1 to start storing the X-Y pairs at the start of the arrays. The READ statement will read and store values in element locations according to the value of I, which is incremented each time around the reading loop. Each time through the loop we check to make sure that I has not exceeded 200; if it has, the data is invalid, for we have no more space in the arrays.

It is assumed that column 21 will be blank on all cards except the last. A blank column in a numeric field on a data card is taken to be a zero, so that the second IF statement will cause a return to the READ statement on all X-Y cards before the last. In other words, we continue reading until the last card is detected, increasing the value of I by 1 each time. The X-Y pairs are thus stored in successive locations in the two arrays. When the last card has been detected, with its nonzero punch in column 21, the IF statement will *not* transfer back to the READ, and we go on to the READ at 43, where the processing begins.

Now we have in storage the pairs of X and Y values, representing a series of straight-line segments, as indicated in Figure 4.6. The deck of cards continues, with a series of cards containing X values only, in columns 1 to 10. We are to read a card, interpolate in the table to find the corresponding Y value, print X and Y, go back to read another card, and so on, until the last data card, which will contain a nonzero punch in column 11.

When we read an X card, we first check to see that the X value (named XE) is not less than the first element of the X array, because if it is the data card will be in error. Assuming this test passes, we set J to 2 in order to start a search through the X values, looking for one that is greater than or equal to XE.

In the arithmetic IF statement at 69 we will go to statement 112 if XE is less than $X(J)$, which would mean that XE is "bracketed" by $X(J-1)$

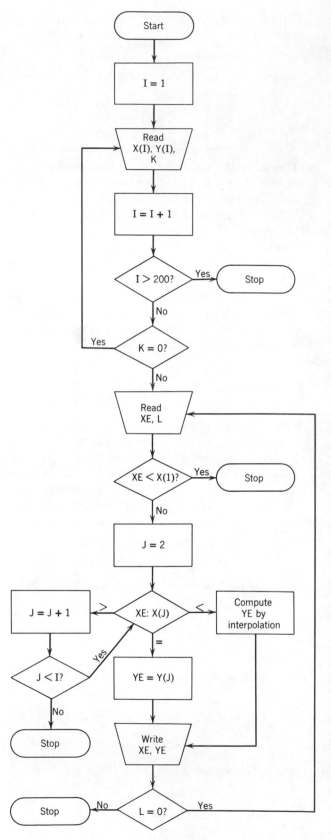

Figure 4.4. Flowchart of a program for linear interpolation. (Case Study 8.)

```
C CASE STUDY 8 - LINEAR INTERPOLATION
C
      DIMENSION X(200), Y(200)
C FOLLOWING STATEMENTS READ THE CARDS DEFINING THE CURVE
      I = 1
  56 READ (5,57) X(I), Y(I), K
  57 FORMAT (2F10.0, I1)
      I = I + 1
      IF (I .GT. 200) STOP
      IF (K .EQ. 0) GO TO 56
C THIS STATEMENT READS A CARD CONTAINING AN X VALUE
  43 READ (5, 70) XE, L
  70 FORMAT (F10.0, I1)
C CHECK FOR X VALUE LESS THAN SMALLEST X ON CURVE
      IF (XE .LT. X(1)) STOP
      J = 2
C THE FOLLOWING ARITHMETIC IF STATEMENT COMPARES THE GIVEN X VALUE
C WITH SUCCESSIVE VALUES ON THE CURVE, LOOKING FOR AN X VALUE ON THE
C CURVE THAT IS GREATER THAN THE GIVEN VALUE
  69 IF (XE - X(J)) 112, 111, 110
C NOT FOUND YET
 110 J = J + 1
C CHECK WHETHER GIVEN X VALUE IS LARGER THAN LARGEST X ON CURVE
      IF (J .LT. I) GO TO 69
      STOP
C EQUAL
 111 YE = Y(J)
      GO TO 200
C TWO CURVE VALUES BRACKET GIVEN X -- INTERPOLATE
 112 YE = Y(J-1) + (Y(J)-Y(J-1))/(X(J)-X(J-1))*(XE-X(J-1))
 200 WRITE (6,201) XE, YE
 201 FORMAT (1P2E15.7)
C CHECK FOR SENTINEL
 202 IF (L .EQ. 0) GO TO 43
      STOP
      END
```

Figure 4.5. A program for linear interpolation. (Case Study 8.)

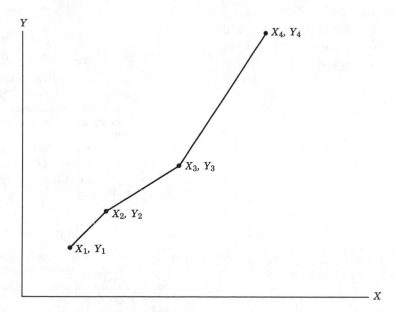

Figure 4.6. Schematic representation of the meaning of the X-Y pairs in linear interpolation. (Case Study 8.)

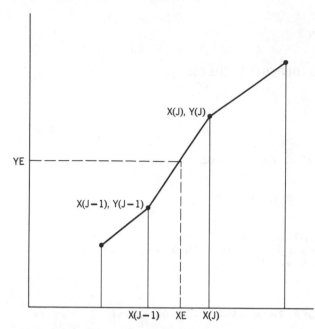

Figure 4.7. The geometrical basis of the method of linear interpolation, once XE has been found to exceed some entry X(J −1) in the table. (Case Study 8.)

and $X(J)$. We go to 111 if XE is equal to $X(J)$, in which case the value we want is simply $Y(J)$. A transfer to 110 will occur if XE is greater than $X(J)$, which means that we have not yet found two X values that bracket XE. In this last case we need only to increment J, check to see that we have not exhausted the list of X values without finding one larger than XE, and go back to the IF statement if the search should continue.

Once we have found that some $X(J)$ is larger than XE, we will have the situation diagrammed in Figure 4.7. By simple geometry we find that the corresponding value of Y is as written in statement 112. However YE was found, we now print it and then return to read another XE value and repeat the whole process as long as column 11 is blank.

The program was run with data cards defining a curve with four points, as in Figure 4.6. The x-y values entered were, in sequence, $(1, 1)$, $(2, 2)$, $(4, 6)$, $(9, 21)$. Figure 4.8 shows a few values of XE and corresponding values of YE.

XE	*YE*
1.1000000E 00	1.1000000E 00
2.5000000E 00	3.0000000E 00
5.0000000E 00	9.0000000E 00

Figure 4.8. The output of the program of Figure 4.5, using the curve stated in the text. (Case Study 8.)

EXERCISES

Note. Include an appropriate DIMENSION statement in each program segment for these exercises, realizing, of course, that in a complete program each subscripted variable is mentioned only once in a DIMENSION statement, usually at the beginning of the program.

*1. Suppose that the coordinates of a point in space are given by the three elements of a one-dimensional array named X. (Note the different usages of the word dimension: the elements of a one-dimensional array are being used as the coordinates of a point in three-dimensional space!) Write a statement to compute the distance of the point from the origin, which is given by the square root of the sum of the squares of the coordinates.

2. If the coordinates of a point in space are x_1, x_2, and x_3, the direction cosines of the line from the origin to the point are given by

$$CA = \frac{x_1}{\sqrt{x_1^2 + x_2^2 + x_3^2}}$$

$$CB = \frac{x_2}{\sqrt{x_1^2 + x_2^2 + x_3^2}}$$

$$CC = \frac{x_3}{\sqrt{x_1^2 + x_2^2 + x_3^2}}$$

Write statements to compute these three numbers, assuming that the coordinates are the elements of a one-dimensional array named X.

*3. Given two arrays named A and B, both two-dimensional, write statements to compute the elements of another two-dimensional array named C from the following equations. The maximum value of all subscripts is 2.

$$c_{11} = a_{11}b_{11} + a_{12}b_{21}$$
$$c_{12} = a_{11}b_{12} + a_{12}b_{22}$$
$$c_{21} = a_{21}b_{11} + a_{22}b_{21}$$
$$c_{22} = a_{21}b_{12} + a_{22}b_{22}$$

Readers familiar with matrix notation will recognize the multiplication of two 2×2 matrices.

4. Given a two-dimensional array named R, the elements of which are to be viewed as the elements of a 3×3 determinant, write a statement to compute the value of the determinant by any method you know. The value of the determinant should be named DET.

*5. Two one-dimensional arrays named A and B each contain 30 elements. Compute

$$D = \left(\sum_{i=1}^{30} (A_i - B_i)^2 \right)^{1/2}$$

(A distance function in 30-space.) Write a program segment to perform the calculation.

*6. If we have a list of tabular values represented by a one-dimensional array, then the *first differences* of the list are formed by subtracting each element except the last from the element immediately following it. Suppose we have a one-dimensional array named X that contains 50 elements. Compute the 49 elements of another array named DX from

$$DX(I) = X(I + 1) - X(I) \qquad I = 1, 2, \ldots, 49$$

Write a program segment to perform this calculation.

7. Suppose we have a one-dimensional array named Y that contains 32 elements; these are to be regarded as the 32 ordinates of an experimental curve at equally spaced abscissas. Assuming that a value has already been given to H, compute the integral of the curve represented approximately by the Y values from

$$TRAP = \frac{H}{2} (Y_1 + 2Y_2 + 2Y_3 + \cdots + 2Y_{31} + Y_{32})$$

8. A two-dimensional array named AMATR contains 10 rows and 10 columns. A one-dimensional array named DIAG contains 10 elements. Write a program segment to compute the elements of DIAG from the formula

$$DIAG(I) = AMATR(I, I) \qquad I = 1, 2, \ldots, 10$$

*9. Given a one-dimensional array named Y, with 50 elements, and numbers U and I, write a statement to compute the value of S from the following equation, written in ordinary mathematical subscript notation.

$$S = y_i + u \frac{y_{i+1} - y_{i-1}}{2} + \frac{u^2}{2} (y_{i+1} - 2y_i + y_{i-1})$$

This is called *Stirling's interpolation formula* (through second differences), which may be described as follows: we have three points of a curve: (x_{i-1}, y_{i-1}), (x_i, y_i), and (x_{i+1}, y_{i+1}), such that $x_{i+1} - x_i = x_i - x_{i-1} = h$, and a value of x. We write $u = (x - x_i)/h$. Then the formula stated gives the interpolated value of y corresponding to x, found by passing a quadratic through the three given points.

10. Using the assumptions of Exercise 9, write a statement to compute the value of T from the following equation:

$$T = y_i + u(y_{i+1} - y_i)$$
$$+ \frac{u(u - 1)(y_{i+2} - y_{i+1} - y_i + y_{i-1})}{4}$$
$$+ \frac{(u - \frac{1}{2}) u(u - 1)(y_{i+2} - 3y_{i+1} + 3y_i - y_{i-1})}{6}$$

This is called *Bessel's interpolation formula* (through third differences). With the notation used in Exercise 9, it finds a value of y corresponding to x by passing a cubic through the four given points. The arrangement of the differences is somewhat different from that in Stirling's formula, however.

*11. Given two one-dimensional arrays named A and B, of seven elements each, suppose that the seven elements of A are punched on one card and the seven elements of B are punched on another card. Each element value is punched in 10 columns in a form suitable for reading with an F10.0 field specification. Write a program to read the cards, then compute and print the value ANORM from

$$ANORM = \sqrt{\sum_{i=1}^{7} a_i b_i}$$

Use a 1PE20.7 field specification for ANORM.

A *norm* may be thought of as a generalization of the concept of distance.

12. Using the assumptions of Exercise 11, write a program to read the data cards and then carry out the following procedure. If every $a_i > b_i$, for $i = 1, 2, \ldots, 7$, print an integer 1; if this condition is not satisfied, print a zero.

*13. Rewrite the program segment for Exercise 5 to use double precision variables for the arrays.

14. Rewrite the program segment for Exercise 10 to use double precision variables for the arrays.

*15. COMPLX is a one-dimensional array containing 30 complex numbers. Write statements to form the sum of the absolute values of the 30 elements, using the CABS function.

16. With assumptions as in Exercise 15, write statements to form the sum of all the imaginary parts of the 30 elements of COMPLX, but include in the sum only those imaginary parts that are positive.

*17. A one-dimensional array named TRUTH contains 40 truth values. Write a program to place in TRUE the count of the number of elements of TRUTH that are .TRUE., and in FALSE the count of the number of elements that are .FALSE.. Note that TRUE is a legitimate variable name; .TRUE., with periods, is a logical constant.

18. A one-dimensional array named COMPLX contains 30 elements. A two-dimensional array of logical variables named QUAD contains 30 rows and 4 columns. For all 30 values of I, if the point represented by COMLX(I) lies in quadrant J, make $QUAD(I, J)$ .TRUE. and the other three elements in row I of QUAD .FALSE..

19. Refer to Exercise 3d in Chapter 2. Suppose that WORD1 and WORD2 are one-dimensional arrays, each containing five alphanumeric variables of one letter each. (See Chapter 6 for a further discussion of alphanumeric variables.) Compare each letter of WORD1 with each letter of WORD2 and place in DUPE the number of letters the two words have in common.

5. THE DO STATEMENT

5.1 Introduction

The DO statement is one of the most powerful and most widely used features of the FORTRAN language. This statement makes it possible to execute a section of a program repeatedly, with automatic changes in the value of an integer variable between repetitions. Coupled with subscripted variables, the DO statement provides a simple way to perform calculations that would be a great deal more difficult otherwise. In view of the importance of the topic, we shall study its application in a variety of examples, including two case studies.

5.2 Fundamentals and Definitions

The DO statement may be written in either of these forms:

$$DO \ n \ i = m_1, m_2$$

or

$$DO \ n \ i = m_1, m_2, m_3$$

In this statement n must be a statement number, i must be a nonsubscripted integer variable, written without a sign, and m_1, m_2 and m_3 must each be either an unsigned integer constant or a nonsubscripted unsigned integer variable. If m_3 is not stated, as in the first form of the statement, it is understood to be 1.

The action of the DO statement is as follows. The statements following the DO, up to and including the one with the statement number n, are executed repeatedly. They are executed first with $i = m_1$; before each succeeding repetition i is increased by m_3; repeated execution continues until the statements have been executed with i equal to the largest value that does not exceed m_2.

To illustrate how the DO statement works and how it may be used, let us consider again the problem stated in connection with subscripting on p. 59. It will be recalled that we were required to form the sum of the squares of the 20 elements of a one-dimensional array named X. This can be done with the program shown in Figure 5.1.

The DIMENSION statement establishes X as a variable with one subscript, the maximum value of which is 20. We first set the sum location to zero, then go into the DO statement. This says to execute repeatedly all the statements following the DO, down to and including the one numbered 180. There is, of course, only one statement in this range, and statement 180 itself is the repeated part. Statement 180 is carried out first with $I = 1$, so that the first time through we get x_1^2 in SUMSQ. Then I is increased by 1 and statement 180 is executed again, this time adding x_2^2 to the x_1^2 that is already in SUMSQ. This process is repeated until statement 180 has been executed with $i = 20$, after which SUMSQ contains the sum of the squares of all 20 numbers. Control then passes on to the statement following 180, whatever it might be.

For another example of a DO statement, suppose we have a one-dimensional array called DATA which contains 21 elements. We wish to form the sum of all the odd-

```
   DIMENSION X(20)
   SUMSQ = 0.0
   DO 180 I = 1, 20
180 SUMSQ = SUMSQ + X(I)**2
```

Figure 5.1. A program segment using a DO loop to form the sum of the squares of 20 numbers.

numbered elements and to place this sum in a location we shall call SUM. The program in Figure 5.2 will do this.

We assume that these three statements are a small part of a larger program and that elsewhere in the program there is a DIMENSION statement which will establish DATA as a one-dimensional variable with 21 elements. The DO statement, in this case, says to execute the statement numbered 500 with K equal to 1, 3, 5, $\cdots$, 17, 19, 21. The first time statement 500 is executed the value of the variable SUM is zero, so that the net effect is to move the first element of DATA to SUM. The second time it is executed the effect is to add to this the value of the third element of DATA, and so on. When it has been executed with K equal to 21, which adds in the last element, control passes to the statement following statement 500.

5.3 Further Definitions

Before proceeding to more examples we present a few definitions that will make it easier to talk about the DO statement.

The *range* of a DO statement is the set of repeatedly executed statements. In short, it consists of the statements beginning with the one immediately following the DO and continuing up to and including the one named in the DO. The integer variable i in the general form of the DO statement is called its *index*. Throughout the execution of the range i is available for any purpose permitted for an integer variable. We have seen how it may be used as a subscript and shall see later how it can be applied in other ways.

There are two ways by which control can transfer outside the range of a DO. The *normal exit* occurs when the DO is *satisfied*, that is, at the completion of the number of executions of the

```
   SUM = 0.0
   DO 500 K = 1, 21, 2
500 SUM = SUM + DATA(K)
```

Figure 5.2. A program segment to form the sum of the odd-numbered elements of an array.

range as specified by the *indexing parameters* m_1, m_2, and m_3. When this happens, as we have seen, control passes to the statement following that named in the DO. The second method by which control can get outside the range of a DO is through a GO TO or IF statement. This can happen when we wish to specify in the DO parameters the *maximum* number of executions of the range but to set up tests in the range to determine the *actual* number of executions.

When control is transferred outside the range of a DO *before* the DO is satisfied, the index i is available for any purpose permitted for an integer variable. This can be quite valuable. After a normal exit, however, i is *not* available (at least not in most versions of FORTRAN). This is no serious inconvenience in practice.

To examine another way in which the index of a DO may be used within the range, consider the following example. In a problem involving combinations we are required to form the product of all integers from 1 to M, in which the value of M has been determined earlier in the program. M is an integer variable; we wish to obtain the product in real form. The program in Figure 5.3 does the necessary computation and places the product in a location called PROD. We first set PROD equal to 1.0 and then go into the DO loop, asking for the range to be executed with I equal to all values from 2 through M. To use the index I in a computation of real variables, we execute the statement $AI = I$, which calls for the conversion of I to real form, assuming the real-integer naming convention. The first time statement 6 is executed the effect is to multiply 1.0 by 2.0 (since PROD has been started at 1.0) and to store the product in PROD. The next time this product is multiplied by 3.0 and the new product is stored back in PROD. The process continues until the two statements in the range have been executed with I equal to M.

Implicit in this formulation is the assumption that M is at least 2. If M could be 1, the DO statement would ask for the range to be executed with I equal to all values from 2 up to 1, which, of course, is impossible. What the DO statement would do in such a case cannot be stated in general.

```
   PROD = 1.0
   DO 6 I = 2, M
   AI = I
6  PROD = PROD * AI
```

Figure 5.3. A program segment to form the product of the integers from 1 to M.

If M were equal to 2, the program would not get into trouble: the two statements in the range would be executed only once and control would pass to the statement following 6.

This example shows that it is important to be sure that the range of a DO is executed the precisely correct number of times. Experience reveals that it is all too easy to make mistakes on this point, especially by calling for one too few or one too many repetitions. A good way to check is to ask, "What would the parameters have to be if the range were to be executed *once*?" Based on this question, it is usually not too difficult to decide whether the actual situation is properly handled.

The DO statement can often be used effectively to run through a set of values of an independent variable. In Case Study 5, for instance, we computed the sine of a series of angles: 30°, 390°, 750°, etc., up to 3990°. It was indicated in Figure 3.2 that these angles were read from cards; the same arguments could have been generated more simply by a DO statement, as shown in Figure 5.4. The index of a DO statement must be an integer variable; we have used K. In the computation the angle is a double-precision variable, called DEGREE in Figure 3.2. Therefore the first operation after the DO is an assignment statement:

$$DEGREE = K$$

With DEGREE having been declared to be double precision, this statement calls for a conversion from integer to double precision. The body of the computation is as before. The end of the range is the WRITE statement that prints the results.

For a second example of this kind of use of the DO statement, consider the modification of the program of Case Study 3, Figure 2.11. In the modified program we needed to run through all values of S from 20.0 to 200.0, in steps of 0.1. This time we cannot use the value of the DO index directly, since it must be an integer variable and we need steps of 0.1. This is only a minor difficulty, however, since we can write

$$DO \ 40 \ I = 200, \ 2000$$
$$S = I$$
$$S = S / 10.0$$

These steps are placed before the body of the computation; statement 40 would be the WRITE statement that prints the results. The DO index will run through the values 200 through 2000 in steps of 1. After conversion to FORTRAN real form and division by 10.0, S will therefore run through the values 20.0 through 200.0 in steps of 0.1.

5.4 Rules Governing the Use of the DO Statement

A great deal of flexibility is permitted in the use of the DO statement as long as certain rules are observed. We shall state all of these rules together and later illustrate the situations that some of them cover.

Rule 1. The first statement in the range of a DO must be one that can be executed. This excludes the DIMENSION and FORMAT state-

```
C CASE STUDY 5 - MODIFIED DOUBLE PRECISION SINE ROUTINE
      DOUBLE PRECISION X, TERM, SUM, XSQ, DENOM, TEST, DEGREE
      DO 78 K = 30, 4000, 360
      DEGREE = K
      X = DEGREE / (180.0 / 3.14159265358979932)
      SUM = X
      TERM = X
      DENOM = 3.0
      XSQ = X**2
   25 TERM = -TERM * XSQ / (DENOM * (DENOM - 1.0))
      SUM = SUM + TERM
      IF (DABS(TERM) .LT. 1.0D-17) GO TO 24
      DENOM = DENOM + 2.0
      GO TO 25
   24 SDEGR = SNGL(DEGREE)
      TEST = DSIN(X)
   78 WRITE (6, 89) SDEGR, X, SUM, TEST
   89 FORMAT (F8.0, 1P3D26.16)
      STOP
      END
```

Figure 5.4. The program of Figure 3.2, modified to use a DO statement to replace the reading of data.

ments and the various type-statements. These *specification statements* provide information to the compiler about the program, rather than causing any computation to take place. We shall see later that several other statements are also nonexecutable.

Rule 2. It is permissible for the range of one DO (which we call the *outer* DO) to contain another DO (which we call the *inner* DO). When this occurs, it is required that all statements in the range of the inner DO also be in the range of the outer DO. This does not prohibit the ranges of two or more DO's from ending with the same statement, but it does prohibit a situation in which the range of an inner DO extends past the end of the range of an outer DO.

Rule 3. The last statement in the range of a DO must not be a GO TO in any form, nor an arithmetic IF, RETURN (discussed in Chapter 7), STOP, PAUSE, or DO statement. Neither can it be a logical IF containing any of the others. These statements, with the exception of the RETURN, may be used freely anywhere else in the range. The CONTINUE statement, described later, is provided for situations that would otherwise violate this rule.

Rule 4. No statement within the range of a DO may redefine or otherwise alter any of the indexing parameters of that DO; that is, it is not permitted within the range of a DO to change the values of i, m_1, m_2, or m_3. As noted before, these numbers may still be used in any way that does not alter their values.

Rule 5. Control, with one exception, must not transfer into the range of a DO from any statement outside its range. Thus it is expressly prohibited to use a GO TO or an IF statement to transfer into the range of a DO without first executing the DO itself. This rule *does* prohibit a transfer from the range of an outer DO into the range of an inner DO, but it *does not* prohibit a transfer out of the range of an inner DO into the range of an outer DO. The latter is permissible because from the standpoint of the outer DO the transfer is entirely within its range. Some illustrations of the application of this rule are provided in Figure 5.5. The brackets here represent the ranges of DO's and the arrows represent transfers of control. Transfers 2, 3, and 4 are acceptable, since 2 and 3 are transfers from the range of an inner DO into the range of an outer DO and 4 is a transfer entirely within the range of a single DO. Transfers 1, 5, and 6 all represent transfers into the range of a DO from outside its range.

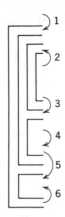

Figure 5.5. Examples of permissible nests of DO's and some correct and incorrect transfers of control. Transfers 2, 3, and 4 are acceptable; 1, 5, and 6 are not.

The one exception to the rule prohibiting transfers into the range of a DO from outside its range is this: it is permissible to transfer control completely outside the nest to which a DO belongs, to perform a series of calculations that makes no changes in any of the indexing parameters in the nest, and then to transfer back to the range of the same DO from which transfer was originally made. The restriction on the exit and re-entry transfer location may be stated another way: no DO and no statement that is the last statement in the range of a DO may lie between the exit and re-entry points.

CONTINUE is a dummy statement that causes no action when the object program is executed. It merely satisfies the rule that the last statement in the range of a DO must not be one that can cause transfer of control. It is also used to provide a statement to which an IF can transfer when the computations in the range of a DO have been completed. This is necessary because a transfer within the range of a DO is not permitted to return to the DO itself, unless, of course, it really is intended to start the execution of the DO from the beginning again. An example of the use of the CONTINUE appears in Figure 5.6, which is discussed in the following section.

5.5 Examples of the Use of the DO Statement

Because the DO statement is so powerful and since it is so heavily used in most FORTRAN applications, we shall give some additional examples of its use.

We shall suppose that the input to a program consists of a series of experimentally measured values. Each point in the experiment consists of an x value and a y value, corresponding to the abscissa and ordinate of a point on a graph. The data points were gathered and entered into the computer in random order; that is, we know that the first x value goes with the first y value, the second x value goes with the second y value, and so on, but we cannot assume that the first x is the smallest of the x values. For the purposes of the calculations that are to be done later in the program, it is necessary to rearrange the data points in storage so that the first x value *is* the smallest and that the second x value is the next larger, and so on. In other words, we must order the data points into ascending sequence on the x values.

We shall assume that the x values as they were originally read (i. e., in scrambled order) are the elements of an array named X and that there are 25 of them. The y values are the 25 elements of another array called Y.

The FORTRAN program to rearrange these data points into ascending sequence of the x values involves a nest of two DO loops. We shall show the development of the program by displaying a simplified version of the inner loop before writing the full program. This simplified loop will place the smallest x value in the first position of the x array. This can be done by the following process. First compare the first and second x values in the original array. If $X(1)$ is smaller than or equal to $X(2)$, leave them as they are; but if $X(1)$ is larger than $X(2)$, interchange these two values within the array. Having inspected the first and second elements and interchanged them if necessary to get the smaller in $X(1)$, we compare $X(1)$ and $X(3)$ and interchange them if $X(1)$ is larger. What is in $X(1)$ as we make this second comparison may well be the value that was originally in $X(2)$, but that does not matter. Similarly, we compare $X(1)$ and $X(4)$, $X(1)$ and $X(5)$, etc., each time interchanging if necessary to get the smaller in $X(1)$. This process guarantees that the smallest x value in the entire array will finally be in $X(1)$, wherever it may have been to begin with. Remembering that to each element of X there corresponds an element of Y, we naturally carry out the same interchange operations on the Y array as we do on the X array, but there is no testing of the Y array values.

To interchange two values from the array in storage, we follow a three-step process: (1) move the first value to a temporary location which we call TEMP; (2) move the second value to the location originally occupied by the first; (3) move the first value, now in TEMP, to the location originally occupied by the second.

A program to carry out all of the steps of this process is shown in Figure 5.6. We are assuming that the data values have been read in by an earlier part of the program, and we are not showing the statements that complete the rearrangement or use of the data values. Elsewhere in the program there would have to be a DIMENSION $X(25)$, $Y(25)$ statement.

The program illustrates a number of points worth noting. We see another example of a DO loop in which the index does not start with 1. We see an example of the use of the CONTINUE statement. This is required, for if the IF statement shows that $X(1)$ is already less than or equal to the other x value with which we are comparing it a transfer of control must be made to skip around the six statements that interchange elements in the X and Y arrays. What we want to do in this case is simply to repeat the whole process with the index J increased by 1. As we have already noted, however, it is not possible to transfer control back to the DO. This would result in starting the DO loop again with J equal to 2—which is not what we want. Therefore we transfer control to the CONTINUE, which has been identified in the DO statement as the end of the range.

In reading this program, it is well to recall the meaning of an arithmetic assignment statement: the value of the variable on the left side of the equal sign is replaced by the value of the expression on the right. Thus a statement such as

$$X(1) = X(J)$$

```
DO 12 J = 2, 25
IF (X(1) .LE. X(J)) GO TO 12
TEMP = X(1)
X(1) = X(J)
X(J) = TEMP
TEMP = Y(1)
Y(1) = Y(J)
Y(J) = TEMP
12 CONTINUE
```

Figure 5.6. A program segment to place the smallest value of X in an array of X's in the first position of the array and to place the corresponding Y in the first position in an array of Y's.

```
      DO 12 I = 1, 24
      IP1 = I + 1
      DO 12 J = IP1, 25
      IF (X(I) .LE. X(J)) GO TO 12
      TEMP = X(I)
      X(I) = X(J)
      X(J) = TEMP
      TEMP = Y(I)
      Y(I) = Y(J)
      Y(J) = TEMP
   12 CONTINUE
```

Figure 5.7. A program segment to rearrange a set of X-Y data points into ascending sequence on the X values.

means that the number identified by the variable name $X(J)$ is to be moved to the location for the number identified by the name $X(1)$. The value in the location for $X(J)$ is unchanged.

In the data as described earlier there may or may not be two equal x values. As the program has been written, it does not matter; if they are equal, there is no point in exchanging them, and we simply transfer control down to the CONTINUE and go around the loop again.

When this loop has been completed (when the DO is satisfied), we are guaranteed that the data points have been rearranged so that the smallest x value is in $X(1)$ and the corresponding y value is in $Y(1)$. What we would like to do next is to get the next larger x value in $X(2)$. This can be done by comparing $X(2)$ with $X(3)$, and following, interchanging when necessary. After that we would like to get the next larger element in $X(3)$. We would similarly like to get the successively larger values in $X(4)$, $X(5)$, and so on.

It appears that what we need to do for the complete program is to make variables of all subscripts that appear as 1's in Figure 5.6. The subscript will then select the element to be compared with all following elements (interchanging if necessary). This subscript, which we shall call I, will start at 1 and run through 24. The subscript that appears as J in the Figure 5.6 will still be J, but it will have to start at one more than the value of the I subscript, and run through 25. All of this is easily done with another DO statement which controls the I subscript. This is the outer DO. There is one complication, however. The inner DO must

specify that the J subscript will start at one more than I. Looking back at the definition of the DO statement, we see that each indexing parameter must be either an integer constant or a single integer variable. It is *not* permitted to write a statement such as

$$\text{DO } 12 \text{ J} = \text{I} + 1, 25$$

To avoid this restriction, we simply insert a statement that computes the value of a variable $IP1$, which is always one more than the value of I. The complete program to arrange the data points in sequence is shown in Figure 5.7.

This technique is by no means the most efficient sorting method known. It is presented here only as an interesting application of the DO statement.

To illustrate a slightly different type of DO loop, let us now make some further assumptions about the purpose of the program just written. Suppose that the data points that have been read and arranged into ascending sequence on the x values lie on a curve and that we are required to find the area under the curve; that is, to find the definite integral of the curve represented approximately by these points. If we now make the further assumption that the distance between successive x values is equal to a constant value h, the approximate integral given by the trapezoidal rule is

$$\text{AREA} = \frac{h}{2}(y_1 + 2y_2 + 2y_3 + \cdots$$
$$+ 2y_{23} + 2y_{24} + y_{25})$$

A DO loop may conveniently be used to form the sum of the y values with subscripts of 2 through 24. Having done so, we can multiply this sum by 2, add the first and last y values, and multiply by $h/2$. This program segment, shown in Figure 5.8, would follow the CONTINUE statement of the segment shown in Figure 5.7. It includes the computation of h on the assumption that it is the interval between any two x values. If, in fact, the x values are not equally spaced, the program naturally gives an incorrect result. If it were required that the program be able to handle unequally spaced x values, the numerical integration method would have to be modified.

```
      SUM = 0.0
      DO 20 I = 2, 24
   20 SUM = SUM + Y(I)
      AREA = (X(2) - X(1))/2.0 * (Y(1) + 2.0*SUM + Y(25))
```

Figure 5.8. A program segment for numerical integration by the trapezoidal rule.

```
         ODD = 0.0
         EVEN = 0.0
         DO 47 I = 2, 24, 2
    47   EVEN = EVEN + Y(I)
         DO 48 I = 3, 23, 2
    48   ODD = ODD + Y(I)
         AREA = (X(2) - X(1))/3.0 * (Y(1) + 4.0*EVEN + 2.0*ODD + Y(25))
```

Figure 5.9.   A program segment for numerical integration by Simpson's rule.

Simpson's rule, with the subscripting scheme we are using, is

$$AREA = \frac{h}{3}(y_1 + 4y_2 + 2y_3 + 4y_4 + 2y_5 + \cdots + 2y_{23} + 4y_{24} + y_{25})$$

A program to evaluate this formula will be a little more complex because of the alternating coefficients of 2 and 4. One fairly obvious way to handle the problem is to set up two DO loops and to accumulate separately the sums of the y's corresponding to the two coefficients. See Figure 5.9.

The computation may also be done with only one DO loop, which saves a little time in the running of the object program, if we proceed as follows. Suppose we set up an index that runs from 2 to 22 in steps of 2. Such an index always references an element that should be multiplied by 4; one plus the index references an element that should be multiplied by 2. The $Y(24)$ element must be added in separately, which is caused by the fact that there are more odd elements than even. See Figure 5.10.

Flexibility in the manner of writing subscripts is very useful here. It is not possible to form the sum of the y values with one DO loop unless some such subscripting arrangement is used.

It may be noted that we have written these integration formulas with the subscripts starting at 1, whereas it is conventional to write them with the subscripts starting at zero. This was done to make it easier to describe the problem, since we recall that a subscript must always be positive and nonzero.

It is possible to program formulas that have zero and negative subscripts, but it is somewhat more effort than it is worth to us at this point. See Figure 6.8 in Case Study 12 for an example of a program based on formulas originally stated in terms of subscripts starting at zero. (It may be noted that some FORTRAN systems, or languages similar to FORTRAN, do permit zero and negative subscripts.)

5.6   Case Study 9: Damped Oscillation

This case study, which in its physical situation is closely related to Case Study 2, provides a simple example of a DO loop not involving subscripting.

The current flowing in a series circuit containing resistance, inductance, and an initially charged capacitor, but no voltage source, is given by

$$i = i_m e^{-Rt/2L} \sin 2\pi f_1 t$$

where

$$i_m = \frac{2\pi f_0^2 Q}{f_1}$$

$$f_0 = \frac{1}{2\pi}\sqrt{\frac{1}{LC}}$$

$$f_1 = \frac{1}{2\pi}\sqrt{\frac{1}{LC} - \frac{R^2}{4L^2}}$$

and i = current flowing at time t, amperes
i_m = maximum current, amperes
R = resistance, ohms
t = time since closing switch, seconds
L = inductance, henrys
f_0 = frequency of undamped circuit $(R = 0)$, cycles per second
f_1 = frequency of damped circuit, cycles per second
C = capacitance, farads
Q = initial charge on capacitor, coulombs

```
         ODD = 0.0
         EVEN = 0.0
         DO 51 I = 2, 22, 2
         EVEN = EVEN + Y(I)
    51   ODD = ODD + Y(I+1)
         AREA = (X(2)-X(1))/3.0*(Y(1) + 4.0*(EVEN+Y(24)) + 2.0*ODD + Y(25))
```

Figure 5.10.   Another version of a program segment for numerical integration by Simpson's rule.

We wish to compute a number of points on the curve of instantaneous current versus time, in order to draw a graph. One of the inputs to the program, along with the physical parameters, will be an integer giving the number of cycles of the curve desired (CYCLES) and another number giving the number of points per cycle to be computed (NPERCY).

The program is shown in Figure 5.11. We begin with type declarations, which in this case are a definite convenience: electrical engineers always write i for current, and with the REAL statement to override the naming convention we can do the same.

The IF statement checks that R^2 is less than $4L/C$, because if not there is a disabling error in the data; a different formulation applies in that case.

We compute $F0$ and $F1$, the undamped and damped frequencies, as intermediate variables to save time in the loop later. Having $F0$ we can get the time interval DELT. The scheme is to have NPERCY points in each cycle at the undamped frequency. One cycle at a frequency of $F0$ cps takes $1/F0$ sec. In order to get NPERCY points in one such cycle, the time interval between points should be $1/(NPERCY*F0)$. $C1$ and $C2$ are further intermediate variables.

The total number of points is the number per cycle, NPERCY, times the number of cycles, CYCLES. This product becomes the value of LIMIT, which we then use as the final value in the DO statement that follows. The DO statement here is used only to count the number of repetitions. The incrementing of T is done within this loop.

Figure 5.12 shows the output from this program with the parameters having been

$$Q = 0.00001 \text{ coulomb}$$

$$R = 1.0 \text{ ohm}$$

$$C = 0.00001 \text{ farad}$$

$$L = 0.002 \text{ henry}$$

$$CYCLES = 3$$

$$NPERCY = 20$$

This program is the basis for Case Studies 11 and 12, in which the results are presented in a more understandable form. See Figures 6.4–6.8.

```
C CASE STUDY 9 - DAMPED OSCILLATION
C
      REAL I, IM, Q, R, C, L, FO, F1, C1, C2, T, DELT, TEMP
      INTEGER CYCLES, NPERCY, LIMIT
C READ PARAMETERS
      READ (5, 612) Q, R, C, L, CYCLES, NPERCY
  612 FORMAT (4F10.0, 2I2)
C CHECK FOR INVALID DATA
      IF (R**2 .GE. 4.0*L/C) STOP
C COMPUTE INTERMEDIATE VARIABLES
      FO = 0.1591549 / SQRT(L*C)
      F1 = 0.1591549 * SQRT(1.0/(L*C) - R**2/(4.0*L**2))
      TEMP = NPERCY
      DELT = 1.0 / (TEMP * FO)
      IM = 6.2831853 * FO**2 * Q / F1
      C1 = R / (2.0 * L)
      C2 = 6.2831853 * F1
C START T AT ZERO BEFORE ENTERING LOOP
      T = 0.0
C COMPUTE NUMBER OF POINTS
      LIMIT = CYCLES * NPERCY
C COMPUTING LOOP - DO STATEMENT USED ONLY FOR COUNTING
      DO 11 J = 1, LIMIT
      I = IM * EXP(-C1 * T) * SIN(C2 * T)
      WRITE (6, 706) T, I
   11 T = T + DELT
  706 FORMAT (1P2E17.5)
      STOP
      END
```

Figure 5.11. A program for computing the instantaneous current flowing in a circuit containing resistance, inductance, and an initially charged capacitor. (Case Study 9.)

T I

T	I
0.	0.
4.44288E-05	2.16099E-02
8.88577E-05	4.06530E-02
1.33287E-04	5.53422E-02
1.77715E-04	6.43512E-02
2.22144E-04	6.69325E-02
2.66573E-04	6.29776E-02
3.11002E-04	5.30128E-02
3.55431E-04	3.81349E-02
3.99860E-04	1.98921E-02
4.44288E-04	1.24362E-02
4.88717E-04	-1.92211E-02
5.33146E-04	-3.62808E-02
5.77575E-04	-4.94535E-02
6.22004E-04	-5.75493E-02
6.66433E-04	-5.98960E-02
7.10861E-04	-5.63927E-02
7.55290E-04	-4.75072E-02
7.99719E-04	-3.42178E-02
8.44148E-04	-1.79079E-02
8.88577E-04	-2.22589E-04
9.33006E-04	1.70957E-02
9.77434E-04	3.23785E-02
1.02186E-03	4.41911E-02
1.06629E-03	5.14661E-02
1.11072E-03	5.35989E-02
1.15515E-03	5.04962E-02
1.19958E-03	4.25731E-02
1.24401E-03	3.07028E-02
1.28844E-03	1.61209E-02
1.33287E-03	2.98814E-04
1.37729E-03	-1.52046E-02
1.42172E-03	-2.88955E-02
1.46615E-03	-3.94884E-02
1.51058E-03	-4.60257E-02
1.55501E-03	-4.79638E-02
1.59944E-03	-4.52160E-02
1.64387E-03	-3.81513E-02
1.68830E-03	-2.75485E-02
1.73272E-03	-1.45118E-02
1.77715E-03	-3.56551E-04
1.82158E-03	1.35222E-02
1.86601E-03	2.57870E-02
1.91044E-03	3.52859E-02
1.95487E-03	4.11602E-02
1.99930E-03	4.29209E-02
2.04373E-03	4.04878E-02
2.08816E-03	3.41886E-02
2.13258E-03	2.47181E-02
2.17701E-03	1.30627E-02
2.22144E-03	3.98854E-04
2.26587E-03	-1.20254E-02
2.31030E-03	-2.30125E-02
2.35473E-03	-3.15305E-02
2.39916E-03	-3.68090E-02
2.44359E-03	-3.84080E-02
2.48801E-03	-3.62538E-02
2.53244E-03	-3.06372E-02
2.57687E-03	-2.21782E-02
2.62130E-03	-1.17579E-02

Figure 5.12. The output of the program of Figure 5.11, using the parameter values stated in the text. (Case Study 9.)

5.7 Case Study 10: The Gauss-Seidel Method for Solving Simultaneous Equations

In this case study we shall see DO statements applied in the way that is most common, in connection with subscripting in arrays. The application is a rather standard numerical technique.

Let us state the method in terms of a system of three simultaneous equations in three unknowns.

$$a_{11}x_1 + a_{12}x_2 + a_{13}x_3 = b_1$$
$$a_{21}x_1 + a_{22}x_2 + a_{23}x_3 = b_2$$
$$a_{31}x_1 + a_{32}x_2 + a_{33}x_3 = b_3$$

Suppose we make guesses at the values of x_2 and x_3 —it doesn't matter whether they are good guesses; zeros will work. Then we solve the first equation for x_1, writing a prime to indicate that this is a new approximation:

$$x_1' = \frac{b_1 - a_{12}x_2 - a_{13}x_3}{a_{11}}$$

Now using this new value for x_1 and the initial guess at x_3, we solve the second equation for x_2:

$$x_2' = \frac{b_2 - a_{21}x_1' - a_{23}x_3}{a_{22}}$$

Finally, using the new approximations to x_1 and x_2, we solve the third equation for x_3:

$$x_3' = \frac{b_3 - a_{31}x_1' - a_{32}x_2'}{a_{33}}$$

This process of computing a new value for each of the variables constitutes one *iteration*. Now we perform another iteration, always using the most recently computed value of each variable. If the system of equations satisfies certain conditions that we shall state shortly, the approximations will converge to a solution of the system, regardless of the initial guesses used.

A *sufficient* condition for convergence is that the main diagonal coefficient in each row should dominate the other coefficients in that row, which means that

$$a_{ii} > \sum_{j \neq i} a_{ij} \quad i = 1, 2, \ldots, n$$
$$n = \text{number of equations}$$

We emphasize that this condition is *sufficient*. *Necessary* conditions are considerably less stringent but unfortunately beyond the scope of this book. In

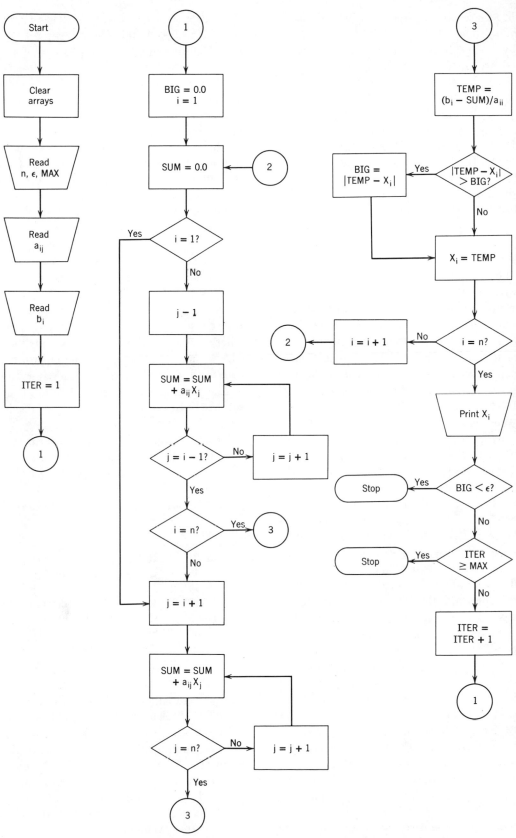

Figure 5.13. A flowchart of a method for solving a system of simultaneous equations by the Gauss-Seidel method. (Case Study 10.)

other words, there are systems of equations in which the main diagonal terms do not all dominate their rows, yet the Gauss-Seidel iteration method, as it is called, still converges to a solution.

We wish to write a program that will apply the Gauss-Seidel method to a system of equations of any size up to 40 equations. The program must include the reading of the coefficients, of which there could be 1600 in the largest case, and the constant terms. It must include a test for convergence, to decide when the approximations are close enough, and an iteration counter to stop the process if for any reason it fails to converge.

Figure 5.13 is a flowchart of the method, drawn to correspond quite closely to the FORTRAN techniques we shall be using. We begin by clearing the arrays for the coefficients, the constant terms, and the unknowns. The idea here is that with many hundreds of data values to enter it might be a considerable convenience not to enter zero values. This is especially true, since some systems of equations arising in practice have a high proportion of zero coefficients. Next we read a card containing the number of equations, the convergence test value ϵ, and the maximum number of iterations to be permitted. We then read the coefficients and constant terms, using a card layout and sentinel scheme that we shall describe in connection with the program. Finally, in the preliminary phase, we set the iteration counter to one.

A connector (the circled 1) takes us to the part of the flowchart that begins an iteration. The convergence test will be as follows: if the maximum absolute difference between the last two approximations to any variable is less than ϵ, the iteration scheme will be stopped. This requires keeping a variable that represents the largest difference found so far; this is BIG, which we set to zero initially. The line $i = 1$ represents part of a DO statement action. The SUM = 0.0 box is the start of the actions for one line, that is, the computation of a new approximation to one variable. This involves accumulating a sum of products in SUM, which we accordingly set to zero.

The rest of the middle column of boxes, beginning with the decision box $i = 1$?, forms the sum of the off-diagonal terms in one row. This is considerably more complex than might seem necessary at first glance, because the first and last equations have to be handled a little differently from all others. Except for these two, all equations have some terms before the diagonal and some after.

The basic idea is to use two DO loops, one running from 1 to $I - 1$, the other from $I + 1$ to N. The first DO loop must be skipped over for equation 1, and the second skipped for equation n.

At connector 3 we carry out certain operations that apply at the end of the accumulation of the sum of products. We set TEMP equal to the new approximation, then ask whether the absolute value of the difference between the new and old values is greater than BIG and, if so, set BIG equal to the difference. BIG thus always contains the largest difference so far found in this iteration. TEMP then becomes the new approximation, and we go back to connector 2 if more equations remain.

If $i = n$ at this point, we have completed an iteration; that is, we have computed a complete set of approximations to the unknowns. These approximations are printed, so that we may see the convergence. If BIG is now less than ϵ, the convergence test constant, we are finished. Otherwise, we ask whether the iteration counter exceeds the limit value MAX and either stop or increment the iteration counter and go back for another iteration.

The program of Figure 5.14 follows the flowchart so closely in most regards that we need only point out a few features of the program.

The first two DO statements form a nest having a common terminal statement, but the inner DO has a smaller range than the outer DO.

In the READ statement at 31 we read the coefficient cards, which have the following format.

Columns	Contents
1–2	Row number of first coefficient
3–4	Column number of first coefficient
5–14	First coefficient
15–16	Row number of second coefficient
17–18	Column number of second coefficient
19–28	Second coefficient
29	Sentinel: zero on all cards except last

The READ statement reads the row and column numbers and then uses them immediately—in the same READ list—as subscripts. This is permitted.

In the sentinel scheme we punch some nonzero digit in column 29 of the last card. Thus we can write IF (NEXT .EQ. 0) GO TO 31 to loop back on all cards except the last. With two coefficients per card, we shall have to enter one coefficient twice if we have an odd number of them, but this is a minor inconvenience.

A very similar scheme reads the constant terms,

```
C CASE STUDY 10 - GAUSS-SEIDEL METHOD FOR SOLVING SIMULTANEOUS EQUATIONS
C
C PROGRAM TO SOLVE N SIMULTANEOUS EQUATIONS IN N UNKNOWNS BY THE
C METHOD OF GAUSS-SEIDEL ITERATION.  N MUST NOT EXCEED 40.
C ONLY THE NON-ZERO ELEMENTS IN THE ARRAYS NEED BE ENTERED.
C
      DIMENSION A(40, 40), B(40), X(40)
C CLEAR ARRAYS
      DO 50 I = 1, 40
      B(I) = 0.0
      X(I) = 0.0
      DO 50 J = 1, 40
   50 A(I,J) = 0.0
C READ  N, EPSILON, AND THE MAXIMUM NUMBER OF ITERATIONS
      READ (5, 20) N, EPS, MAX
   20 FORMAT (I2, F10.0, I2)
C READ THE COEFFICIENTS, WHICH ARE PUNCHED TWO-TO-A CARD
   31 READ (5, 21) I, J, A(I, J), I1, J1, A(I1, J1), NEXT

   21 FORMAT (2I2, F10.0, 2I2, F10.0, I1)
      IF (NEXT .EQ. 0) GO TO 31
C READ THE CONSTANT TERMS
   32 READ (5,22) I, B(I), NEXT
   22 FORMAT (I2, F10.0, I1)
      IF (NEXT .EQ. 0 ) GO TO 32
C BEGIN THE ITERATION SCHEME
      ITER = 1
C STATEMENT 99 IS EXECUTED ONCE PER SWEEP
   99 BIG = 0.0
C INDEX I SELECTS A ROW
      DO 100 I = 1, N
C STATEMENT 102 IS EXECUTED ONCE PER ROW
  102 SUM = 0.0
C SEGMENT FROM HERE THROUGH STATEMENT 107 GETS THE SUM OF THE
C TERMS IN A ROW, EXCLUDING THE MAIN DIAGONAL TERM
      IF (I .EQ. 1) GO TO 105
      LAST = I - 1
      DO 106 J = 1, LAST
  106 SUM = SUM + A(I,J)*X(J)
      IF (I .EQ. N)  GO TO 103
  105 INITL = I + 1
      DO 107 J = INITL, N
  107 SUM = SUM + A(I,J)*X(J)
C COMPUTE NEW VALUE OF A VARIABLE
  103 TEMP = (B(I) - SUM) / A(I,I)
C AT END OF SWEEP, THIS STATEMENT HAS PUT LARGEST RESIDUAL IN BIG
      IF (ABS(TEMP-X(I)) .GT. BIG) BIG = ABS(TEMP - X(I))
  100 X(I) = TEMP
C ONE SWEEP HAS NOW BEEN COMPLETED - PRINT VARIABLES
      DO 42 I = 1, N
   42 WRITE (6,200) I, X(I)
  200 FORMAT (I5, 1PE16.7)
C IF LARGEST RESIDUAL IS LESS THAN EPSILON, PROCESS HAS CONVERGED
      IF (BIG .LT. EPS) STOP
C IF ITERATION COUNTER EXCEEDS MAXIMUM ALLOWABLE, GIVE UP
  110 IF (ITER .GE. MAX)  STOP
      ITER = ITER + 1
      GO TO 99
      END
```

Figure 5.14.   A program for solving a system of simultaneous equations by the Gauss-Seidel method. (Case Study 10.)

except that we have arranged to punch only one per card.

The rest of the program is an almost literal transcription of the flowchart.

The program was run with $\epsilon = 0.001$ and the following system of equations:

$$12.418x_1 - 1.061x_2 + 2.669x_3 + 4.361x_4 - 0.119x_5 = 4.508$$

$$-1.501x_1 + 19.832x_2 + 0.694x_3 - 4.816x_4 + 2.274x_5 = -8.449$$

$$2.308x_1 + 1.728x_2 - 15.165x_3 - 2.023x_4 + 1.104x_5 = -33.031$$

$$3.359x_1 - 0.913x_2 - 6.441x_3 + 27.864x_4 + 3.737x_5 = -106.909$$

$$-1.562x_1 + 1.168x_2 - 2.004x_3 + 1.818x_4 + 9.490x_5 = 30.268$$

Figure 5.15 is the output produced. We see that after six iterations the method has produced a set of approximations quite close to the exact solution 1, −2, 3, −4, 5.

EXERCISES

*1. Two one-dimensional arrays named A and B each contain 30 elements. Write a program segment

I	$X(I)$
1	3.6302141E−01
2	−3.9855308E−01
3	2.1879428E 00
4	−3.3878742E 00
5	4.4093195E 00
1	1.0907347E 00
2	−1.7483377E 00
3	2.9178269E 00
4	−3.9424675E 00
5	4.9555971E 00
1	1.0185336E 00
2	−1.9766591E 00
3	2.9945729E 00
4	−3.9967688E 00
5	4.9984232E 00
1	1.0020108E 00
2	−1.9986924E 00
3	2.9959091E 00
4	−4.0000091E 00
5	5.0001631E 00
1	1.0001360E 00
2	−2.0000074E 00
3	3.0000329E 00
4	−4.0000309E 00
5	5.0000466E 00
1	1.0000035E 00
2	−2.0000137E 00
3	3.0000064E 00
4	−4.0000056E 00
5	5.0000152E 00

Figure 5.15. The output of the program of Figure 5.14 for the system of equations displayed in the text. (Case Study 10.)

using a DO statement to compute

$$D = \left(\sum_{i=1}^{30} (A_i - B_i)^2 \right)^{\frac{1}{2}}$$

2. Given a one-dimensional array named X that contains 50 elements, write a program segment using a DO statement to compute the 49 elements of another array, named DX, from

$$DX(I) = X(I + 1) - X(I) \qquad I = 1, 2, \ldots, 49$$

3. A two-dimensional array named AMATR contains 10 rows and 10 columns. A one-dimensional array named DIAG contains 10 elements. Write a program segment to compute the elements of DIAG from

$$DIAG(I) = AMATR(I, I) \qquad 1 = 1, 2, \ldots, 10$$

*4. A one-dimensional array named M contains 20 integers. Write a program segment using a DO statement to replace each element by itself, multiplied by its element number. In other words, replace m_i by $i \cdot m_i$, $i = 1, 2, \ldots, 20$.

*5. Two one-dimensional arrays named R and S have a *maximum* of 40 elements each. The *actual* number of elements is given by the value of a previously computed integer variable M. Compute the first M elements of an array named T, which also has a maximum of 40 elements, according to

$$T(i) = R(i) + S(i) \qquad i = 1, 2, \ldots, M$$

6. Two one-dimensional arrays, A and B, have a maximum of 18 elements each. N is an integer, the value of which does not exceed 18. Compute

$$C = \sum_{k=1}^{N} A_k B_k$$

*7. A one-dimensional array named F contains at most 50 elements. Each of the first M elements, except the first and Mth, is to be replaced by

$$F_i = \frac{F_{i-1} + F_i + F_{i+1}}{3}$$

This is an example of techniques for *smoothing* experimental data to reduce the effect of random errors.

*8. A one-dimensional array named B contains 50 elements. Place the largest of these elements in BIBG and the element number of BIGB in NBIGB.

9. Two one-dimensional arrays named X and Y contain 50 elements each. A variable named XS is known to be equal to one of the elements in X. If $XS = X_i$, place Y_i in YS.

This kind of *table search* has a wide variety of applications, such as finding a value in a table of electric utility rates from a rate code or finding the numerical code corresponding to an alphabetic name.

*10. A two-dimensional array A contains 15 rows and 15 columns. A one-dimensional array X contains 15 elements. Compute the 15 elements of a one-dimensional array B according to

$$B_i = \sum_{j=1}^{15} A_{ij} X_j \qquad i = 1, 2, \ldots, 15$$

This is multiplication of a matrix and a vector.

11. Three two-dimensional arrays A, B, and C have 15 rows and 15 columns each. Given the arrays A and B, compute the elements of C from

$$C_{ij} = \sum_{k=1}^{15} A_{ik} B_{kj} \qquad i, j = 1, 2, \ldots, 15$$

This is matrix multiplication.

*12. A two-dimensional array RST has 20 rows and 20 columns. Compute the product of the main diagonal elements of RST and store it in DPROD. A main diagonal element is one that has the same row and column number, so that

$$DPROD = \prod_{i=1}^{20} RST(I, I)$$

*13. The formula

$$Y = 41.298\sqrt{1 + x^2} + x^{1/3} e^x$$

is to be evaluated for

$$x = 1.00, 1.01, 1.02, \ldots, 3.00$$

Each xy pair is to be printed on a line, with 1PE20.7 field specifications. Write a program using a DO loop to do this.

14. The formula

$$z = \frac{e^{ax} - e^{-ax}}{2} \sin(x + b) + a \log \frac{b + x}{2}$$

is to be evaluated for all combinations of

$$x : 1.0(0.1)2.0$$

$$a : 0.10(0.05)0.80$$

$$b : 1.0(1.0)10.0$$

where $x : 1.0(0.1)2.0$ means $x = 1.0, 1.1, 1.2, \ldots, 2.0$, and so on. For each combination of x, a, and b (there are 1650 combinations) a line giving x, a, b, and z is to be written. Write a program containing three DO loops to do this.

15. A solution to the following specialized system of equations is to be found:

$$a_{11}x_1 = b_1$$
$$a_{21}x_1 + a_{22}x_2 = b_2$$
$$a_{31}x_1 + a_{32}x_2 + a_{33}x_3 = b_3$$
$$\cdot \quad \cdot \quad \cdot \quad \cdot \quad \cdot \quad \cdot \quad \cdot \quad \cdot \quad \cdot \quad \cdot \quad \cdot \quad \cdot$$
$$a_{n1}x_1 + a_{n2}x_2 + a_{n3}x_3 + \cdots + a_{nn}x_n = b_n$$

First write a program to solve this system on the assumption that the a's are contained in a two-dimensional array that will have about half zeros for the missing elements. This is a moderately simple program: first solve for x_1, substitute this result into equation 2, and so on.

The difficulty, from the standpoint of computer solution, is that there is a great deal of wasted space in the array, which uselessly restricts the size of the system that can be solved. Devise a method of storing the coefficients in a *one-dimensional* array and write a program to find the unknowns. Assume that it must be possible to handle a maximum of 100 equations in 100 unknowns. The actual number of equations is given by the value of N.

16. Same as Exercise 15, except that the system of equations is

$$a_{1,1}x_1 + \cdots + a_{1,n-2}x_{n-2} + a_{1,n-1}x_{n-1} + a_{1,n}x_n = a_{1,n+1}$$
$$\cdot \quad \cdot \quad \cdot \quad \cdot \quad \cdot \quad \cdot \quad \cdot \quad \cdot \quad \cdot \quad \cdot \quad \cdot \quad \cdot \quad \cdot \quad \cdot \quad \cdot$$
$$a_{n-2,n-2}x_{n-2} + a_{n-2,n-1}x_{n-1} + a_{n-2,n}x_n = a_{n-2,n+1}$$
$$a_{n-1,n-1}x_{n-1} + a_{n-1,n}x_n = a_{n-1,n+1}$$
$$a_{n,n}x_n = a_{n,n+1}$$

Note that it is *not* possible to write a statement like

$$DO \ 12 \ I = N, 1, -1$$

which would be handy here. An equivalent "IF loop" must be written to work backward through the x's. Alternatively, we may write

$$DO \ 12 \ II = 1, N$$

$$I = N - II + 1$$

I is then used as the subscript; it will vary from N downward to 1.

17. Given a two-dimensional array named C, with 10 rows and 11 columns, compare $C(1, 1)$ with all other elements in the first column, looking for the element with the largest absolute value; make the value of L equal to the row number of the element in column 1 with the largest value. If at the end of these operations $L = 1$, do nothing more; otherwise exchange the elements in row 1 with the elements in row L, whatever it is.

18. A great many important computer applications involve logical manipulations of non-numerical data. As one small sample of the techniques used, let us explore some of the service routines that would be necessary in a chess program. We do not claim that chess playing by computer is in itself important, but that the techniques we can learn are and that they have broad applicability.

For the benefit of readers who may not be familiar with chess the following is a brief statement of the rules for the moves of the various pieces.

Each player, black and white, begins the game with 16 pieces: a king, a queen, two bishops, two knights, two rooks (also called castles), and eight pawns. At the start of the game the pieces are arranged as shown in Figure 5.16, in which the abbreviations used are as follows:

K	king
Q	queen
B	bishop
N	knight
R	rook
P	pawn

The (horizontal) rows are called ranks and the (vertical) columns are called files. Figure 5.16 shows the numbering system we shall use for the computer array described later.

The rook may move any distance along a rank or a file.

The bishop may move any distance along a diagonal.

The queen combines the powers of the rook and the bishop, and may thus move any distance in a straight line, along a rank, a file, or a diagonal.

The king may move in any direction also, but only one square at a time.

The knight moves by leaping to the nearest square of opposite color that is not adjacent. The move may also be described as "one over and two the other way," which is hardly precise but perhaps more descriptive. Figure 5.17 shows the eight possible squares to which the knight shown could move.

The pawn may move forward and must stay on its original file except when capturing. For its first move the

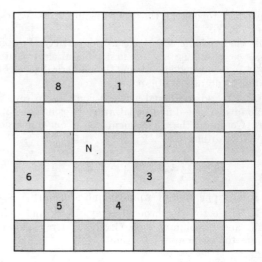

Figure 5.17. Schematic representation of the move of a knight, in chess.

pawn may advance either one square or two, but after the opening move the pawn moves only one square at a time.

The knight's move is a point-to-point move and is thus unaffected by the presence of any intervening pieces. All of the other moves are restricted to the distance that the piece may move without encountering any other, whether the player's own or his opponent's.

All pieces except the pawn capture by moving in the normal manner to the square occupied by the piece being captured. The captured piece is removed from the board. The pawn captures diagonally forward.

(Capturing *en passant* and castling are two additional moves, but they will not be needed in the exercises.)

For the programming exercises we have a two-dimensional integer array named BOARD, in which the rows and columns are numbered as in Figure 5.16. Each element of BOARD contains a number to identify what is on the square, according to the following coding of the pieces:

1	pawn
2	rook
3	knight
4	bishop
5	queen
6	king

If a given square is not occupied, the corresponding element of BOARD is zero. Positive values for the piece codings indicate white pieces and negative black. The integer variables $I1$ and $J1$ in all exercises give the row and column, respectively, of a piece under consideration. $I2$ and $J2$ give the location of some other square, when appropriate. We assume throughout that the game has been in progress for some time, so that the pieces are considerably removed from their starting positions.

*a. Write a routine to print the row and column numbers of all unoccupied squares adjacent to $I1$, $J1$. The possibility that the subject square will be on the edge of the board must be taken into account.

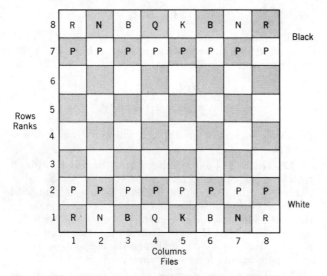

Figure 5.16. The arrangement of the pieces at the start of a chess game.

b. Write a routine to print the row and column numbers of all unoccupied squares that can be reached in a single move by a knight at $I1, J1$.

*c. A rook is on square $I1, J1$. If the path from there to square $I2, J2$ is unobstructed, set MOVE to .TRUE., and to .FALSE. otherwise. (The square $I2, J2$ *itself* may or may not be occupied.) Do this only if $I1 = I2$ or $J1 = J2$; if neither of these is true, set LEGAL to .FALSE..

d. A bishop is on square $I1, J1$. If the path from there to $I2, J2$ is unobstructed, set MOVE to .TRUE., and to .FALSE. otherwise. Make these moves only if the path is on a diagonal; if not, set LEGAL to .FALSE.

*e. The following scale, among others, is used to evaluate the relative value of the pieces:

pawn	1
knight	3
bishop	3
castle	5
queen	10

No weight is given to the king, since capture of the king ends the game.

Write a program to compute the value of all pieces, including pawns, for white, and place this integer in WPIECE.

f. The black king is at $I1, J1$. White claims to have the black king in check (under attack) by an unspecified piece on an unspecified square. Write a routine to determine whether the black king actually is in check. (This is much harder than the preceding exercises!)

6. INPUT AND OUTPUT

6.1 Introduction

The beginning programmer must necessarily concentrate on the basic ideas of data processing: writing expressions, translating a flowchart into a program, making good use of DO statements, and so on. Once these things are well learned, however, most people discover that the work of the programmer revolves to a large extent around questions of input and output.

These questions range from matters of convenience in card preparation, to the effective presentation of results in an easily understood and pleasing arrangement, to economic issues of the time required for input and output of very large arrays, to name some.

In this chapter we shall primarily be extending the reader's command of input and output beyond the rather elementary techniques presented while we were concentrating on other topics. However, in order to make the chapter more useful as a reference, we shall repeat some things that have been mentioned before.

6.2 Basics

Reading input data or writing output requires the programmer to provide four categories of information in the source program.

1. The selection of an input or output device, which is handled by a combination of the statement verb and the unit designation. We write READ or WRITE to indicate input or output, and, in some circumstances, as we shall see in Section 6.7, we may also use PRINT and PUNCH. Ordinarily, however, we use READ and WRITE, with the first number in parentheses designating the input or output unit.

2. The variables to receive new input valves or to have their values sent to an output device, as specified by the list of variables in the input or output statement.

3. The order in which the values are to be transmitted, as governed by the order in which the variables are named in the list.

4. The format in which the data appears for input, or is to be written for output, as specified by a FORMAT statement that must be referenced by the input or output statement in all but a few special cases.

Each of these four areas has been discussed in more or less depth in preceding chapters, and there have been many examples of their application. Each of them is the subject of further elaboration in the interest either of simplicity of programming or, more commonly, of more powerful techniques directed toward greater usefulness of the computer.

We shall investigate the various advanced topics in a sequence suited to study rather than in the order just named.

6.3 The List of an Input or Output Statement

The simplest type of list is one in which all the variables are named explicitly and in the order in which they are to be transmitted. There are more complicated (and more powerful) types of lists, as we shall see shortly. In all cases, however, the fundamental idea of "scanning" carries through: the first data field is associated with the first variable name and with the first field specification and so on.

The first additional list feature is a useful one that does not complicate the scanning process: it is permissible to use integer variables in a list as subscripts elsewhere in the list. This is subject to one restriction: when it is done with input, any variable used as a subscript must appear in the list as an input variable *before* it appears as a subscript. "Before" means in the sense of the scanning process, but it also means, in fact, "to the left."

We have already seen examples of the usefulness of this flexibility. In Case Study 10, for instance, (pp. 74–78), we wanted to be able to enter array element values in random order. Accordingly we punched the row number and column number on the data card along with the element. We had statements of the following kind.

READ $(5, 21)$ I, J, A$(1, J)$, I1, J1, A$(I1, J1)$
21 FORMAT $(2I2, F10.0, 2I2, F10.0)$

There were two elements punched on each card. As each card was read, the subscripting information on the card was immediately used to determine where to store the element, that is, to establish which element it was.

When entire arrays or parts of arrays are to be transmitted, it is often not necessary to name each element explicitly. To transmit an entire array, it is necessary only to name the array in a list without any subscripts. The name of the array must, of course, appear elsewhere in the program in a DIMENSION statement or in a COMMON statement that gives dimensioning information, but in the list it need not carry any subscripting information. The elements ordinarily all have the same field specification; this one field specification may be given by itself in the FORMAT statement. For instance, we can write

WRITE $(6, 21)$ A
21 FORMAT $(1PE20.8)$

where A is an array of any size.

Whenever an entire array is moved this way, the elements are transmitted in a sequence in which the first subscript varies the most rapidly and the last subscript the least rapidly, as discussed on p. 60.

When only some of the array elements are to be transferred, or when the "natural order" just mentioned is not wanted, it is often still possible to avoid naming each element explicitly. The elements can be specified instead in the list in a way that parallels a DO loop. For instance, the statements

READ $(5, 200)$ $(A(1, J), J = 1, 10)$
200 FORMAT $(10F7.0)$

would call for 10 numbers to be read from a card and stored as the first 10 elements of the first row of an array named A. The same 10 numbers would be stored as the first 10 elements of the first *column* of A by

READ $(5, 200)$ $(A(I, 1), I = 1, 10)$

We see that the indexed variable (or variables), along with the indexing information, must be enclosed in parentheses.

Just as it is possible to have nests of DO's, it is possible to have nests of *implied DO's*, as they are called. Suppose, for example, that we want to print 60 numbers, taking the first 12 from the first row of R, the next 12 from the *third* row of R, the next 12 from the *fifth* row of R, and so on. This can be done with

WRITE $(6, 91)$ $((R(I, J), J = 1, 12), I = 1, 9, 2)$
91 FORMAT $(4E20.7)$

In a certain sense this list may be thought of as equivalent to the schematic nest:

$$\text{DO } 462 \text{ I} = 1, 9, 2$$
$$\text{DO } 462 \text{ J} = 1, 12$$
$$462 \text{ RESULT (I, J)}$$

We see that the idea of inner and outer DO's carries over to inner and outer list indexing. A comma is always required between the last variable name in an implied DO and the indexing information.

The implied DO is a powerful feature of the input and output capability of FORTRAN. The serious student will take the trouble to learn it thoroughly. In fact, some people urge the use of implied DO's even where it might be possible to write the name of an array without subscripts. The implied DO is simple and precise, whereas experience shows that the use of array names without subscripting can cause complications.

The scanning of a list can be considerably more complex than it is in a simple list which names each variable explicitly. Still, the sequence of transmission of values is completely specified in all cases. It should also be realized that the scanning of the list and the scanning of the FORMAT statement entries keep in step: each time another variable is obtained from the list the next field specification is obtained from the FORMAT statement. If the closing parenthesis of the FORMAT is reached while more variables still remain in the list, a new card or a new line is called for and FORMAT scanning returns to the start of the FORMAT statement. Thus, if A is a one-dimensional array with 20 elements, the statements

$$\text{WRITE (6, 582) } A$$
$$\text{582 FORMAT (1PE16.7)}$$

would print 20 separate lines with one value each. On the other hand these statements

$$\text{WRITE (6, 583) } A$$
$$\text{583 FORMAT (1P5E16.7)}$$

would print five numbers on each of four lines. And we could also write

$$\text{WRITE (6, 584) } A$$
$$\text{584 FORMAT (F10.1, F10.2, F10.3, F10.4)}$$

which would put four numbers on each of five lines. *In each line* the first number would have one decimal place, the second two, and so on.

This "repeat scanning," as we might call it, is an important feature of FORMAT statement usage. We shall discuss it further in Section 6.5, in which we shall also see how it can be modified by parentheses within the FORMAT.

6.4 The FORMAT Statement

It is the business of the FORMAT statement to describe how the information is arranged on input or is to be arranged on output. To each value transmitted there must correspond a field specification which lists the kind of information the field contains (in terms of its internal representation) and what it "looks like" externally.

The subject may conveniently be described under two headings: (1) what each of the types of field specifications does and (2) how the field specifications may be arranged in the FORMAT statement, in keeping with the scanning process. Item (1) is the subject of this section and item (2), of the next.

We shall discuss eight types of field specification. In each case a complete field specification consists of the following:

1. A letter (I, F, E, D, L, A, H, or X) to designate the kind of information and how it is to be handled.

2. A number to designate how many card columns or printing positions are in use.

The D, E, and F field specifications require a second number to prescribe decimal-point handling.

To save repetition, we may note a few items that apply to D, E, F, and I field specifications.

On *input* a sign, if any, must be the first nonblank character of the field. The use of a plus sign is always optional; if no sign appears, the number is considered positive. Blanks are taken to be zeroes. A field that is entirely blank is zero.

On *output* the number will appear at the right of the output field if more character positions are specified for the field than there are characters in the number. If too few characters are specified, the sign and high-order digits will be lost and no warning will be given. Plus signs are neither punched nor printed in most FORTRAN systems.

In all types except H and X it is permissible to specify that the same field specification applies to several successive fields by writing a *repetition number* in front of the field specification.

Whenever a scale factor is written with a D, E, or F field specification, it automatically applies to all succeeding D, E, and F field specifications, until some other scale factor is encountered. If a given scale factor is applied to one field specification only, the next field specification must have an 0P scale factor.

Field specification I (integer). The form of this specification is Iw. I specifies conversion between an internal integer and an external decimal integer. The total number of characters in the field, including sign and any blanks, is w. Decimal points are not permitted.

Field specification F (external fixed point). The form of this specification is Fw.d. The F indicates conversion between an internal real value and an external number written without an exponent. The total number of characters in the field, including sign, decimal point, and any blanks, is w. The number of decimal places after the decimal point is d.

On *input* the use of a decimal point is optional; if one is supplied in the card, it overrides d.

On *output* there will be d places to the right of the decimal point, which is always supplied.

A scale factor may be used with the F field

specification by writing the specification in the general form

sPrFw.d

where s is the scale factor and r the repetition number. The effect is

external number = internal number . 10^s

The scale factor may be positive or negative. The formula applies both to input and output, although use with input is rare. There are many possible reasons for using a scale factor. One would be to change units for printing. An internal number giving current in amperes could be printed as milliamperes by use of scale factor of 3. This is illustrated in Case Study 11.

Field specification E (floating point). The form of this specification is Ew.d. E specifies conversion between an internal real value and an external number written with an exponent. The total number of characters in the external medium is w, including sign, decimal point, exponent, and any blanks. The number of decimal places after the decimal point (not counting the exponent) is d.

On *input* the use of an actual decimal point is optional; if it is supplied in the card, it overrides d. The exponent part of the field takes the general form E±ee, as in a floating point constant in a statement. However, several shortcuts are permitted to simplify card punching. A positive exponent may appear with the + omitted or replaced with a blank, that is, E ee or Eee. If the first digit of the exponent is zero, it may be omitted. If the exponent is written with a sign, the E may be omitted. Thus all of the following are permissible and equivalent forms for the exponent *plus 2*: E+02, E 02, E02, E+2, E2, +2.

The exponent must be punched at the extreme right of the card field to convey the correct meaning, since blanks are taken to be zeros.

For example, all of the following data fields convert to the same internal number if read in under control of E14.7, but it must be remembered that an actual decimal point overrides d in the field specification:

$$+12345678E03$$
$$12345678.E-4$$
$$1234.5678E0$$
$$+0.12345678+4$$

On *output* the number will normally appear in the form ±0.nn . . . E±ee (except that plus signs are replaced with blanks), in which the number of places after the decimal point is specified by d.

A scale factor has no effect on input with an E field specification. On output the effect is to multiply the "fractional" part by 10^s and to reduce the exponent by s. The scale factor may be positive or negative.

Field specification D (double precision). In the Dw.d specification the internal value must be double-precision. The exponent is written with D instead of E, but in all other respects this is analogous to the E field specification.

Field specification L (logical). In the Lw form the L specifies conversion between an internal logical value (.TRUE. or .FALSE.) and one of the letters T or F externally. The total number of character positions is w.

On *input* the first nonblank character in the field must be T or F, which will cause storage of a value of .TRUE. or .FALSE., respectively. Any other letters following the T or F are ignored, making it possible, for instance, to specify L5 and then to punch the word TRUE or FALSE in the card.

On *output* the letter T or F is placed at the extreme right of the allotted space, preceded by w-1 blanks.

Field Specification A (Alphameric). In the Aw form of field specification the associated variable may be of any kind. The field specification causes w characters to be read into, or written from, the associated list element. The "alphameric" characters may be any symbols representable in the particular computer: letters, digits, punctuation, and the "character" *blank.* The precise action depends on the number of characters held in one storage location in the particular machine, which, as a general indication, ranges from four to eight. Call this number g.

On *input,* if w is greater than or equal to g, the rightmost g characters will be taken from the internal input field; these g characters fill the storage location. If w is less than g, the w characters will appear "left justified" (at the extreme left) in storage, followed by trailing blanks.

On *output* if w is greater than g, the external result will consist of w-g blanks followed by the g characters. If w is less than or equal to g, the external result will be the leftmost w characters from storage.

For instance, in Case Study 12 we shall see

field specifications of A1 used for input and output. On input this places one character in the leftmost character position of a storage location. When this location is later printed under control of A1, that one leftmost character is the one printed.

Field specification H (Hollerith). This specification takes the form wH. The w characters immediately following the letter H are printed or punched in the position indicated by the position of the Hollerith field specification in the FORMAT statement. The Hollerith field specification is different from the others so far discussed in that it does not call for the transmission of any values from the list. Instead, it calls for the input or output of the text *itself*. Any character available in the computer may be used, as it can with the A field specification. This, incidentally, is the only case in which a blank in a statement is not ignored by the FORTRAN compiler.

No indication of the presence of the Hollerith text is required in the list of the input or output statement that refers to the FORMAT statement containing the text. Whenever a Hollerith field specification is encountered in the scanning of the FORMAT statement, the text is transmitted without any variable from the list having been transmitted.

On *input* the w characters from the input record are inserted into the FORMAT statement. This makes it possible to change Hollerith information within a FORMAT. The variation of FORMAT statements, however, is more commonly accomplished with FORMAT specifications in arrays, as discussed in Section 6.6.

On *output* the w characters following the letter H are written out.

Hollerith field specifications are commonly used to provide headings and other identification on printed reports, as we shall see in the case studies.

Another very frequent application controls the spacing of lines in printing. The first character of the line printed with a WRITE statement is ordinarily not actually printed but is used instead to control spacing, according to the following table:

Control Character	Action
Blank	Normal single spacing
0	Double space
1	Skip to top of next page before printing
+	Suppress spacing

Common practice, and strongly recommended, is to start every FORMAT statement for output with a Hollerith field giving the desired spacing. If, by accident, the first data field places a nonblank character into the carriage control position, *strange* spacing can result.

Field specification X (blank). This specification has the form wX

On *input* the effect is to skip over w columns. The reason might be that the columns are blank and that the purpose is to avoid having to make the succeeding field specification longer than it really is to take the blanks into account. On the other hand, the columns skipped might have punches that simply are not needed in the computer, such as, for example, card identification used only by the programmer and the computer operator.

On *output* the effect is to insert w blanks into the output record. This is commonly done to space heading information or to spread out results across the line.

6.5 Additional FORMAT Statement Features

Just as it is possible to repeat a field specification by writing a repetition number in front of it, it is also possible to repeat a *group* of field specifications. The group is enclosed in parentheses and the desired number of repetitions is written before it. For instance, suppose that eight fields on a card are alternately described by I2 and F10.0. We can write

$$4(I2, F10.0)$$

to get the desired action. This is *not* the same as

$$4I2, 4F10.0$$

which describes a card with four I2 fields, then four F10.0 fields, rather than the desired alternation.

Two levels of parentheses, in addition to those required by the FORMAT statement, are permitted. The second level facilitates the transmission of complex quantities, which require two field specifications for each list variable.

When the list of an input or output statement is used to transmit more than one *record* (card or line) and the different records have different formats, a slash (/) is used to separate the format specifications for the different lines. For example, suppose that two cards are to be read with a single READ statement; the first card has only a four-digit integer and the second has six real numbers. We could write

FORMAT (I4/6E14.0)

The slash terminates the reading of the first card (skipping over any other punching that it might contain) and, if list variables remain, initiates the reading of another card, using the field specifications after the slash.

It is possible to specify a special format for the first (one or more) records and a different format for all subsequent records. This is done by enclosing the last record specifications in parentheses. For instance, if the first card of a deck has an integer and a real number and all following cards contain two integers and a real number, we could write

FORMAT (I4, E14.0/(2I4, E14.0))

The principle here is that when all field specifications in a FORMAT statement have been used and more list variables remain, control reverts to the group-repeat specification terminated by the last preceding right parenthesis, if there is one, or to the beginning of the statement. For instance, suppose we have

FORMAT (2E10.3, 2(I2, I3),
(I4, 2(F12.4, F12.6)), D26.16)

If more list variables remain after the D26.16 specification has been used, control reverts to the group-repeat specification (I4, 2(F12.4, F12.6)), which is the one terminated by the last preceding right parenthesis.

It is possible to call for the skipping of entire records by writing successive slashes, which are often useful when line spacing is desired and it is not convenient to use a carriage control character in the FORMAT statement for the next line. When $n + 1$ consecutive slashes appear at the end of a FORMAT specification, they are treated as follows: for input $n + 1$ records are skipped; for output n blank records are written, unless after doing so control reverts for the transmission of additional values, in which case a total of $n + 1$ blank records is written. When $n + 1$ consecutive slashes appear in the middle of the FORMAT specification, n records are skipped or written.

If a FORMAT statement contains nothing but Hollerith and blank field specifications, there must be no variables listed in the associated input or output statement. This is most commonly done with the WRITE statement to produce page and column headings or to cause line and page spacing. A not uncommon FORMAT statement is

FORMAT (1H1)

Referenced by a WRITE statement with no list, this causes the printer paper to space to the top of the next page.

6.6 Object Time FORMAT Statements

The ability to read a FORMAT statement at the time of execution of the object program adds great flexibility to FORTRAN. To do this we must establish an array that will hold the format specifications in the form of alphameric data. The formats are read into this array at object time. To use these variable formats we reference the array *by name* in the READ or WRITE statement. Let us study an example.

Suppose that we wish to print the values of four variables named I, J, X, and Y, the first two being integers and the last two real. The formats for printing them are to be read in at object time. Let us assume further that our computer has storage locations that hold six characters each. Consider the program shown in Figure 6.1. The DIMENSION statement establishes FMT as a one-dimensional array with five elements, which will be considered as alphameric variables and therefore can hold 30 characters (five "words," we assume, of six characters each). The READ statement references a FORMAT statement which says to expect five words of six characters each, and these characters are to go into the five storage locations of the array FMT. The card might contain something like this:

(I10, I16, 1PE20.8, 0PE16.2)

Counting the parentheses and the blanks, we have 28 characters up through the closing parenthesis. These characters, plus two more blanks from columns 29 and 30, fill out the 30 characters in the FMT array. This is how the object-time format

```
      DIMENSION FMT(5)
      READ (5, 209) (FMT(I), I = 1, 5)
  209 FORMAT (5A6)
      •
      •
      •
      WRITE (6, FMT) I, J, X, Y
```

Figure 6.1.   A program segment using object-time format statements.

information must be entered: with the enclosing parentheses, but without the word FORMAT. The specifications just written would be entered into the FMT array exactly as they were punched on the card.

Later in the program we can use the "formatting" information that has been read into storage, as in the WRITE statement, by writing the name of the format array in place of the statement number of a FORMAT statement. The field specifications will be taken from storage as they have been read.

Reading in a complete set of format specifications is by no means the only thing that can be done with object time formats. Suppose we have an array named RESULT, which contains ten real numbers. These are to be printed across one line, using F8.2 specifications for nonzero values and replacing zeros with blanks. This will avoid printing the 0. that most FORTRAN systems put out for zero values and which some users might not consider attractive. The lines are to be double spaced.

Figure 6.2 shows one way in which this requirement can be met. We establish the arrays for the format and for the results. The READ statement should get a card containing the following table, in which small b's stand for blanks:

Columns	Contents	Program Name
1–6	(bbbbb	LEFT
7–12	//)bbb	RIGHT
13–18	A8,bbb	ASPEC
19–24	F8.2,b	FSPEC
25–30	bbbbbb	BLANKS

In FORM(1) we place the opening left parenthesis. This is followed in the format in storage by five blanks, but blanks in a format are ignored except in a Hollerith field. To get the required double spacing we place two slashes before the closing right parenthesis that falls in FORM(12).

Now we have ten storage locations, FORM(2) through FORM(11), into which to place field specifications corresponding to the ten values in the array RESULT. For each element in RESULT that is nonzero we shall place in the corresponding position of FORM the field specification F8.2. Each

```
C ILLUSTRATION OF OBJECT-TIME FORMATS
C
      DIMENSION RESULT(10), FORM(12)
      REAL LEFT, RIGHT, ASPEC, FSPEC, BLANKS
C THE CARD READ BY THE NEXT READ CONTAINS THE FOLLOWING
C     COLUMNS  1- 6    (         LEFT
C     COLUMNS  7-12    //)       RIGHT
C     COLUMNS 13-18    A8,       ASPEC
C     COLUMNS 19-24    F8.2,     FSPEC
C     COLUMNS 25-30              BLANKS
      READ (5, 19) LEFT, RIGHT, ASPEC, FSPEC, BLANKS
   19 FORMAT (5A6)
C SET UP OPENING AND CLOSING PARENTHESES
      FORM(1) = LEFT
      FORM(12) = RIGHT
C LOOP TO READ SAMPLE DATA
      DO 27 I1 = 1, 5
      READ (5, 1033) RESULT
 1033 FORMAT (10F3.0)
C LOOP TO PROCESS ALL 10 ITEMS IN RESULT
      DO 47 I = 1, 10
      IF (RESULT(I) .EQ. 0.0) GO TO 46
C NON-ZERO IF HERE -- PUT F8.2, INTO FORMAT IN STORAGE
      FORM(I+1) = FSPEC
      GO TO 47
C ZERO IF HERE -- PUT A8, INTO FORMAT IN STORAGE AND BLANKS IN RESULT
   46 FORM(I+1) = ASPEC
      RESULT(I) = BLANKS
   47 CONTINUE
C WRITE THE ARRAY UNDER CONTROL OF THE COMPUTED FORMAT
   27 WRITE (6, FORM) RESULT
      STOP
      END
```

Figure 6.2. A program segment using object-time formatting to blank out zero values.

1.00	2.00	3.00	4.00	5.00	6.00	7.00	8.00	9.00	10.00
1.10	0.	2.20	0.	3.30	4.40	0.	0.	0.	5.50
0.	0.	10.00	20.00	0.	0.	30.00	40.00	0.	0.
0.10	0.	0.	0.	0.	0.	0.	0.	0.20	0.
0.01	0.02	0.03	0.	0.	0.	0.	0.	0.04	0.05

1.00	2.00	3.00	4.00	5.00	6.00	7.00	8.00	9.00	10.00
1.10		2.20		3.30	4.40				5.50
		10.00	20.00			30.00	40.00		
0.10								0.20	
0.01	0.02	0.03						0.04	0.05

Figure 6.3. Sample data values, printed with F8.2 field specifications (first five lines), and the output of the program of Figure 6.2 for the same data values (second five lines).

element of RESULT that is zero will be replaced in RESULT by an alphameric "value" consisting of six blanks, and in the corresponding element of FORM we will place the field specification A8. An alphameric value in RESULT contains only six blanks, whereas the field specification indicates eight printing positions. The extra positions are filled with blanks, which is entirely suitable in this case.

A simple DO loop runs through the 10 elements of RESULT, processing each appropriately, after which the array is printed under control of the format that we have assembled in FORM.

Figure 6.3, in the first five lines, shows sample data printed with F8.2 field specifications throughout. The second five lines are the output of the program of Figure 6.2 for the same data values.

Very complex and flexible formatting can be built up by using techniques like these. The result can be a program that has more statements for input and output than for other data processing, which is more or less typical of the work of professional programming.

6.7 Additional Input and Output Statement Features

Throughout this book we have tacitly assumed that input comes into the computer from magnetic tape unit 5, after a preliminary card-to-tape conversion, and that output is written on tape unit 6 from which it is printed. We have assumed furthermore that FORMAT statements are always used. It is now appropriate to discuss these matters a little more fully, because there are several other ways of working with input and output devices.

Conventions on magnetic tape numbering vary greatly from one installation to the next; the programmer must get the list of functions for his system. The conventions used on the computer employed to run the programs in this book are more or less representative, as given in Table 6.1.

TABLE 6.1

FORTRAN Tape Unit	Mode	
1	Binary	Input or Output
2	Binary	Input or Output
3	Binary	Input or Output
4	Binary	Input or Output
5	BCD	Input
6	BCD	Output
7	Binary	Output
8	BCD	Input or Output

"BCD" and "binary" refer to the method of storage of information on the magnetic tape and also to the question whether the information is formatted. Binary tapes 1–4 are used with READ and WRITE statements that do not reference a FORMAT statement. The information is placed on tape in a format that cannot be printed; the purpose of such storage is to hold information that is too extensive to keep in main storage at one time. We shall find an example in Case Study 13, in which we work with an array containing as many as 90,000 elements. We write the entire array on tape a row at a time in binary form, without FORMAT statements, then read the rows back one at a time for repeated processing.

FORTRAN tapes 5 and 6 are the familiar units we have used for program data and results.

FORTRAN tape 7 is used for the output of object programs, which also are written without formatting by the compiler. FORTRAN tape 8 is available to the programmer for whatever purposes he may wish.

These tape designations are symbolic, which means that a given FORTRAN tape unit may correspond to any of the physical tape units of the computer, depending on the operating system specifications, which may be changed by control cards. The symbolic designations we have listed can also be changed; those we have given are conventional but not fixed.

The designation of the input or output unit desired may be specified at the time of execution of the object program by writing an integer variable in place of the unit number and assigning a suitable value to the variable. We might write, for instance,

$$READ\ (N, 106)\ A, B, C$$

Earlier in the program we might assign to N the value 5 or 8 to select the corresponding *BCD* input tape.

The *off-line* operation we have assumed (card-to-tape before reading, tape-to-print after writing) is a routine procedure on large computers. In most cases, with present equipment and methods, it is not economical to use the *on-line* reader, printer, or punch. Nevertheless, almost all computers have such devices, and there are occasional reasons for the FORTRAN programmer to use them. There are, of course, smaller computers that have no off-line operations at all.

For a number of reasons, therefore, we should learn how to call for on-line reading of cards, on-line printing of information, and on-line punching of cards. It is quite simple, actually. To read on-line

we merely write a READ statement of the following form:

$$READ\ n,\ list$$

where n is a FORMAT statement number. To print on-line we write

$$PRINT\ n,\ list$$

and to punch on-line we write

$$PUNCH\ n,\ list$$

In these forms the FORMAT statement features are the same as those we have discussed and the list is the same.

There are three statements specifically for use with magnetic tape. In each case the verb is followed by an integer constant or variable designating the FORTRAN unit number.

The END FILE statement places an end-of-file mark on the designated tape. Its primary use, from our standpoint, is to serve as a signal to the off-line printer that no more valid information follows. The REWIND statement returns a tape to its beginning. This step is necessary, for instance, when a binary tape has been written with intermediate results and we want to read the data back into the computer. Tape cannot be read backward in FORTRAN, so we rewind the tape and use a binary read to get the information.

The BACKSPACE statement backs up the specified tape by one "record." A record, for our purposes, may be defined as the information corresponding to one card or one printer line.

The object program is set up to test for inadvertent attempts to destroy the standard input and output tapes. For instance, a BACKSPACE statement that names FORTRAN tape 6 will be ignored, because this could cause destruction of some of the information already written on the tape.

6.8 Case Study 11: Damped Oscillation with Headings

The calculations in this case study are identical with those in Case Study 9 (pp. 72–74). We now wish to modify the program so that it will produce an attractive and easily readable report.

```
C CASE STUDY 11 - DAMPED OSCILLATION WITH HEADINGS
C
        REAL I, IM, Q, R, C, L, F0, F1, C1, C2, T, DELT, TEMP
        INTEGER CYCLES, NPERCY, LIMIT
C READ PARAMETERS
        READ (5, 612) Q, R, C, L, CYCLES, NPERCY
    612 FORMAT (4F10.0, 2I2)
C PRINT PARAMETERS, WITH IDENTIFICATION, AND COLUMN HEADINGS
        WRITE (6, 613) Q, R, C, L
    613 FORMAT (1H1, 17HINITIAL CHARGE = , F10.6, 10H   COULOMB, 6X,
      1    13HRESISTANCE = , F9.3, 6H   OHM/15HOCAPACITANCE = , F10.6,
      2    8H   FARAD, 11X, 13HINDUCTANCE = , F7.3, 8H   HENRY///
      3    21H0   TIME        CURRENT/7H    MS, 10X, 2HMA///)
C CHECK FOR INVALID DATA
        IF (R**2 .GE. 4.0*L/C) STOP
C COMPUTE INTERMEDIATE VARIABLES
        F0 = 0.1591549 / SQRT(L*C)
        F1 = 0.1591549 * SQRT(1.0/(L*C) - R**2/(4.0*L**2))
        TEMP = NPERCY
        DELT = 1.0 / (TEMP * F0)
        IM = 6.2831853 * F0**2 * Q / F1
        C1 = R / (2.0 * L)
        C2 = 6.2831853 * F1
C START T AT ZERO BEFORE ENTERING LOOP
        T = 0.0
C COMPUTE NUMBER OF POINTS
        LIMIT = CYCLES * NPERCY
C COMPUTING LOOP - DO STATEMENT USED ONLY FOR COUNTING
        DO 11 J = 1, LIMIT
        I = IM * EXP(-C1 * T) * SIN(C2 * T)
        WRITE (6, 706) T, I
     11 T = T + DELT
C NOTE THAT SCALE FACTOR (3P) APPLIES TO BOTH FIELD SPECIFICATIONS
    706 FORMAT (1H , 3PF8.3, F12.3)
        STOP
        END
```

Figure 6.4. The program of Figure 5.11, modified to produce identifications and headings. (Case Study 11.)

There are four input parameters in the calculation: the initial charge Q, the resistance R, the capacitance C, and the inductance L. The values of these parameters are to be printed at the top of the first page, with identifications and units. The two columns of output are to be headed with their meanings and the units: time in milliseconds, identified MS, and current in milliamperes, identified MA. The actual units in the program are seconds and amperes; a scale factor will be used to convert to milliseconds and milliamperes.

Figure 6.4 shows the program of Figure 5.11 as modified to get the desired actions.

The reading of the parameters is as before. Now, however, we immediately print the four physical parameters, referencing a long FORMAT statement that produces the headings. Figure 6.5 shows the result of all this; it may be helpful to follow the output in studying the FORMAT.

The 1H1 is for carriage control. Each report

should normally begin at the top of a new page to avoid printing it on the same page as the end of the preceding report. 17HINITIAL CHARGE b=b, is identification information. Note that the blank spaces (b's) before and after the equal sign must be counted in the 17H. F10.6 is the first field specification that corresponds to a list entry, namely Q. After that we have 10HbbbCOULOMB, which is the unit of charge. We now skip six spaces, which is readily done with 6X. The FORMAT statement is continued on another line, which, of course, does *not* mean that the output will go to a new line now; nothing has been said about a new line in the output, and in fact we continue on the same line. The word RESISTANCE is followed by the value of R from the list and then the word OHM, the unit of resistance. Now comes a slash, which will cause the line just assembled to be printed and will start the assembly of another line, since more list variables remain.

INITIAL CHARGE =   0.000010   COULOMB   RESISTANCE =   1.000   OHM

CAPACITANCE =   0.000010   FARAD   INDUCTANCE =   0.002   HENRY

TIME MS	CURRENT MA
0.	0.
0.044	21.610
0.089	40.653
0.133	55.342
0.178	64.351
0.222	66.933
0.267	62.978
0.311	53.013
0.355	38.135
0.400	19.892
0.444	0.124
0.489	-19.221
0.533	-36.281
0.578	-49.453
0.622	-57.549
0.666	-59.896
0.711	-56.393
0.755	-47.507
0.800	-34.218
0.844	-17.908
0.889	-0.223
0.933	17.096
0.977	32.378
1.022	44.191
1.066	51.466
1.111	53.599
1.155	50.496
1.200	42.573
1.244	30.703
1.288	16.121
1.333	0.299
1.377	-15.205
1.422	-28.896
1.466	-39.488
1.511	-46.026
1.555	-47.964
1.599	-45.216
1.644	-38.151
1.688	-27.549
1.733	-14.512
1.777	-0.357
1.822	13.522
1.866	25.787
1.910	35.286
1.955	41.160
1.999	42.921
2.044	40.488
2.088	34.189
2.133	24.718
2.177	13.063
2.221	0.399
2.266	-12.025
2.310	-23.013
2.355	-31.531
2.399	-36.809
2.444	-38.408
2.488	-36.254
2.532	-30.637
2.577	-22.178
2.621	-11.758

Figure 6.5. Output of the program of Figure 6.4.

The second line is put together in much the same manner. Extra blanks were inserted by using 11X, whereas we had 6X before, to line up the second halves of the two lines. After the word HENRY, the unit of inductance, we have three slashes. This will cause termination of the second heading line and the printing of two blank lines.

The list variables have now been exhausted, but all remaining Hollerith text will nevertheless be printed. The next Hollerith field specification is

21H0bbbTIMEbbbbbbCURRENT

The zero after the H will cause double spacing before printing. This could, of course, have been accomplished by putting one more slash before it; the choice is essentially arbitrary, although the way shown is faster in the printer by a trivial amount.

A slash separates the time-current heading from the units heading; there will be only the normal single spacing between these two lines. Following the slash is a Hollerith field in which the first character is a carriage-control character of blank, calling for single spacing. The other four blanks are for separation. They could just as well have been inserted with a 4X; there is little to choose between in the two methods. The three slashes at the end of the FORMAT statement will cause two extra lines to be inserted. It would not be convenient to get either of these blank lines by a carriage-control character in the FORMAT statement for the next line because the next line is regular output. Unless we wish to use a different FORMAT statement for the first line of regular output (non-heading) than for all following, we cannot call for different spacing on the first line.

In the FORMAT statement at 706 we have carriage-control character of blank for single spacing, followed by an F field specification with a scale factor, which we have not seen before. A scale factor of 3 on an F field causes the internal value to be multiplied by 10^3, and there is, of course, no compensating change in the exponent, since there is no exponent. This is just what we want: to convert from seconds to milliseconds it is indeed necessary to multiply by 10^3.

The other field specification here is also of the F type, but with more printing positions allowed to provide some separation between the two numbers. We have not written this field specification with a scale factor; once a scale factor has been established, it stays in effect in that FORMAT

statement until another scale factor is encountered in the scan.

6.9 Case Study 12: Graphing

It not infrequently happens that what a person wants from a computer, in the early stages of a study, is a *general* idea how a proposed system will work. Great accuracy may be of very little importance. In many such cases a graphical presentation may be the best solution.

In others the nature of the problem may be such that a graphical presentation will give the best intuitive understanding of the system, even though considerable accuracy may be required in the calculation.

In this case study we shall see an example of each of these points, as indications of what can be done to make computer results more meaningful than they sometimes are when presented as a stack of numbers.

For the first example let us graph the results of the damped oscillation calculation (Figure 6.6) we considered in Case Study 11 and in Case Study 9. We shall produce a graph in which the y axis is a line of dots *across* the page and the x axis is a row of dots *down* the page, printed one to each line. Each line printed (after the initial line of dots) will contain the letter X somewhere in the line; this is the plotted point. The page can be turned sideways for normal viewing. The reader may wish to glance at Figures 6.7 and 6.8 to get a clear picture of what we shall be doing. Figure 6.7 is a page of output (one graph) in the orientation of the printer, somewhat reduced. Figure 6.8 shows three other graphs, turned on the page and very much reduced.

We have chosen to provide 61 printing positions in each line, a line, remember, being parallel to the y axis as we interpret the graph. The choice of 61 was largely arbitrary. There can be as many lines as there are points; in other words, the graph is of indefinite length in the x direction (down the page).

Figure 6.6 contains additions required in the program of Figure 5.11. We set up a one-dimensional variable LINE that will contain 61 alphameric elements, each containing one character. We get the symbols we shall be using by reading a card in which the first three columns contain a blank, a decimal point, and the letter X, in that order. In

```
C CASE STUDY 12A - DAMPED OSCILLATION GRAPHING
C
      REAL I, IM, Q, R, C, L, F0, F1, C1, C2, T, DELT, TEMP, LINE
      INTEGER CYCLES, NPERCY, LIMIT, J
      DIMENSION LINE(61)
C READ PLOTTING SYMBOLS
      READ (5, 100) BLANK, DOT, X
  100 FORMAT (3A1)
C READ PARAMETERS
      READ (5, 612) Q, R, C, L, CYCLES, NPERCY
  612 FORMAT (4F10.0, 2I2)
C CHECK FOR INVALID DATA
      IF (R**2 .GE. 4.0*L/C) STOP
C PRINT A LINE OF DOTS, WHICH WILL BE VERTICAL AXIS WHEN PAPER IS TURNED
      DO 101 J = 1, 61
  101 LINE(J) = DOT
C NOTE THAT INDEXING IS NOT NEEDED, SINCE ENTIRE ARRAY IS PRINTED
      WRITE (6, 102) LINE
  102 FORMAT (1H1, 61A1)
C BLANK THE LINE
      DO 103 J = 1, 61
  103 LINE(J) = BLANK
C PUT A DOT IN LINE(31), TO PRODUCE HORIZONTAL AXIS WHEN PAPER IS TURNED
      LINE(31) = DOT
C COMPUTE INTERMEDIATE VARIABLES
      F0 = 0.1591549 / SQRT(L*C)
      F1 = 0.1591549 * SQRT(1.0/(L*C) - R**2/(4.0*L**2))
      TEMP = NPERCY
      DELT = 1.0 / (TEMP * F0)
      IM = 6.2831853 * F0**2 * Q / F1
      C1 = R / (2.0 * L)
      C2 = 6.2831853 * F1
C START T AT ZERO BEFORE ENTERING LOOP
      T = 0.0
C COMPUTE NUMBER OF POINTS
      LIMIT = CYCLES * NPERCY
C COMPUTING LOOP - DO STATEMENT USED ONLY FOR COUNTING
      DO 11 J1 = 1, LIMIT
      I = IM * EXP(-C1 * T) * SIN(C2 * T)
C COMPUTE DESIRED LOCATION OF PLOTTING SYMBOL
      J = 30.0 * (I/IM + 1.0) + 1.5
C PUT X IN SELECTED LOCATION
      LINE(J) = X
      WRITE (6, 104) LINE
  104 FORMAT (1H , 61A1)
C PUT A BLANK IN SELECTED POSITION, WHICH MIGHT HAVE BEEN ON AXIS
      LINE(J) = BLANK
C PUT DOT BACK IN AXIS LOCATION, IN CASE IT WAS BLANKED
      LINE(31) = DOT
   11 T = T + DELT
      STOP
      END
```

Figure 6.6. The program of Figure 5.12, modified to plot the results. (Case Study 12a.)

the program these symbols are named BLANK, DOT, and X. A simple DO loop fills all 61 elements of LINE with decimal points, which we then print. LINE is written without subscripts, since we want all 61 elements in the natural order. The associated FORMAT statement has a carriage-control character of 1 to space to the top of the next page. These decimal points are replaced with blanks, and

a decimal point is put back in the "middle" of the line.

After each value of I (the current) has been found, we wish to use it to decide where in the line to place an X, to stand for the point. There are many ways to do this; the system here is indicative of what can be done. We know from the formulation of the problem that IM is the maximum ab-

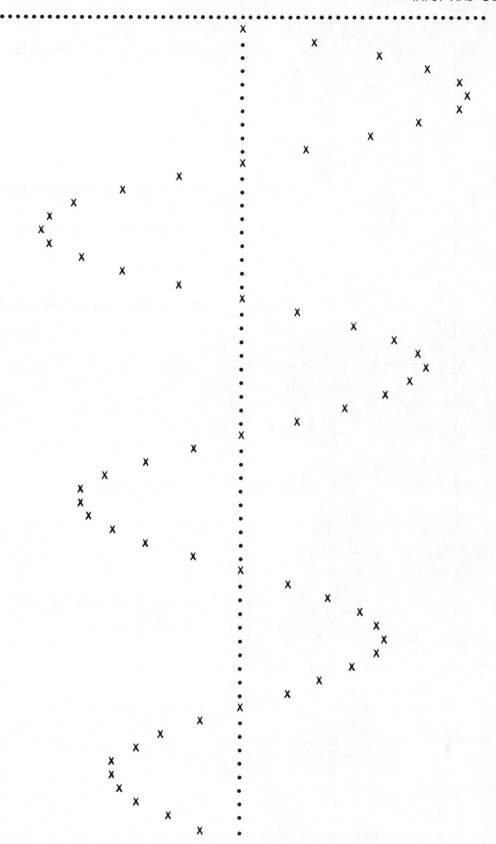

Figure 6.7.   The output of the program of Figure 6.6. (Case Study 12a.)

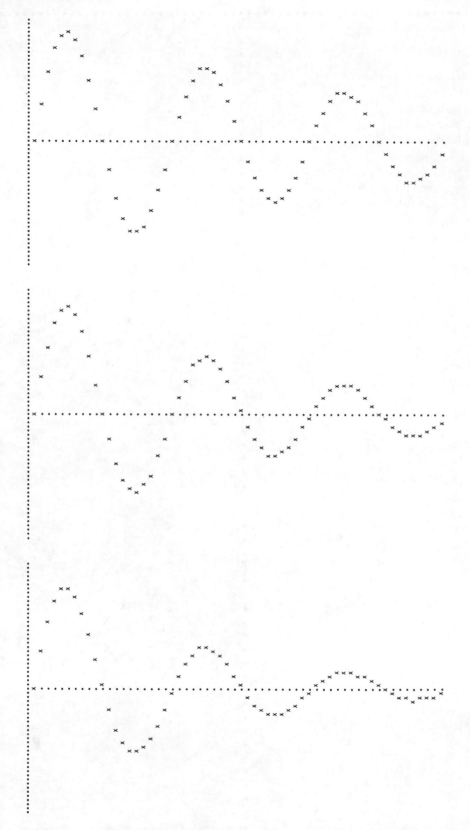

Figure 6.8.   The output of the program of Figure 6.6. for three other values of the resistance. The plots have been turned on the page for normal viewing. (Case Study 12a.)

solute value of I that can ever arise. The formula

$$J = 30.0*(I/IM + 1.0) + 1.5$$

transforms I/IM, which lies between -1 and $+1$, into a number which falls between 1 and 61, the range of subscripts, as follows. The 1.0 inside the parentheses changes the range from $(-1, 1)$ to $(0, 2)$, the multiplier of 30 changes it to $(0, 60)$, and the added 1.5 changes it to $(1, 61)$; we remember that in the conversion of the real expression into an integer any fractional part will be truncated. The extra 0.5 in 1.5 is for rounding.

This subscript may now be used to place the X in one of the 61 elements of LINE, after which we print the line. The FORMAT statement for this WRITE must have a carriage-control character of blank to get single spacing. (The first version of this program was tried thoughtlessly, using FORMAT 102 for the purpose, which meant that the printer spaced to the top of a new page for every line. This is a bit wasteful of paper.)

After printing the line we replace the X with a blank and then put a decimal point in LINE(31) against the possibility that the X, which we would have erased, had been there. A test could be made to see whether the X had been in LINE(31), but it would be a lot more trouble than the untested assignment statement.

The actions programmed at the bottom of the page in Figure 6.6 are carried out for every computed value of I, producing one line for each.

The usefulness of this kind of output is perhaps best seen in Figure 6.8, in which we have plots for different values of resistance. The damping caused by the increased resistance is clearly pictured in this way.

It would have been good practice, of course, to have printed some kind of identification on these plots. It was not done here partly because the identification would have been unreadable in Figure 6.8 after the great reduction necessary to produce them in printable size.

This program illustrates only one of many approaches to the graphing of this kind of function. The method shown has the advantage that the plotting can be done as the points are produced, without requiring any storage of the values.

It is quite possible to print a complete graph on one page in normal orientation. It is most easily done if there is sufficient storage in the computer to be able to set up a two-dimensional array with as many rows as we need lines and as many columns as we need horizontal printing positions. This array could be as large as about 60 x 120, or 7200 storage locations, which in many computers is no problem at all.

With such an array, translation formulas, such as the foregoing, can translate x and y values into subscript values, which can then be used to place a plotting point in the computed location. Unless a great deal is known about the function being plotted (e.g., that it decreases monotonically), it is impossible to print any of the graph until it is all ready, which, of course, is why we must have a two-dimensional array. It is entirely possible to print grid lines, indications of units on the axes, and axis identifications. A complete plotting program of this sort is quite elaborate. Most installations have such a program available as a library subroutine, to which we supply the data and some scaling information.

A second example of graphing involves a rather different sort of thing. In this problem we have a 61 x 61 array containing temperatures in the range of 0 to 200°. There are 529 elements in the "middle" of the array that contain no values, but, not counting these elements, there are still 3192 temperatures to be presented, and the problem is to be solved for five different values of the temperature inside the pipe. Getting any meaning out of such a mass of data is virtually impossible, so we turn to a way of making it graphic.

Each temperature will be translated into a blank or a letter, according to the pattern of Table 6.2.

TABLE 6.2

Temperature	Symbol
0–11.7	A
23.6–35.3	B
47.1–58.7	C
70.6–82.3	D
94.2–105.8	E
117.9–129.4	F
141.4–152.9	G
164.8–176.3	H
188.3–200.0	K

The basic idea here is that each letter will represent a band of temperatures about 11.7° wide. Between each of these bands will be a band of the same width for which a blank will be printed. The temperatures in the 61 x 61 array are the solution to Laplace's equation for a certain square pipe, so

```
C CASE STUDY 12B - PIPE TEMPERATURE MAP
      DIMENSION U(61,61), G(61), SYMBOL(17)
C READ GRAPHING SYMBOLS AND BLANK
      READ (5,700) (SYMBOL(I), I = 1, 17), BLANK

  700 FORMAT (18A1)
C FROM HERE THROUGH STATEMENT 15 IS THE SOLUTION OF THE EQUATION
      READ (5, 100) OMEGA, EPS, MAXIT
  100 FORMAT (2F10.0, I3)
      DO 777 INT = 1, 201, 50
      DO 1 I = 1, 61
      DO 1 J = 1, 61
    1 U(I, J) = 0.0
      DO 2 J = 32, 61
      FJ = J
      BOUND = 100.0 * (FJ - 31.0) / 30.0
      U(1, J ) = BOUND
    2 U(61, J) = BOUND
      DO 3 I = 2, 60
    3 U(I, 61) = 100.0
      DO 4 I = 19, 43
      U(I, 43) = INT - 1
    4 U(I, 19) = INT - 1
      DO 5 J = 19, 43
      U(43, J) = INT - 1
    5 U(19, J) = INT - 1
      ITN = 1
      A = OMEGA / 4.0
      B = 1.0 - OMEGA
   10 D = 0.0
      DO 14 J = 2, 60
      DO 14 I = 2, 60
      IF(I.GE.19.AND.I.LE.43.AND.J.GE.19.AND.J.LE.43) GO TO 14
      UNEW = A*(U(I+1,J) + U(I-1,J) + U(I,J+1) + U(I,J-1)) + B * U(I,J)
      RESID = ABS(UNEW - U(I,J))
      IF (RESID .GT. D) D = RESID
      U(I,J) = UNEW
   14 CONTINUE
      ITN = ITN + 1
      IF (ITN .GT. MAXIT) STOP
   15 IF (D .GE. EPS) GO TO 10
C MOVE TO TOP OF NEW PAGE
      WRITE (6,956)
  956 FORMAT (1H1)
C SET ROW INDEX, J, TO 61 FOR TOP ROW
      J = 61
C RUN THROUGH COMPLETE ROW
  602 DO 701 I = 1, 61
C CHECK IF POINT IS IN CENTER OF PIPE
      IF( I.GE.20.AND.I.LE.42.AND.J.GE.20.AND.J.LE.42) GO TO 702
C NOT IN CENTER - SELECT LETTER OR BLANK TO REPRESENT TEMPERATURE
      K = U(I,J)/11.765 + 1.0
C  PLACE SELECTED SYMBOL IN APPROPRIATE POSITION IN LINE
      G(I) = SYMBOL(K)
      GO TO 701
C INSERT BLANK IF IN CENTER OF PIPE
  702 G(I) = BLANK
  701 CONTINUE
C WRITE ENTIRE LINE, SO INDEXING NOT NEEDED
  703 WRITE (6,704) G
  704 FORMAT (1H , 61A1)
C MOVE TO NEXT ROW OF MAP
      J = J - 1
C CHECK COMPLETION
      IF (J- .NE. 0) GO TO 602
  777 CONTINUE
      STOP
      END
```

Figure 6.9. A program for solving LaPlace's equation for a certain square pipe and plotting the solution. (Case Study 12b.)

Figure 6.10. The output of the program of Figure 6.9. This is a graphical presentation of the solution of LaPlace's equation in a certain square pipe. (Case Study 12b.)

that when the temperatures are plotted there will be lines of constant temperature, represented in our system by a letter. The letters to be used were selected to be of about the same size, visually, which will perhaps make the graph easier to interpret.

As promised in Chapter 5, the program in Figure 6.9 includes the solution of Laplace's equation for those who may be interested. Our concern here, however, is with plotting, which is a rather small part of the total program, as it turns out.

At the beginning of the program we read a card which contains the following in columns 1 to 17, including the blanks:

A B C D E F G H K

The A is in column 1. These 17 characters become the 17 elements of the one-dimensional array named SYMBOL. The variable BLANK receives the character in column 18, which is a blank.

From this point down through statement 15 is the setup of the problem and its solution.

In the WRITE statement just before 956 we reference the FORMAT at 956 without an output list to cause page spacing. The subscripting scheme for working through the 61 lines and the 61 elements is of no interest to us in this case study. The long logical IF statement asks whether the element selected by the row-and-column subscripts is one of those in the middle, because we wish to produce blanks in this area. If not, we come to a translation formula which converts a temperature into a symbol. Division of a temperature in the range $(0, 200)$ by 11.765 provide a quotient in the range $(0, 16.999)$; adding 1.0 produces a number in the range $(1, 17.999)$; when this is truncated to an integer value for the variable K, the range becomes $(1, 17)$. SYMBOL(K) is then a blank or one of the letters contained in Table 6.2. The selected symbol goes into the appropriate place in an array named G which has 61 elements. When a complete line of symbols has been assembled, it is printed.

The result is shown in Figure 6.10, somewhat reduced. The physical problem was this. We have a square pipe, with an inside dimension of 4 in. and and outside dimension of 10 in. The pipe is half submerged along its length in ice water at $0°$; the temperature along the vertical sides increases linearly from $0°$ at the water level to $100°$ at the top, which is also the temperature along the top. The pipe is carrying a fluid at $200°$. The output in Figure 6.10 shows the temperature at the interior points after solution of the differential equation. The pic-

ture is not square because there are 10 printing positions per inch horizontally but only six lines per inch vertically. This is no serious inconvenience.

One useful way to use this program is to visualize the effect of changing fluid temperatures on the temperature distribution through the pipe material. Figure 6.11 shows plots, very much reduced, for inside temperatures of 0, 50, 100, and $150°$.

6.10 Case Study 13: The Gauss-Seidel Method with Very Large Systems of Equations

In this case study we shall modify the program of Case Study 10 to make it apply to systems of equations as large as 300 x 300. The coefficients for such a system number 90,000, which exceeds the storage capacity of most computers. The coefficients are accordingly written onto magnetic tape as they are read, and during the iteration process are read back one row at a time. It is one of the advantages of the Gauss-Seidel method that it requires only one row of coefficients to be in main storage at one time.

The logic of the solution is quite close to that of Case Study 10, and the modifications do not greatly complicate the logic. Therefore we shall dispense with a flowchart this time. The program shown in Figure 6.12 can be examined directly.

The array for the coefficients now is *one*-dimensional; we shall never have the entire array in storage at once. We see two small arrays set up to hold the input and output formats. With thousands of coefficients to be read and hundreds of results to be printed, it is almost essential that some flexibility be permitted in card and printing formats.

After clearing the X array to zeros, reading the formats, and reading the input and output formats and the values of N, EPS, and MAX, we come to a REWIND statement, which may seem pointless: we have not yet written anything on the tape. The problem is that we cannot know for sure that the tape is at its initial point, even though it ordinarily will be.

If by chance it is positioned somewhere else, we will have no trouble in writing, but when we later rewind the tape and try to read the information we have written we will encounter tape area before the point at which we began writing. Usually, there will be information on it from some previous usage of the tape, and we will be in trouble. It is good

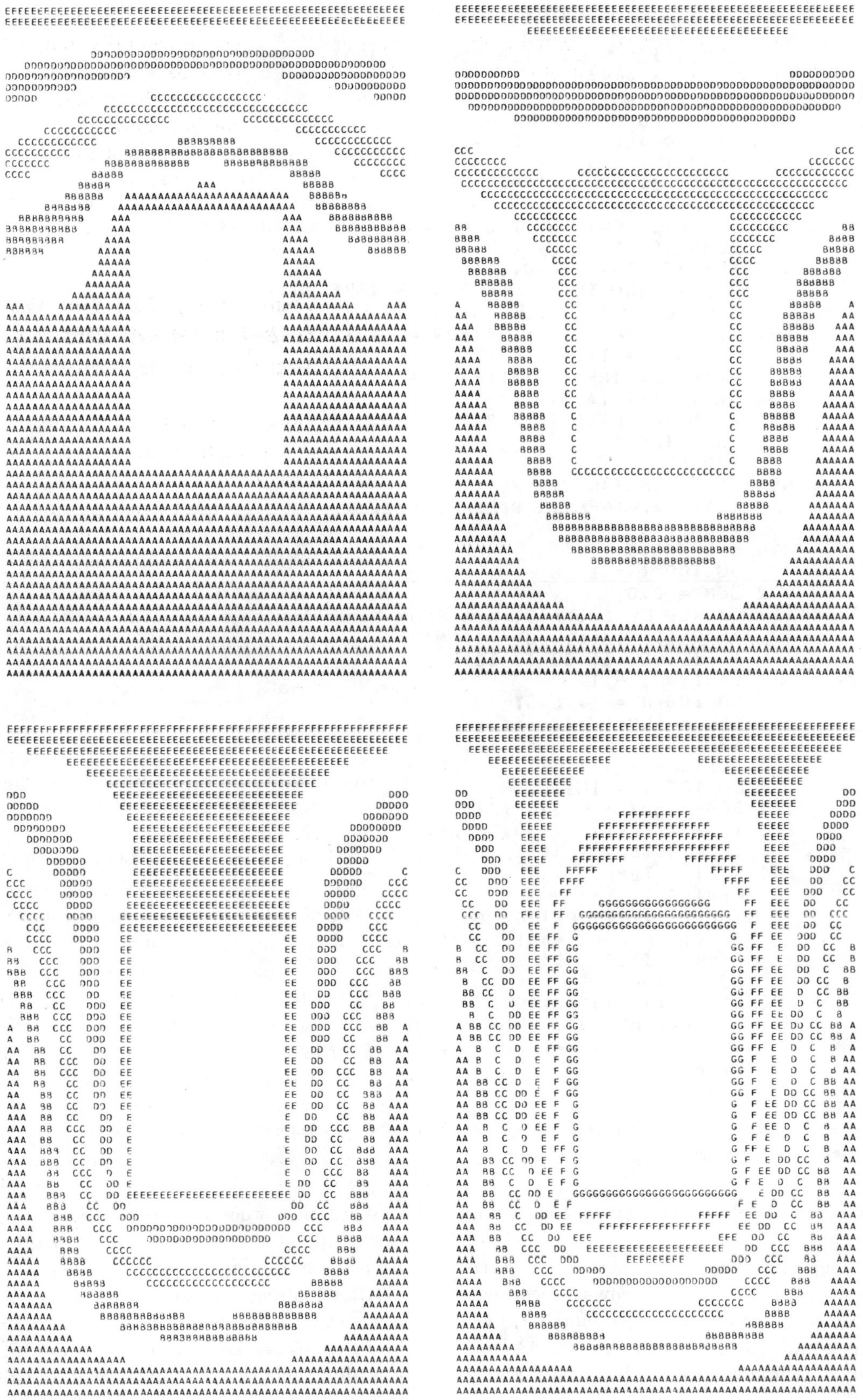

Figure 6.11. The output of the program of Figure 6.9, greatly reduced, for four other temperatures at the inside of the pipe. (Case Study 12b.)

```
C CASE STUDY 13 - LARGE SIMULTANEOUS EQUATIONS WITH TAPE
C
      DIMENSION A(300), B(300), X(300), INFMT(12), OUTFMT(12)
C CLEAR THE X ARRAY
      DO 50 L = 1, 300
   50 X(L) = 0.0
C READ THE OBJECT-TIME FORMATS
      READ (5, 87) INFMT
      READ (5, 87) OUTFMT
   87 FORMAT (6X, 12A6)
C READ N, EPSILON, AND THE MAXIMUM NUMBER OF ITERATIONS
      READ (5, 101) N, EPS, MAX
  101 FORMAT (I3, F10.0, I3)
C INITIAL REWIND TO ASSURE PROPER TAPE POSITION
      REWIND 1
C READ THE COEFFICIENTS, A ROW AT A TIME, AND WRITE ON TAPE
      DO 60 I = 1, N
      READ (5, INFMT) (A(L), L = 1, N)
   60 WRITE (1) (A(M), M = 1, N)
C WRITE END OF FILE TO MARK THE END OF VALID INFORMATION
      END FILE 1
      REWIND 1
C READ THE CONSTANT TERMS
      READ (5, INFMT) (B(L), L = 1, N)
      ITER = 1
   99 BIG = 0.0
      DO 100 I = 1, N
  102 SUM = 0.0
C READ A ROW OF COEFFICIENTS FROM TAPE
      READ (1) (A(L), L = 1, N)
      IF(I .EQ. 1) GO TO 105
      LAST = I - 1
      DO 106 J = 1, LAST
  106 SUM = SUM + A(J)*X(J)
      IF(I .EQ. N) GO TO 103
  105 INITL = I + 1
      DO 107 J = INITL, N
  107 SUM = SUM + A(J)*X(J)
  103 TEMP = (B(I) - SUM) / A(I)
      IF(ABS(TEMP - X(I)) .GT. BIG) BIG = ABS(TEMP - X(I))
  100 X(I) = TEMP
      REWIND 1
      IF(BIG .LT. EPS) GO TO 752
      IF (ITER .GE. MAX) GO TO 752
      ITER = ITER + 1
      GO TO 99
  752 WRITE (6, 147) ITER, EPS, BIG
  147 FORMAT(1H0, I5, 2E14.7   )
      WRITE (6, OUTFMT) (X(L), L = 1, N)
      STOP
      END
```

Figure 6.12. A program for solving a system of as many as 300 equations in 300 unknowns by the Gauss-Seidel method, using magnetic tape for storage of the coefficients. (Case Study 13.)

programming practice to rewind every tape before using it.

The DO loop that follows is executed N times. On each repetition of the loop one row of coefficients is read from card records on tape, under control of the object-time formats read earlier. As each row is read, it is immediately written onto binary tape 1.

When this process is completed, we end-file and rewind the tape, in order to be ready to read it from the beginning.

After reading the constant terms we go into the iteration scheme, which is similar to the program of Figure 5.14. The major difference, of course, is that for each row we must read the binary tape into the one-dimensional array A. We write statements such as

$$SUM = SUM + A(J)*X(J)$$

with the knowledge that the proper row will be occupying the *A* array at every point. We must rely on the fact that the rows are being used in the same order in which they were read. Prudence would normally dictate that the coefficient array should be printed for checking, since so much depends on a correct deck make-up.

After each iteration we rewind the coefficient tape so that it is correctly positioned for the next iteration.

This program was tested with the same system of equations used to test the earlier program. The input format card contained, in columns 1 to 14,

$$IN \qquad (5F10.0)$$

Notice that in FORMAT statement 87 we have a 6X field specification, to skip over whatever identification might be punched in columns 1 to 6. The format information was set up to accommodate the coefficients from one row on one card, which was a convenient way to arrange the data in this case. The output format card read

$$OUT \qquad (I5, 1PE16.7)$$

which is the same as we used earlier.

The output from the modified program was identical with the earlier results.

EXERCISES

1. Show how the given data values would be printed under control of the field specifications stated.

a. I5: 0, 1, 10, −587, 90062, 123456
b. F7.2: 0.0, 1.0, 16.77, −586.21, 0.04, 12.34
c. F5.0: 0.0, 1.0, 16.87, −12.32
d. E10.3: 0.0, 0.00072, 601000., −473., −0.0123
e. 1PE10.3: 0.0, 10.0, 0.000076, 6780000., −627., −0.000456

2. Given that the values of three variables are as follows,

$$M = 12$$

$$X = 407.8$$

$$Y = -32.9$$

Show exactly what would be printed by

$$WRITE (6, 107) M, X, Y$$

with each of the following FORMAT statements.

*a. 107 FORMAT (1Hb, 3HM=b, I3, 3HX=b, F6.1, 3HY=b, F6.1)

b. 107 FORMAT
   (1H1, 17HREADINGbNUMBERb=b,
   I3/ 1H0, 11HPRESSUREb=b, F6.1,
   7HTEMPb=b, F6.1)
c. 107 FORMAT
   (1H1, 17HREADINGbNUMBERb=b,
   I3/ 1H0, 8HPRESSURE, 6X,
   11HTEMPERATURE/1H0,
   F7.1, 9X, F6.1)

*3. Four numbers are punched on a card; they are new values of real variables named BOS, EWR, PHL, and DCA. Each number is punched in eight columns, the first beginning in column 1. Each number contains a decimal point. Write READ and FORMAT statements to read the card.

4. Same as Exercise 3, except that there is no decimal point. The numbers are to be treated as if they had two decimal places, that is, two places to the right of an assumed decimal point.

5. Same as Exercise 3, except that each number occupies 14 columns and is punched with a decimal point and an exponent.

*6. A card is punched in the following format.

Columns	Sample Format	Variable Name
1–3	±xx	LGA
4–6	xxx	JFK
7–20	±x.xxxxxxxE±ee	BAL
21–34	±x.xxxxxxxE±ee	TPA

LGA and JFK are integer variables; BAL and TPA are real. The small letters stand for any digits. Write statements to read such a card.

*7. Given a WRITE statement,

$$WRITE (6, 92) I, J, R, S$$

I and *J* are integer variables and *R* and *S* are real. For each of the following, write a FORMAT statement that could produce such a line or lines with the given WRITE statement.

a. bbbb-16bb92017bbb16.82bb437.89
b. bbbb-16bb92017bbb17.bb438.
c. bbb-16bbb92017bb0.16824Eb02bb0.43789Eb03
d. bbb-16bbb92017bb1.6824Eb01bb4.3789Eb02
e. I=bbb-16bbJ=b92017bbR=bb16.8bbbS=b437.9
f. I=bbb-16
   J=b92017
   R=bb16.8
   S=b437.9

[Write only one FORMAT statement for (f).]

8. Same as Exercise 7, but given the WRITE statement

$$WRITE (6, 93) M, P, Q, R$$

M is an integer variable and the others are real.

a. b9bb-33.b1.6E-04bb1.439024Eb06
b. b9bb-32.62bb0.00016bb0.1439024Eb07
c. b9bb-32.62bb0.16E-03bb1439024.

d. M   RHO   GAIN   OUTPUT
   b9bb-32.62bb1.6E-04bbbb1.439024Eb06

(Write only one FORMAT statement.)

e. M=b9bbbRHO=b-32.62bbbGAIN=b1.6E-04
   OUTPUT=b1.439024Eb06

(Write only one FORMAT statement.)

*9. DATA is a one-dimensional array of at most 10 elements. A card is punched with a value of N in columns 1 and 2 and with 1 to 10 elements of DATA in succeeding columns. The numbers of elements is given by the value of N. Each number is punched with a decimal point but no exponent, in seven columns. Write statements to read such a card.

10. Same as Exercise 9 except that the numbers are the *odd-numbered* elements of DATA; there are therefore at most five of them. N is the *element* number of the last one, not the total number of elements.

*11. Describe in words what card format and deck make-up would be required for each of the following groups of statements to be meaningful:

a.   DIMENSION X(10)
     READ (5, 69) (X(I), I = 1, 7)
  69 FORMAT (10F4.0)
b.   DIMENSION X(10)
     READ (5, 70) N, (X(I), I = 1, N)
  70 FORMAT (I2, 10F4.0)
c.   DIMENSION X(10)
     READ (5, 71) N, (X(I), I = 1, N)
  71 FORMAT (I2/10F4.0)
d.   DIMENSION X(10)
     READ (5, 72) N, (X(I), I = 1, N)
  72 FORMAT (I2/(F4.0))

12. Same as Exercise 11.

a.   DIMENSION Y(10, 10)
     READ (5, 79) K, (Y(K, I), I = 1, 10)
  79 FORMAT (I2, 10F5.0)
b.   DIMENSION Y(10, 10)
     READ (5, 80) K, M, (Y(K, I), I = 1, M)
  80 FORMAT (2I2, 10F5.0)
c.   DIMENSION Y(10, 10)
     READ (5, 81) M, N, ((Y(I, J), J = 1, N), I = 1, M)
  81 FORMAT (2I2/(10F8.0))
d.   DIMENSION Y(10, 10)
  83 READ (5, 82) I, J, Y(I, J), L
  82 FORMAT (2I2, F10.0, I1)
     IF (L .EQ. 0) GO TO 83

*13. The values of the real variables A, B, X, and Z are to be printed on one line. A and B are to be printed without exponents, X and Z with exponents. Twelve spaces should be allowed for A and B, and they should have four decimal places. Twenty spaces should be allowed for X and Z, and they should be printed with eight decimal places and no scale factor. Write appropriate statements.

14. Same as Exercise 13 except that a positive integer named K is to be printed in six spaces between A and B and the decimal point is to be moved one place to the right in X and Z.

*15. A two-dimensional array named *ABC* consists of 10 rows and 4 columns. Write a program to print a page as follows: at the top of the page is the heading MATRIX ABC. After two blank lines the elements are printed in the normal row-and-column arrangement for a two-dimensional array, using 1PE20.7 field specifications. (*Hint.* Be sure that exactly four numbers are printed on each line.)

16. A one-dimensional array named *CVG* contains a maximum of 40 elements. The input deck to be read has one element per card; each card contains the element number in columns 1 and 2 and the element itself in columns 3 to 12, punched with a decimal point but without an exponent. The cards cannot be assumed to be in sequence on the element numbers. It is not known how many cards there are, but the last card of the deck is blank, which will look like an element number of zero. Write a program segment to read the deck and place each value in the correct location in the array.

*17. A two-dimensional array named *STL* is named in the statement

DIMENSION STL(10, 13)

The actual number of rows and columns is given by the values of the variables M and N, respectively. Write a program to punch on cards as many elements as there actually are in the array, in row order. Each element should be punched on a separate card along with its row and column numbers. Use I2 for the integers and 1PE20.7 for the real numbers.

*18. Given an integer variable I, with $1 \leq I \leq 12$, set up a program that will print in three printing positions one of the abbreviations JAN, FEB, MAR, APR, etc., depending on the value of I. Assume a computer in which one alphameric variable can hold six characters.

19. Given an integer variable J, with $1 \leq J \leq 7$. Set up a program to print one of the words MONDAY, TUESDAY, etc., depending on the value of J. Assume a computer in which one alphameric variable can hold six characters, which, of course, is not enough to hold a word such as TUESDAY.

*20. Given the following program segment.

     DIMENSION FMT(12), X(10)
 101 READ (5, 102) (FMT(I), I = 1, 12)
 102 FORMAT (12A6)
        .
        .
        .

     WRITE (6, FMT) (X(I), I = 1, 10)

Show exactly what should be punched on the card read by the foregoing READ statement in order to print the 10 numbers in each of the following ways:

a. All 10 on one line, using F10.2 for each.
b. Five on each of two lines, using 1PE20.6 for each number.
c. $X(1)$ on first line, using F10.2;
   second line blank;
   $X(2)$, $X(3)$, and $X(4)$ on third line, 1PE20.6 for each;

$X(5)$, $X(6)$, and $X(7)$, on fourth line, 1PE20.6 for each;

$X(8)$, $X(9)$, and $X(10)$ on fifth line, 1PE20.6 for each.

21. Given the following program segment.

```
      DIMENSION FMT(12), A(80, 80)
201   READ (5, 202) (FMT(L), L = 1, 12)
202   FORMAT (12A6)
203   READ (5, FMT) I, J, T
      IF (I .EQ. 0) GO TO 204
      A(I, J) = T
      GO TO 203
204 whatever follows.
```

State what should be on the card read by the READ at 201 to permit cards of the following types to be read by the READ at 203.

a. Columns 1–2: I
   Columns 3–4: J
   Columns 5–14: T, in form suitable for use with F10.0

b. Columns 1–2: I
   Columns 3–4: J
   Columns 5–14: T, in form suitable for use with F10.4

c. Columns 1–2: I
   Columns 3–4: J
   Columns 5–18: T, in form suitable for use with E14.7

d. Columns 1–2: I
   Columns 3–4: J
   Columns 5–16: T, for use with F12.0

There are five such groups per card; the second starts in column 17, and so on.

e. Columns 1–2: I
   Columns 3–4: J
   Columns 5–10: T, for use with F6.3

There are eight such groups per card; the second starts in column 11, and so on.

f. Columns 21–22: I
   Columns 31–32: J
   Columns 47–61: T, for use with E15.6

Ignore the contents of all other columns on the card.

22. Modify the program of Figure 6.2 so that a zero value is replaced with the word ZERO instead of blank.

23. Modify the program of Figure 6.6 so that the vertical scale is variable. ("Vertical" means as the final graph is normally viewed, that is, after turning the page from the way it was printed.) Make a suitable change in the DIMENSION statement and in the conversion formula so that there may be between 20 and 100 points vertically.

*24. Following the scheme suggested on p. 97, write a routine to plot a unit circle on a graph. Use 48 lines vertically and 80 horizontally; assuming a printer with 6 lines per inch vertically and 10 printing positions per inch horizontally, such a graph will be square. Print rows of dots for the axes. Given the x-y coordinates of a point, it will be necessary to use two different conversion formulas to find the element in which to store the character for plotting. Let 1 in. = 1 unit on both axes.

Generate and plot 40 points equally spaced around a circle of radius 1 with center at the origin.

25. Modify the program of Exercise 24 so that it reads two numbers from a data card, one of which gives the number of vertical lines that are to represent one unit and the other the number of horizontal printing positions. These numbers become parameters in the formulas that locate the element in which to store the plotting character.

26. Modify the program of Exercise 25 so that points in the first quadrant are plotted with the character "1," points in the second quadrant are plotted with the character "2," and so on.

27. Produce a plot of the unit circle with each point plotted as its quadrant number. Consider the graph to be the complex plane. For each point $x + iy$ plot also the point $\text{CEXP}(x + iy)$. If $x + iy$ is in quadrant j, plot both the point itself and $\text{CEXP}(x + iy)$ with the character j, even though in this case all of the function points will be in the first quadrant.

7. FUNCTIONS AND SPECIFICATION STATEMENTS

7.1 Introduction

One of the major reasons for using electronic computers is that they reduce the human effort required to carry out calculations. Our attitude is, roughly speaking, "Why do anything ourselves that the computer can do for us?" This approach applies as well to writing programs. In this chapter we explore the question: "Why do anything twice if once will do?"

This, among other things, is what the various types of *functions* in the FORTRAN system will do. We write a statement or group of statements once and then refer to the statement or to the group whenever we want to carry out the operations described in the one place. The use of functions not only saves programming time but also conserves computer storage space, in most cases, and has certain advantages in program organization.

There are several types of functions, which serve different purposes and follow different rules of formation and use. We shall explore each of them in turn, starting with a type we have already discussed briefly, the functions supplied with the system. We shall then investigate in some detail two additional statements, COMMON and EQUIVALENCE, which are related to the effective use of the computer with two of the types of functions. Finally, we shall consider a means of entering program data with the program, using the DATA statement.

7.2 Supplied Functions

Most FORTRAN systems provide several dozen functions to compute such things as trigonometric functions, logarithms, and absolute values. The exact list depends not only on the computer and the version of FORTRAN used, but on the particular installation. Most installations provide special-purpose functions to meet their individual needs. An installation doing orbit calculations, for instance, might have a special function to compute air density as a function of altitude. Each programmer must have an up-to-date list of the functions available at his installation, as well as a precise write-up containing such information as accuracy, speed, the form of the data (whether angles are in degrees or radians, for instance), and so on.

The functions listed in Appendix 3, it is expected, will be found in virtually all FORTRAN systems.

In order to use these functions, it is necessary only to write their names where they are needed, entering the desired expression(s) for the argument(s). (Many permit several arguments, such as the function that finds the smallest of the values of the arguments listed.)

The names of these functions are established in advance, and the programmer must write them exactly as specified. Although he has no control over their naming, we may note that if the value produced by the supplied function is real or integer the first letter of the function name must comply with the IJKLMN naming convention.

The functions available as part of the system are actually of two different kinds, depending on the mechanics of their insertion into the object program. The *open* functions require only a few machine instructions, which are inserted into the object program every time the function is used. The *closed* functions, in general, are considerably longer; they are inserted into the object program in one place only, and the object program transfers to that one place whenever it is needed. The closed functions are more common.

7.3 Statement Functions

It often happens that a programmer will find some relatively simple computation recurring through his program, making it desirable to be able to set up a function to carry out the computation. This function would be needed in only the one program, so that there would be no point in setting up a new supplied function for the purpose—which is a bit of work. Instead, a function can be defined for the purpose of the one program and then used whenever desired in that program. It has no effect on any other program.

A statement function is *defined* by writing a single statement of the form $a = b$, where a is the name of the function and b is an expression. The name, which is invented by the programmer, is formed according to the same rules that apply to a variable name: one to six letters or digits, the first of which must be a letter. If the name of the statement function is mentioned in a prior type statement, there is no restriction on the initial letter; if the name is not mentioned in a type statement, the initial letter distinguishes between real and integer in the usual way. The name, of course, must not be the same as that of any supplied function.

The name of the function is followed by parentheses enclosing the argument(s), which must be separated by commas if there is more than one. The arguments *in the definition* must not be subscripted.

The right-hand side of the definition statement may be any expression not involving subscripted variables. It may use variables not specified as arguments and it may use other functions (except itself). All function definitions must appear before the first executable statement of the program. If the right-hand side of a statement function uses another statement function, the other function definition must have appeared *earlier* in the program.

As an illustration, suppose that in a certain program it is frequently necessary to compute one root of the quadratic equation, $ax^2 + bx + c = 0$, given values of a, b, and c. A function can be defined to carry out this computation, by writing

$$ROOT(A, B, C) = (-B + SQRT(B**2 - 4.*A*C))/(2.*A)$$

The compiler will produce a sequence of instructions in the object program to compute the value of the function, given three values to use in the computation.

This is *only* the definition of the function; it does not cause computation to take place. The variable names used as arguments are only dummies; they may be the same as variable names appearing elsewhere in the program. The argument names are unimportant, except as they may distinguish between integer and real.

A statement function is *used* by writing its name wherever the function value is desired and substituting appropriate expressions for the arguments. "Appropriate" here means, in particular, that if a variable in the definition is real the expression substituted for that variable must also be real, and similarly for the other types of variables. The values of these expressions will be substituted into the program segment established by the definition and the value of the function computed. The actual arguments may be subscripted if desired.

Suppose, now, that we wish to use this function with 16.9 for a, $R - S$ for b, and $T + 6.9$ for c; the value of the function (root) is to be added to the cosine of x and the sum stored as the new value of ANS. All this can be done with the statement

$$ANS = ROOT(16.9, R - S, T + 6.9) + COS(X)$$

Suppose that later in the program it is necessary to compute the function with DATA(I) for a, DATA(I + 1) for b, and 0.087 for c; the function value is to be cubed and stored as the value of TEMP:

$$TEMP = ROOT(DATA(I), DATA(I + 1), 0.087)**3$$

It must be emphasized that the variables A, B, and C in the function definition have no relation to any variables of the same names that may appear elsewhere in the program. To illustrate, suppose that the value of the root is needed for the equation

$$22.97x^2 + ax + b = 0$$

where a and b are variables in the program. The root may be found by writing

$$\text{VAL} = \text{ROOT}(22.97, \text{A}, \text{B})$$

The A and B that appear here in the *use* of the function are completely unrelated to the A and B in the *definition* of the function. In summary, the definition variables are dummies that establish how the expression values in the use should be substituted into the object program set up from the definition.

For another example of the usefulness of statement functions, suppose that in a certain program it is frequently necessary to evaluate the function

$$E = \frac{1}{x^5 \left(e^{\frac{1.432}{Tx}} - 1 \right)}$$

The argument this time is to be just x. This is easily set up as a function:

$$\text{E(X)} = 1.0/(\text{X**5*}(\text{EXP}(1.432/(\text{T*X})) - 1.0))$$

The X here, as always in a function definition, is only a dummy variable that defines a computational procedure; when an expression is later written in using the function, the same actions are carried out on the actual value of the argument as are shown being done with X in the definition.

There is no prohibition against using X as an actual variable, of course. The function just defined could be used in statements like these:

$$\text{SUM4} = \text{SUM4} + \text{E(X)}$$

$$\text{SUM2} = \text{SUM2} + \text{E(X + H)}$$

$$\text{EFFIC} = 64.77*\text{H}/3.0*(4.0*\text{SUM4} + 2.0*\text{SUM2}$$
$$+ \text{E(A)} + 4.0*\text{E(B} - \text{H)} + \text{E(B)})/\text{T**4}$$

We see in this function an example of something that was mentioned earlier: the use of a variable in the function definition that is not an argument. The only argument here is X; this is a dummy. T, however, since it is not an argument, is *not* a dummy: it is the same T that presumably appears elsewhere in the program. This use of variables that are not arguments is perfectly legal; as we see, it saves the effort of making arguments out of variables for which we shall never want to substitute anything but their own values. (It is *logically* possible to

think of a statement function with *no* arguments: all the variables would simply take on their current values in the program, as T did in the last example. This is not permitted with statement functions. We shall see that it *can* be done with a SUBROUTINE subprogram.)

7.4 FUNCTION and SUBROUTINE Subprograms

Useful as a statement function often is, it does have two rather serious restrictions: the definition is limited to one statement and it can compute only one value. The FUNCTION and SUBROUTINE subprograms remove these restrictions.

This is only half the story, however. The outstanding feature of these two types of functions is that they are *subprograms;* they can be compiled independently of the main program of which they are a part. Their variable names are completely independent of the variable names in the main program and in other subprograms. They may have their own DIMENSION statements (and the other specification statements described below). In short, FUNCTION and SUBROUTINE subprograms can be completely independent of the main program— yet it is quite easy to set up "communication" between the main program and the subprogram(s). This means that a large program can be divided into parts that can be compiled independently, making possible two important kinds of flexibility in writing programs.

The ability to compile a subprogram independently of the main program of which it is a part means that one subprogram can be used with different main programs. For instance, many different programmers in a installation may need a subprogram to solve a system of simultaneous equations. Since arrays are involved and since many statements are required, statement functions are out of the question. However, a SUBROUTINE subprogram can be written to do the job. It can be compiled by itself, and the compiled object program can be combined with *any* main program. All that is necessary is for the main program to have been written with the conventions of the subprogram in mind.

The other flexibility provided by separate compilation is the freedom to compile and run segments of one program independently of each other. This means that parts of a program can be checked out as they are written, which can be an important advantage. For example, if there are many subprograms, all called by one main program, individual subprograms can be checked out and tested before all of the others are finished.

Subprograms thus have three major advantages. One is the primary motivation of any function, as stated in the introduction to this chapter: a group of statements written in one place in a program can be called into action from anywhere else in the program, thus avoiding wasteful duplication of effort in writing the source program and the waste of storage space that would be caused by the duplication of segments of the object program. A second advantage is that of avoiding duplication of effort by making it possible for a subprogram to be used with many different main programs. The third advantage is that of separate checkout.

Whatever the motivation for their use, subprograms are a powerful feature of the FORTRAN language.

As with the arithmetic statement functions, we must distinguish carefully between the definition and the use. The computation desired in a FUNCTION subprogram is *defined* by writing the necessary statements in a segment, writing the word FUNCTION and the name of the function before the segment, and writing the word END after it. The name is formed as for variables and statement functions: one to six letters or digits, the first of which must be a letter. The letter must be chosen according to the naming convention in the absence of a type declaration. If the naming convention is to be overridden, or if the type is other than real or integer, the word FUNCTION is preceded by one of the five types.

The name of the subprogram is followed by parentheses enclosing the argument(s), which are separated by commas if there is more than one.

The name of the function must appear at least once in the subprogram as a variable on the left-hand side of an assignment statement or in the list of an input statement. In other words, the name of a FUNCTION subprogram is associated with a value; a value must therefore be given to it in the subprogram.

As before, the arguments in the subprogram definition are only dummy variables. The arguments in the function definition must be distinct nonsubscripted variables or array names. Within the subprogram itself, however, subscripted variables may be used freely. The subprogram must contain at least one RETURN statement, for reasons that we shall see shortly.

To *use* a FUNCTION subprogram it is necessary only to write the name of the function where its value is desired, with suitable expressions for arguments. The mechanics of the operation of the object program are as follows: the FUNCTION subprogram is compiled as a set of machine instructions in one place in storage, and wherever the name of the subprogram appears in the source program a transfer to the subprogram is set up in the object program. When the computations of the subprograms have been completed, a transfer is made back to the section of the program that brought the subprogram into action. The RETURN statement(s) in the subprogram results in object program instructions to transfer back to the place in the main program from which the subprogram was called. (This is actually quite similar to the way a statement function is set up, except that in that case there can be only one statement in the definition and there is no question when the function's operations are complete.)

As a simple example of the use of a FUNCTION subprogram, suppose that in a certain program there is frequent need for the function shown on page 21. The function can be defined with the statements shown in Figure 7.1, in which the name Y has been given to the function.

If we now want to compute the value of this function for an argument equal to GRS — 6.8 and divide the result by 12.99 to get the value of EWR, we can write

$$EWR = Y(GRS - 6.8) / 12.99$$

To get the value of this function of the square root of one plus RHO, with SFO set equal to the square root of the result, we can write

$$SFO = SQRT(Y(SQRT(1.0 + RHO)))$$

A FUNCTION subprogram can be set up to have many arguments, including arrays. For example, suppose that it is necessary to find the product of the main diagonal elements (those having the same

```
      FUNCTION Y(X)
      IF (X .GT. 2.1) GO TO 30
   40 Y = 0.5 * X + 0.95
      RETURN
   30 Y = 0.7 * X + 0.53
      RETURN
      END
```

Figure 7.1. An example of a FUNCTION subprogram.

row and column number) of square arrays. The arrays from which this product is computed must have been mentioned in a DIMENSION statement in the "calling" program, as always, and all the arrays must have the same dimensions. (We shall see shortly how to remove the same-dimension restriction.) The array names in the FUNCTION argument list and subprogram will be dummies, but the dummy array names must still be mentioned in a DIMENSION statement in the subprogram. Suppose that the arrays in question are all 10 x 10 but that they are not necessarily full; the value of an integer variable gives the number of rows and columns. The subprogram could be as shown in Figure 7.2.

Now, if we want the product of the main diagonal elements of a 10 x 10 array named X, in which the actual size is 8 x 8, with the extra elements containing nothing, we can write

$$DET = DIAGPR(X, 8)$$

To find the square of the product of the main diagonal elements of an array named SAM, in which the number of rows and columns containing meaningful data is given by the value of an integer variable named JACK, we could write

$$EIG = DIAGPR(SAM, JACK)**2$$

A FUNCTION subprogram is seen to be quite similar to a statement function, except that it can use many statements instead of just one and it can use any of the FORTRAN statements instead of just an assignment statement. A subprogram can call on other subprograms as long as it does not call itself and as long as two subprograms do not call each other.*

A FUNCTION subprogram has been described as computing just one value, the one associated with the name of the FUNCTION. Actually, there can be any number of output values: any of the arguments may refer to output. For an example of how this can be useful, consider the following extension

*A subprogram that calls itself is said to be *recursive*. This *is* permitted in the ALGOL language and others, in which it finds greatest utility in non-numerical applications, such as compiler programs, processing natural languages (e.g., English), and in operations on the *symbols* of mathematics as distinguished from their values. Recursiveness can be accomplished in some cases in FORTRAN by "stacking" arguments in arrays. We shall see a rudimentary example of some of these ideas in Case Study 15, on the translation from ordinary algebraic notation to Polish notation.

```
      FUNCTION DIAGPR(A, N)
      DIMENSION A(10, 10)
      DIAGPR = A(1, 1)
      DO 69 I = 2, N
   69 DIAGPR = DIAGPR * A(I, I)
      RETURN
      END
```

Figure 7.2. A FUNCTION subprogram to find the product of the main diagonal elements of an array.

of the requirements of the preceding illustration. Suppose that if the product of the main diagonal elements is less than or equal to 100 we wish to go to statement 12; if it is between 100 and 1000, we wish to go to statement 123; if it is greater than or equal to 1000, we wish to go to statement 1234. All of these statement numbers refer to statements in the *main* program. This could, of course, be done with IF statements in the main program, but if it has to be done frequently we prefer a simpler way.

To accomplish the simplification, let us first add a type specification to make the value associated with the name of the integer type. This is done by writing the word INTEGER in front of the word FUNCTION in the subprogram definition. We then write the modified subprogram so that the value of DIAGPR is negative, zero, or positive, depending on whether the product is less or equal to 100, between 100 and 1000, or greater or equal to 1000. We also add PROD as an argument and within the subprogram give it the value of the product of the main diagonal elements. The modified program is shown in Figure 7.3.

Now suppose that we want the product of the main diagonal elements of a 10 x 10 array named BETA in which seven rows and seven columns are used; the product is to be called GAMMA. We are to transfer to one of the three statements numbered 12, 123, or 1234, as already described.

$$IF (DIAGPR(BETA, 7, GAMMA)) 12, 123, 1234$$

The appearance of the name of the function, written with appropriate arguments, causes the function to be called into operation, in the course of which a value is given to its name and also to the other output parameter, which is GAMMA in this case. Control returns from the subprogram to the arithmetic IF statement in the main program, where the proper transfer is made. At any of these locations the newly computed value of GAMMA may be used.

The basics of a SUBROUTINE subprogram, although quite similar to those of a FUNCTION subprogram, show three differences.

```
      INTEGER FUNCTION DIAGPR(A, N, PROD)
      DIMENSION A(10, 10)
      PROD = A(1, 1)
      DO 69 I = 2, N
   69 PROD = PROD * A(I, I)
      IF (PROD .LE. 100.0) DIAGPR = -1
      IF (PROD .GT. 100.0 .AND. PROD .LT. 1000.0) DIAGPR = 0
      IF (PROD .GE. 1000.0) DIAGPR = 1
      RETURN
      END
```

Figure 7.3. The FUNCTION subprogram of Figure 7.2 modified to store the product as a argument and to give an integer value for the function

1. A SUBROUTINE has no value associated with its name. All outputs are defined in terms of arguments; there may be any number of outputs.

2. A SUBROUTINE is not called into action simply by writing its name, since no value is associated with the name. Instead, we write a CALL statement to bring it into operation; this specifies the arguments and results in storing all the output values.

3. Since the output of a SUBROUTINE may be any combination of the various types of values, there is no type associated with the name and likewise no convention attached to the first letter of the name. The naming of a SUBROUTINE is otherwise the same as the naming of a FUNCTION.

In all other respects the two subprograms are entirely analogous.

The essential features of the SUBROUTINE subprogram are illustrated in the following example. Suppose that in a certain program it is frequently necessary to find the largest element (in absolute value) in a specified row of a 50 x 50 array. The input to the SUBROUTINE is therefore the array name and the row number. The output will be the absolute value of the largest element in that row and its column number. The SUBROUTINE could be as shown in Figure 7.4.

Now suppose that the largest element in the third row of a 50 x 50 array named ZETA is needed. The absolute value of the element is to be called DIVIS

and column number is to be called NCOL. We write the statement

CALL LARGE (ZETA, 3, DIVIS, NCOL)

This brings the subprogram into operation, stores the values of DIVIS and NCOL found by the subprogram, and returns control to the statement following the CALL. If, later, it is necessary to find the largest element in row $M + 2$ of an array named DETAIL, storing its absolute value in SIZE and the column number in KW, we can write

CALL LARGE(DETAIL, M + 2, SIZE, KW)

To emphasize the independence of the variable names between the main program and any subprograms, we note that it would be possible and legal to write the statement

CALL LARGE(ARRAY, I, BIG, J)

If this is done, all of the input variables to the subprogram must be defined and given values in the calling program and all output variables from the subprogram must be defined in the calling program. The name I in the calling program and the name I in the subprogram are unrelated. And this must logically be so: the name I in the subprogram tells *what to do with* a value from the the calling program, whereas the name I in the calling program

```
      SUBROUTINE LARGE(ARRAY, I, BIG, J)
      DIMENSION ARRAY(50, 50)
      BIG = ABS(ARRAY(I, 1))
      J = 1
      DO 69 K = 2, 50
      IF (ABS(ARRAY(I, K)) .LT. BIG) GO TO 69
      BIG = ABS(ARRAY(I, K))
      J = K
   69 CONTINUE
      RETURN
      END
```

Figure 7.4. A SUBROUTINE subprogram to find the largest element in a specified row of an array.

must *specify a value,* one that has already been computed by the calling program. In the case of output variables, *J,* for instance, the variable *J* in the subprogram identifies a value that the subprogram computes, whereas *J* in the calling program identifies a result transmitted from the subprogram.

7.5 Adjustable Dimensions

It is possible for a subprogram to be defined in terms of arrays that are of adjustable size. We do this by writing in the subprogram a DIMENSION statement in which we write integer variable names instead of integer constants. The integer variables must appear in the argument list and be given values by the calling program.

This is much easier to understand in an example. Consider the program in Figure 7.4, which we rewrite with adjustable dimensions in Figure 7.5. It will be noted that another variable, *N,* has been added to the argument list, which gives the number of rows and columns in the array to be searched. The DIMENSION statement says that the array is *N* x *N,* and the DO statement says to inspect rows 2 through *N.*

With this revision, the subroutine can be used to find the largest element in a specified row of *any* square array. We might write, for instance,

CALL LARGE (ALPHA, 49, 6, BIGGST, M)

This will find the largest element in row 6 of a 49 x 49 array named ALPHA, placing the largest element in BIGGST and its row number in M. Or we might write.

CALL LARGE (GAMMA, L, M, DELTA, K98)

The array this time is *L* x *L,* where *L* would have to have been given a value before the call.

The adjustable dimension facility has a number of advantages. One, of course, is that a very general sort of subprogram can be adapted to the needs of a particular main program, without the awkwardness and potentially wasted storage of specifying a maximum size and then using only some of the elements. A given subprogram can be called many times from one main program, each time if necessary with arrays of different sizes. Looking at another aspect of the usefulness of subprograms, a prewritten subprogram can serve the rather different requirements of many programmers.

We have noted that it is permissible for one subprogram to call another. When this is done, adjustable dimension information may be passed "through" subprograms. For instance, a main program might call a subprogram with array dimension information given by the value of a variable in the argument list. The subprogram called might in turn call another subprogram, "passing" the dimension information to the subprogram *it* called.

The restrictions on the usage of adjustable dimensions are reasonable. The subprogram must not use a subscript value greater than specified in the call; the subprogram must not redefine the value of an adjustable dimension; the calling program must not leave the value of a dimensioned variable undefined. We may also note at this point that an array mentioned in a COMMON statement (see Section 7.7) must not have adjustable dimensions.

7.6 Summary of the Four Types of Functions

FORTRAN provides for four types of functions: those supplied with the system, statement functions, FUNCTION subprograms, and SUBROUTINE subprograms. The salient features of the four types are summarized in Table 7.1.

```
SUBROUTINE LARGE(ARRAY, N, I, BIG, J)
DIMENSION ARRAY(N, N)
BIG = ABS(ARRAY(I, 1))
J = 1
DO 69 K = 2, N
IF (ABS(ARRAY(I, K)) .LT. BIG) GO TO 69
BIG = ABS(ARRAY(I, K))
J = K
69 CONTINUE
RETURN
END
```

Figure 7.5. The SUBROUTINE of Figure 7.4 modified to accept arrays of adjustable size.

TABLE 7.1

	Supplied	Statement	FUNCTION	SUBROUTINE
Naming	1–6 characters, first of which is a letter	1–6 characters, first of which is a letter	1–6 characters, first of which is a letter	1–6 characters, first of which is a letter
Type	Implied by first letter; can be overridden in some FORTRAN's by REAL, INTEGER, COMPLEX, LOGICAL, or DOUBLE PRECISION	Implied by first letter unless overridden by REAL, INTEGER, COMPLEX, LOGICAL, or DOUBLE PRECISION	Implied by first letter unless overridden by REAL, INTEGER, COMPLEX, LOGICAL, or DOUBLE PRECISION	None—no value associated with name
Definition	Provided with the compiler	One arithmetic statement before first usage of function	Any number of statements after word FUNCTION	Any number of statements after word SUBROUTINE
How called	Writing name where function value is desired	Writing name where function value is desired	Writing name where function value is desired	CALL statement
Number of arguments	One or more, as defined	One or more, as defined	One or more, as defined	Any number, including *none*, as defined
Number of outputs	One	One	One is associated with function name; others may be specified as arguments	Any number

7.7 The EQUIVALENCE and COMMON Statements

These two nonexecutable statements make possible certain conveniences in the naming of variables and the assignment of storage locations to them.

The EQUIVALENCE statement causes two or more variables to be assigned to the same storage location, which is useful in two rather different ways.

In one usage the EQUIVALENCE statement allows the programmer to define two or more variable names as meaning the same thing. It might be that after writing a long program the programmer will realize that he has inadvertently changed variable names and that X, X1, and RST7 all mean the same thing. Rather than going back and changing the variable names in the program, a time-consuming and error-prone process, he can write

EQUIVALENCE (X, X1, RST7)

and the mistake is corrected.

The other application is in making use of the same storage location to contain two or more variables that are different but are never needed at the same time. Suppose that in a certain program the variable I27 appears in the initial READ statement and in a few subsequent statements but is never used after that. Later in the program a value is given to the variable NPL, which is then used as a DO parameter. Later the variable JJM2 is applied to a similar purpose. At the end of the variable NEXT1 is given a value and then used in the final WRITE statement. As things now stand, four storage locations will be allocated to these variables, which is pointless, since their usage never overlaps. If the programmer is short of storage space, he can assign all four variables to one location by writing

EQUIVALENCE (I27, NPL, JJM2, NEXT1)

The same thing could, of course, be accomplished by changing the variable names, but using an EQUIVALENCE is obviously simpler.

These two applications of EQUIVALENCE differ only in viewpoint; the statement and its treatment by the compiler are the same in either case.

One EQUIVALENCE statment can establish equivalence between any number of sets of variables. For instance, if A and B are to be made equivalent, as are X, Y, and Z, we can write

EQUIVALENCE (A, B), (X, Y, Z)

Seldom is storage so "tight" that the EQUIVALENCE statement is *really* needed for nonsubscripted variables. The value comes in establishing equivalences between arrays.

In many versions of FORTRAN array names

must be mentioned with a single constant subscript, regardless of the actual dimensionality of the array. We might, for instance, have statements like

DIMENSION A(50), B(5, 10), C(2, 5, 5)

EQUIVALENCE (A(1), B(1), C(1))

This EQUIVALENCE statement causes storage to be assigned so that the elements of the three arrays occupy the same 50 storage locations. It is not required, however, that the arrays made equivalent have the same number of elements. If they do not, and if the arrays in the EQUIVALENCE statements all have element number 1, as above, then the extra elements at the end of the longer array will simply not be shared locations.

It is also permissible to specify that equivalence be established between element locations other than the first. If, for instance, X is a one-dimensional array with ten elements, and D, E, and F are all nonsubscripted variables, we might write

EQUIVALENCE (X(1), D),

(X(2), E), (X(10), F)

The single variable D would be assigned to the same location as the first element of X, E would be assigned to the same location as the second element of X, and F would be assigned to the same location as the tenth element of X.

Arrays can be overlapped by the same techniques. We might write

EQUIVALENCE (A(1), B(20))

The general idea is that the storage assignments are made in such a manner that the specified equivalence is established, and both arrays are stored in consecutive locations just as arrays always are. The question we need to be able to answer, often, is, "In a two- or three-dimensional array, which element *is* the twentieth or the Nth?"

The answer is given by the *element successor* rule, which tells where a given element is stored in the linear sequence of storage locations. Table 7.2 gives the needed information. A, B, and C in this table

are dimensions, as given by a DIMENSION, COMMON, or type statement; a, b, and c are the values of subscript expressions. By "subscript declarator" we mean the dimensioning information given in the DIMENSION, or COMMON, or type statement. For instance, in

DIMENSION X(3, 12)

the subscript declarator is (3, 12).

Consider an example. In the statement just given, in terms of the notation of Table 7.2, $A = 3$, $B = 12$. Now where, for instance, is the element in row 2, column 9, that is, $X(2, 9)$? Table 7.2 says that the "value" of this subscript is $2 + 3 \cdot (9 - 1) = 26$. In other words, we are to think of the 36 elements of the array arranged in a linear sequence in storage. Then, if element $(1, 1)$ is in position 1 in this string, element $(2, 9)$ in in position 26.

Study will show that Table 7.2 is a formal expression of the rule given earlier: arrays are stored in such a way that the first subscript varies most rapidly and the last varies least rapidly. This was the convention described in connection with using array names in input or output statements without subscripts.

All of the preceding has assumed that the variables in question were real, integer, or logical and furthermore that each takes up one storage location. (There are local exceptions to the latter.) In the case of complex and double precision variables two storage locations usually are required for each element, and when a single element is made equivalent to a double element it is the first part of the double element that is involved.

The reader is cautioned that the various versions of FORTRAN vary considerably on the matter of storage assignments for arrays, in the effect of complicated EQUIVALENCE and COMMON statements, in the presence or absence of special rules governing complex and double precision arrays, etc., etc. Different FORTRANs vary as much in this area as anywhere. The description given here is intended to conform to the proposed American Stand-

TABLE 7.2

Dimensionality	Subscript Declarator	Subscript	Subscript Value
1	(A)	(a)	a
2	(A, B)	(a, b)	$a + A \cdot (b - 1)$
3	(A, B, C)	(a, b, c)	$a + A \cdot (b - 1) + A \cdot B \cdot (c - 1)$

ards Association FORTRAN, but every programmer must get the details for his system.

The COMMON statement. It has been stated that each subprogram has its own variable names: the name X in the main program is not necessarily taken to be the same as the name X in a subprogram. However, if the programmer *wishes* them to mean the same thing, he can write

COMMON X

in *both* the main program and the subprogram. The compiler will then assign the two variables (and they still are distinct, in principle) to the same storage location, which as a practical matter makes them the same.

But the statement is not limited to this kind of use. Suppose we write

main program:	COMMON X, Y, I
subprogram:	COMMON A, B, J

Then X and A are assigned to the same storage location, as are Y and B and I and J.

EQUIVALENCE and COMMON have a somewhat similar function. What is the difference between them?

EQUIVALENCE assigns two variables *within the same main program or within the same subprogram* to the same storage location; COMMON assigns two variables *in different subprograms or in a main program and a subprogram* to the same location.

When an array is named in an EQUIVALENCE statement *and* in a COMMON statement, the equivalence is established in the same general way as described earlier. This may increase the size of the COMMON block of storage and thus change the correspondences between the COMMON block described and some other COMMON block in another program.

For instance, consider a program containing the following three statements.

DIMENSION A(4), B(4)

COMMON A, C

EQUIVALENCE (A(3), B(1))

Without the EQUIVALENCE statement, the COMMON block would contain five storage locations in the sequence

A(1), A(2), A(3), A(4), C

With the EQUIVALENCE statement, the B array is brought into COMMON, so to speak, and requires the following sequence of storage locations

A(1), A(2), A(3), A(4), C

B(1), B(2), B(3), B(4)

COMMON is now six storage locations long.

COMMON may be lengthened in this way, but it may *not* be lengthened by any attempt to push the start of a COMMON block forward. For instance, with the same DIMENSION and COMMON statement just considered, the following EQUIVALENCE would be illegal.

EQUIVALENCE (A(1), B(2))

The storage assignment in COMMON would need to be

A(1), A(2), A(3), A(4), C

B(1), B(2), B(3), B(4)

Since B is not mentioned in the COMMON statement, but is brought into COMMON by the EQUIVALENCE, the first element of B now precedes the start of this block of COMMON. This is not permitted.

As we have mentioned several times in passing, a variable named in a COMMON or type statement may have subscripting information. We might write

COMMON A(23), J(2, 8) LOGIC (3,3,7)

REAL X(10)

DOUBLE PRECISION VARNCE(5, 20)

A variable that is written with subscripting information in a COMMON or type statement must *not* be mentioned in a DIMENSION statement. On the other hand, it is still permissible to name a variable in a DIMENSION statement and also to name it, without subscripting information, in a COMMON or type statement.

Two variables in COMMON must not both be named in an EQUIVALENCE statement. The reason for this is instructive. EQUIVALENCE says that two or more variables in *one program* (main program or subprogram) are to be assigned to the same storage location. COMMON says that variables in *different programs* are to be assigned to the same location. The way COMMON works is that all the variables named in a COMMON statement are assigned to storage in the sequence in which the names appear in the COMMON statement. This is true even when there is only one COMMON statement, in which case COMMON does not cause multiple assignments at all. But then if there are two or more COMMON statements, correspondences are established simply because the COMMON statement is treated the same way wherever it appears.

For example, if in a main program we write

COMMON A, B, C, D

the four variables named are assigned to storage locations in the order named, in a special section of storage called "COMMON storage." Thus A is a specific storage location, followed by B, etc. Now suppose that in some subprogram we have

COMMON W, X, Y, Z

This means that W is assigned to the first storage location in COMMON, X is assigned to the next one, and so on, and the "COMMON block" used by the subprogram is the same as that used in the main program. Ergo, A and W have been assigned to the same location—without the compiler ever knowing about more than one COMMON statement at a time. Indeed, the two programs may very well have been compiled entirely separately.

Now suppose that we had the combination

COMMON A, B, C, D

EQUIVALENCE (A, B)

The net effect is a contradiction: the COMMON says to put the four variables named into a special area of storage, in the order named and *in separate locations*, whereas the EQUIVALENCE says that A and B are to be assigned to the *same* location.

In the description just given we have said that there is only one COMMON block in storage. This is actually too limited: we can establish as many distinct blocks of COMMON storage as we please by *labeling* COMMON. What we have been discussing so far is in fact called *blank COMMON* to signify that it has no label.

Each COMMON block—blank COMMON and as many labeled COMMON blocks as there may be—is set up as described above. That is, variables and arrays are assigned storage locations in the order in which they are listed. Any rearrangements made necessary by EQUIVALENCE statements are made.

Labeled COMMON may be used, if there is some need to do so, simply to guarantee a particular arrangement of storage locations. This is probably rare in normal usage, being limited to what might be called "extra-legal" programming. (For instance, in a particular compiler and computer it may be possible to refer to the data adjacent to an array by using subscripts larger than the maximum given in dimensioning information.)

In "normal" or "legal" usage, the value of labeled COMMON is to have two COMMON blocks with the same name in two programs that are executed together. When this is done, the two blocks must be the same length. Assuming this to be the case, the variables in the two blocks are assigned to the same storage locations, just as with blank COMMON.

Labels are written between slashes in front of the variable names. We might write, for instance

COMMON/X/A, B, C

If a single COMMON statement includes labeled COMMON and blank COMMON, the blank COMMON portion may either be written first without a name, as we have done heretofore, or the name may be omitted between slashes.

For a final example, suppose we were to write the following two statements in a main program and in a subprogram.

COMMON A, B, C /B1/D, E/B2/F (20), G (2, 5)

COMMON R, S, T /B1/U, V/B2/X (10), Y (10, 2)

Blank COMMON would contain A, B, and C, in that order, in the program containing the first COMMON, and R, S, and T in the program containing the second. A and R would thus be assigned to the same storage location, as would B and S, and C and T. The COMMON block labeled B1 would establish D and U in the same location and E and V in the same. We assume that all of the foregoing variables were not mentioned elsewhere in a DIMENSION statement. B2 in the first program contains the 20 elements of F and the 10 elements of G. The same 30 locations would also contain the 10 elements of X and the 20 elements of Y. The overlap between the four arrays involved would cause the compiler no difficulty—indeed the compiler would never really consider the situation. Such a pair of statements would put $F(11)$ and $Y(1, 1)$ in the same location, for instance. If that is the intended action, then everything will work nicely. If not, naturally there will be some surprises in store for the programmer. As a matter of fact, the intricacies of things like labeled COMMON and the interrelationships between COMMON and EQUIVALENCE account for a disproportionate percentage of the questions programmers have to ask about FORTRAN.

7.8 The DATA Statement

More frequently than one might imagine it happens to be convenient to compile data into the object program from source program statements. We saw an example in the case studies involving plotting, where in Figure 6.9, for instance, we needed to enter 18 alphameric values. There is no such thing in FORTRAN as an alphameric constant, so we had to read a data card to get the characters entered. This works, but it is slightly annoying, since the card has to be read every time the program is executed even though it never changes. Other examples could be cited.

The DATA statement provides the capability we need. It takes the form

DATA list/d_1, d_2,$\cdots$,d_n/,

$\qquad$ list/d_1, d_2, $k*d_3$,$\cdots$$d_m$/$\cdots$

In this symbolic description, a "list" contains the names of the variables to receive values, the d's are values, and k, if it is used, is an integer constant. Consider some examples.

$\qquad$ DATA A, B, C/14.7, 62.1, 1.5E − 20/

This statement would assign the value 14.7 to A, 62.1 to B, and 1.5 x 10^{-20} to C.

This is done at the time of compilation, not at the time of execution of the object program. The DATA statement is not executable. The values assigned by the DATA statement are placed in storage when the object program is loaded and that is the end of the actions instituted by the DATA statement. It is legal to redefine the values of these variables, but having done so it is NOT possible to "re-execute" the DATA statement to put the values back to their initial values.

The following two statements have the same effect; the choice is a matter of personal preference.

$\qquad$ DATA A/67.87/, B/54.72/, C/5.0/

$\qquad$ DATA A, B, C/67.87, 54.72, 5.0/

The following statement assigns the value 21.7 to all six variables.

$\qquad$ DATA R, S, T, U, V, W/6*21.7/

A DATA statement may contain Hollerith text.

$\qquad$ DATA DOT, X, BLANK/1H., 1HX, 1H /

If the number of characters of text is not the same as the number of characters in a storage location, the treatment is the same as that for reading alphameric data from cards. In the foregoing example, the period would be left-adjusted in DOT and the rest of DOT filled with blanks, and similarly with X. BLANK would be filled entirely with blanks, as intended in this case.

A DATA statement may use an implied DO to specify the elements of an array, as we see in the following statement, which handles the example cited at the beginning of this section.

```
DATA (SYMBOL(L), L = 1, 17)/1HA, 1H ,
1    1HB, 1H , 1HC, 1H , 1HD, 1H ,
1    1HE, 1H , 1HF, 1H , 1HG, 1H ,
1    1HH, 1H , 1HK/, BLANK/1H /
```

Data may never be entered into blank COMMON with a DATA statement. In order to enter data into labeled COMMON it is necessary to write a BLOCK DATA subprogram. This is a small subprogram that begins with the words BLOCK DATA and which contains only the DATA, COMMON, DIMENSION, and type statements associated with the data being defined. It must not contain any executable statements.

```
BLOCK DATA
COMMON /BLK1/R, S, T/BLK2/X, Y(2)
DIMENSION R(6)            '
COMPLEX S
INTEGER T(2)
LOGICAL X
DATA (R(I), I = 1, 6)/1.0, 2.0, 4 * 7.5/, S/(1.0, 2.0)/,
1    X/.TRUE./, Y(1), Y(2)/7.5, 8.0/
END
```

Figure 7.6.   An example of a BLOCK DATA subprogram for initializing labeled COMMON.

Figure 7.6 illustrates a BLOCK DATA subprogram. We see two labeled COMMON blocks, BLK1 and BLK2. All the variables in each block must be listed, even though not all variables receive values from the DATA statement (T does not appear there). We see examples of all three ways of writing the dimensioning information for a subscripted variable: in a DIMENSION statement, in the COMMON statement, and in a type statement.

7.9 Functions as Arguments: the EXTERNAL Statement

FORTRAN permits the use of a function name as an argument in a subprogram call. When this is done, it is necessary to list the function name in an EXTERNAL statement in the calling program to distinguish the function name from a variable name.

As an example of what can be done, Figure 7.7 contains a main (calling) program and a SUBROUTINE subprogram. The subprogram contains exactly one executable statement:

$$Y = F(X)$$

The arguments listed are X, F, and Y, making the function F a matter of choice in the subprogram call.

The main program calls this subprogram three times. Each time the value of X is 2.0 and the actual variable corresponding to Y is RESULT. The arguments corresponding to F are successively SIN, COS, and SQRT; these three supplied function

```
      EXTERNAL SIN, COS, SQRT
      CALL SUBR (2.0, SIN, RESULT)
      WRITE (6, 129) RESULT
129   FORMAT (11HOSIN(2.0) = , F10.6)
      CALL SUBR (2.0, COS, RESULT)
      WRITE (6, 130) RESULT
130   FORMAT (11HOCOS(2.0) = , F10.6)
      CALL SUBR (2.0, SQRT, RESULT)
      WRITE (6, 131) RESULT
131   FORMAT (12HOSQRT(2.0) = , F10.6)
      STOP
      END


      SUBROUTINE SUBR(X, F, Y)
      Y = F(X)
      RETURN
      END
```

Figure 7.7. A main program that calls a subprogram with function names as arguments, and therefore uses the EXTERNAL statement; the SUBROUTINE that is called by the main program.

```
SIN(2.0)  =   0.909297

COS(2.0)  =  -0.416147

SQRT(2.0)  =   1.414214
```

Figure 7.8. The output of the program of Figure 7.7.

names are listed in an EXTERNAL statement. Figure 7.8 shows the three lines printed, indicating that the subprogram really was executed with three different functions for F.

In place of the standard mathematical functions, we could also have specified some FUNCTION subprograms that we might have written.

7.10 Case Study 14: Quadratic Equation Solution with Subprograms

This case study illustrate some of the ideas about subprograms and the COMMON statement that we have been discussing. The numerical aspects of the example are quite simple; the solution of quadratic equations by the familiar formula presents no new concepts. The emphasis instead is on program organization and input-output formats.

A program is to be set up to solve the quadratic equation $Ax^2 + Bx + C = 0$. The program must be able to read from cards the coefficients of many such equations—possibly hundreds—and to produce an easily readable report showing for each equation the coefficients and the roots. A data card contains the coefficients of two equations, six values in all. However, each equation is to be written on a line by itself. The roots can be real or complex, although we shall do all arithmetic using FORTRAN real variables. A heading is to be printed at the top of each page, the pages are to be numbered, and the lines are to be counted as they are printed, so that each page will contain only 20 lines of output, double-spaced.

The program will be written to use two SUBROUTINE subprograms. Each subprogram can be called twice for each data card, avoiding duplication and perhaps making the complete program easier to correct and modify. The main routine will handle reading of data cards, printing of page headings, page numbering, line counting, and detecting the end of the deck, which is signaled by a blank card, placed at the end of the deck for the purpose. The detection of this card can be set up as a test for a data card in which $A = 0$. A can never properly be zero with valid data; if $A = 0$, the equation is not quadratic.

The first subprogram will get the solutions, taking into account that if the discriminant $B^2 - 4AC$ is negative the roots are complex. The input to this subprogram, named SOLVE, consists of the names of the three coefficients; they are named as arguments of the subprogram. The output consists of the real and imaginary parts of the two roots, which are named X1REAL, X1IMAG, X2REAL, and X2IMAG. These four variables are needed in the main program and in both subprograms. They are named in COMMON statements in all three places, making it unnecessary to write them as arguments of the subprograms.

The second subprogram, named OUTPUT, writes the coefficients and the roots. It is desired to print the results in such a way that the reader can tell at a glance if the roots are pure real or pure imaginary. If the roots are real, the space for the imaginary parts is to be left blank, and if they are pure imaginary the space for the real parts is to be left blank. We recall that complex roots always occur as complex conjugates; it can never happen that only one root is complex or that two complex roots have different real parts.

Figure 7.9 is a flowchart of the main program, which is seen to be straightforward.

Figure 7.10 is a flowchart of the subprogram for finding the roots. The procedure shown steers a middle course between the bare minimum required to distinguish between real and complex roots and the more complicated tests that could be made to take advantage of every special situation. The bare minimum would be to go to the complex section if the discriminant is negative and to the real section if it is zero or positive. Since the arithmetic IF statement automatically gives a three-way branch, it seems reasonable to take special action if the discriminant is zero to avoid computing the square root of zero. We could, however, go further with this testing for special conditions. If C is zero, both roots are real, one being zero and the other $-B/A$. If B is zero, the formulas simplify slightly. If B and C are both zero, then, of course, both roots are zero—but it is hard to see why such a case would ever be entered.

In any such case it is necessary to draw the line somewhere. Time can indeed be saved by taking advantage of special situations, unless testing for them wastes all the saving. Even where there is a net saving, though, a thorough series of tests may simply not be worth the trouble and the program complexity.

The flowchart of the output subprogram, Figure

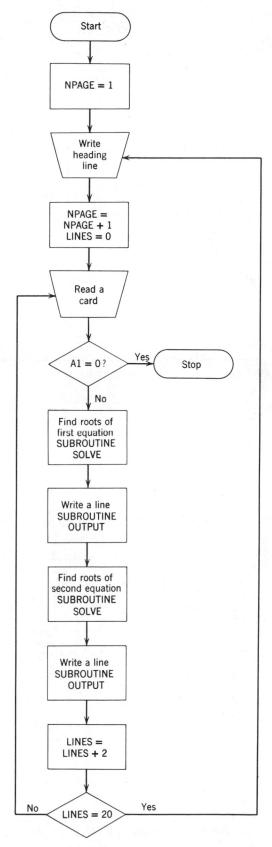

Figure 7.9. Flowchart of the main program for Case Study 14.

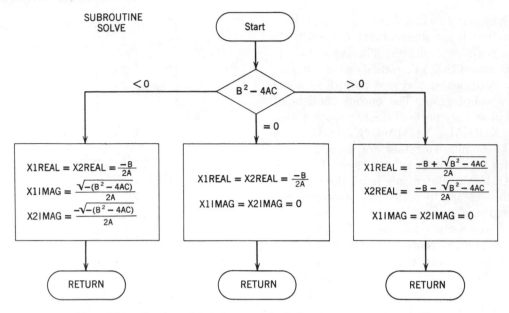

SUBROUTINE
SOLVE

Figure 7.10.   Flowchart of the subprogram for finding the roots in Case Study 14.

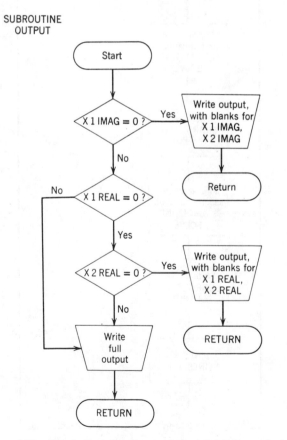

Figure 7.11.   Flowchart of the subprogram for printing the results in Case Study 14.

7.11, is also fairly simple. Note that it is not necessary to test both imaginary components for zero values, since both will always be zero or nonzero. This is not true of the real parts.

The main program is shown in Figure 7.12. We begin with a COMMON statement naming the real and imaginary parts of the two roots. The same statement appears in both subprograms, so that these four variables are assigned to the same storage locations by all three programs, even though the three will be compiled quite separately. This would not be true, of course, without the COMMON statements.

Next we set the page number to 1 and write the heading line, the bulk of which consists of column identifications; in fact, the only variable in the line is the page number itself. The carriage control character of 1 in the first Hollerith field specification causes spacing to the top of a new page. The two slashes at the end of the FORMAT force an extra line space between the heading line and the first line of regular output.

After incrementing the page counter and initializing the line counter, we read a data card. The READ statement must have different names for the three coefficients of the two equations. A test of the first value for A detects the sentinel card and stops if this is the sentinel.

Now we are ready to find the roots for the first set of coefficients, and we call into operation the subprogram that solves the equation. The arguments are the first set of coefficients. When control returns from SOLVE, values will have been given

```
C CASE STUDY 14 - QUADRATIC EQUATION SOLUTION WITH SUBROUTINES
C THIS IS THE MAIN PROGRAM
C
      COMMON X1REAL, X1IMAG, X2REAL, X2IMAG
C INITIALIZE PAGE NUMBER
      NPAGE = 1
C PRINT HEADING, INCLUDING PAGE NUMBER
    5 WRITE (6, 8) NPAGE
    8 FORMAT (1H1, 9X, 1HA, 14X, 1HB, 14X, 1HC, 11X, 7HX1 REAL, 8X,
   1      7HX1 IMAG, 8X, 7HX2 REAL, 8X, 17HX2 IMAG        PAGE, I4//)
C INCREMENT PAGE NUMBER
      NPAGE = NPAGE + 1
C INITIALIZE LINE COUNTER
      LINES = 0
C READ A DATA CARD
   14 READ (5, 15) A1, B1, C1, A2, B2, C2
   15 FORMAT (6F10.0)
C CHECK FOR SENTINEL
      IF (A1 .EQ. 0.0) STOP
C SOLVE BOTH EQUATIONS AND PRINT RESULTS
      CALL SOLVE (A1, B1, C1)
      CALL OUTPUT (A1, B1, C1)
      CALL SOLVE (A2, B2, C2)
      CALL OUTPUT (A2, B2, C2)
C INCREMENT LINE COUNTER
      LINES = LINES + 2
C CHECK IF PAGE IS FULL
      IF (LINES .EQ. 20) GO TO 5
      GO TO 14
      END
```

Figure 7.12. The main program for Case Study 14.

```
C CASE STUDY 14 - QUADRATIC EQUATION SOLUTION WITH SUBROUTINES
C THIS IS THE SUBROUTINE FOR FINDING THE ROOTS
C
      SUBROUTINE SOLVE (A, B, C)
      COMMON X1REAL, X1IMAG, X2REAL, X2IMAG
C MAKE INTERMEDIATE VARIABLE OF THE DISCRIMINANT
      DISC = B**2 - 4.0 * A * C
C TEST DISCRIMINANT
      IF (DISC) 50, 60, 70
C HERE IF THE DISCRIMINANT IS NEGATIVE -- ROOTS ARE COMPLEX
   50 X1REAL = -B / (2.0 * A)
      X2REAL = X1REAL
      X1IMAG = SQRT(-DISC) / (2.0 * A)
      X2IMAG = - X1IMAG
      RETURN
C HERE IF THE DISCRIMINANT IS ZERO -- ROOTS ARE REAL AND EQUAL
   60 X1REAL = - B / (2.0 * A)
      X2REAL = X1REAL
      X1IMAG = 0.0
      X2IMAG = 0.0
      RETURN
C HERE IF THE DISCRIMINANT IS POSITIVE -- ROOTS ARE REAL AND UNEQUAL
   70 S = SQRT(DISC)
      X1REAL = (-B + S) / (2.0 * A)
      X2REAL = (-B - S) / (2.0 * A)
      X1IMAG = 0.0
      X2IMAG = 0.0
      RETURN
      END
```

Figure 7.13. The subprogram for finding the roots in Case Study 14.

```
C CASE STUDY 14 - QUADRATIC EQUATION SOLUTION WITH SUBROUTINES
C THIS IS THE SUBROUTINE FOR PRINTING THE RESULTS
C
      SUBROUTINE OUTPUT (A, B, C)
      COMMON X1REAL, X1IMAG, X2REAL, X2IMAG
C CHECK IF ROOTS ARE PURE REAL
      IF (X1IMAG .NE. 0.0) GO TO 90
C HERE IF ROOTS ARE PURE REAL
      WRITE (6, 95) A, B, C, X1REAL, X2REAL
   95 FORMAT (1H0, 1P4E15.4, 15X, 1PE15.4)
      RETURN
C CHECK IF ROOTS ARE PURE IMAGINARY
   90 IF (X1REAL .NE. 0.0 .OR. X2REAL .NE. 0.0) GO TO 100
C HERE IF ROOTS ARE PURE IMAGINARY
      WRITE (6, 103) A, B, C, X1IMAG, X2IMAG
  103 FORMAT (1H0, 1P3E15.4, 15X, 1PE15.4, 15X, 1PE15.4)
      RETURN
C HERE IF ROOTS ARE NEITHER PURE REAL NOR PURE IMAGINARY
  100 WRITE (6, 110) A, B, C, X1REAL, X1IMAG, X2REAL, X2IMAG
  110 FORMAT (1H0, 1P7E15.4)
      RETURN
      END
```

Figure 7.14. The subprogram for printing the results in Case Study 14.

to X1REAL, X1IMAG, X2REAL, and X2IMAG. Now we call the subprogram for writing the output, naming only the three coefficients; the four parts of the roots are communicated via COMMON. Another call of each of the subprograms computes and writes the roots for the second set of coefficients from the data card. After incrementing the line counter by two, an IF statement determines whether the page is full and goes back to write the heading line if it is.

The coding of the two subprograms, Figures 7.13 and 7.14, should not be hard to follow. Two new variables, DISC and S, are set up in the SOLVE subprogram to avoid computing certain expressions twice. Advantage is taken of the fact that complex roots occur only as complex conjugates, once again to avoid computing an expression twice.

The OUTPUT subprogram is not complicated, but the FORMAT statements should be studied carefully. The blank spaces for the two special cases of pure real and pure imaginary roots are introduced by 15X field specifications. Note the carriage control characters to get double spacing.

The main program of Figure 7.12 and the subprograms of Figures 7.13 and 7.14 were submitted to the computer center as three separate programs at different times. When the three object decks were returned, they were combined into one deck, data cards were added, and the object program was executed. The compiler had arranged the object program decks so that when they were subsequently loaded the computer knew where to start executing

the main program, and the interrelationships between main program and the subprograms were handled automatically, so far as we are concerned.

Figure 7.15 is a page of output produced by the combined program.

7.11 Case Study 15: Translating Algebraic Expressions to Polish Notation

In this case study we shall consider an application that, although highly practical, is quite different from others in this book. The application is that of translating an expression written in ordinary algebraic notation, with parentheses and operators written between the forms they operate on, into what is called *Polish notation*,* in which there are never any parentheses and in which operators are written *after* the forms on which they operate.

Let us start by seeing what an expression written in Polish notation means. Consider the expression

$$AB + C*$$

The plus sign applies to the two operands preceding it; the plus sign is the first operator that appears in a left-to-right "scan" of the expression, and it is carried out first. After doing the addition, we keep scanning the expression, looking for another opera-

* So called because it was developed by the Polish logician J. Lukasiewicz.

A	B	C	X1 REAL	X1 IMAG	X2 REAL	X2 IMAG
1.0000E 00	-2.0000E 00	1.0000E 00	1.0000E 00		1.0000E 00	
1.0000E 00	-1.0000E 01	2.5000E 01	5.0000E 00		5.0000E 00	
1.0000E 00	-3.0000E 00	2.0000E 00	2.0000E 00		1.0000E 00	
2.0000E 00	-6.0000E 00	4.0000E 00	2.0000E 00		1.0000E 00	
1.0000E 00	1.0000E 00	-2.5500E 03	5.0000E 01		-5.1000E 01	
1.0000E 01	-2.0000E 01	1.0000E 01	1.0000E 00		1.0000E 00	
1.0000E 03	-2.0000E 03	1.0000E 03	1.0000E 00		1.0000E 00	
2.0000E-02	-4.0000E-02	2.0000E-02	1.0000E 00		1.0000E 00	
1.4320E 00	9.8760E 00	-4.5670E 00	4.3500E-01		-7.3316E 00	
8.8130E 00	-1.3108E 01	0.	1.4873E 00		0.	
2.3009E 00	1.9917E 00	0.	-3.2381E-09		-8.6562E-01	
1.0000E 00	0.	-1.0000E 00	1.0000E 00		-1.0000E 00	
1.0000E 00	0.	1.0000E 00		1.0000E 00		-1.0000E 00
9.0000E 00	0.	3.6000E 01		2.0000E 00		-2.0000E 00
1.0000E 00	2.0000E 00	5.0000E 00	-1.0000E 00	2.0000E 00	-1.0000E 00	-2.0000E 00
6.3190E 00	4.3380E 00	2.3294E 01	-3.4325E-01	1.8891E 00	-3.4325E-01	-1.8891E 00
-9.0000E 00	2.3000E 01	3.7000E 01	-1.1189E 00		3.6744E 00	
6.1000E 01	0.	8.7000E 01		1.1942E 00		-1.1942E 00
6.1000E 01	2.0000E 00	8.7000E 01	-1.6393E-02	1.1941E 00	-1.6393E-02	-1.1941E 00
6.1000E 01	1.5900E 02	8.7000E 01	-7.8145E-01		-1.8251E 00	

Figure 7.15. Output produced when the object program decks from the programs of Figures 7.12, 7.13, and 7.14 were combined and run with suitable data.

123

tor. When we find it, it is applied to the two quantities preceding it, which now are $A + B$ and C. The Polish expression is thus equivalent to the ordinary algebraic expression $(A + B)*C$.

Consider the Polish expression

$$ABC + *$$

We scan across the expression looking for an operator; when we find the plus sign, we apply it to the last two operands preceding it, to get $B + C$. Finding the asterisk, we apply it to the last two things in the list, which are now A and $B + C$. The expression is thus equivalent to $A*(B + C)$.

Here are a few more Polish expressions and their ordinary equivalents.

Polish	Algebraic
$AB + C + D +$	$A + B + C + D$
$ABC* + D +$	$A + B*C + D$
$AB + CD + *$	$(A + B)*(C + D)$
$ABCDEF + * + * +$	$A + B*(C + D*(E + F))$

Figure 7.19, the output of the program we shall write, contains some more pairs of this sort.

The work of this case study will be to translate an expression written in the ordinary manner into Polish notation. We shall work entirely with the expression, never evaluating it or even asking what the values of the variables might be. The example thus illustrates one type of *non-numeric* data processing. The application is entirely practical: things of this general sort are an essential part of many compilers, for instance, along with many other important areas of computer application.

The program we shall consider will read an expression from a card. We shall restrict ourselves to expressions involving variables only (no constants), with variable names that are always just one letter. We shall further restrict ourselves to the four arithmetic operations of addition, subtraction, multiplication and division. Exponentiation is excluded, as is the unary subtraction operator. (In the expression $-(A - B)$, for instance, the first minus is a unary operator, since it operates on only one operand.) These and many other forms could be included, of course, but we prefer to restrict the complexity in order to gain a full understanding of the basic ideas. We shall assume, finally, that there are no errors of any sort in the input expression.

The first action in the program, after reading the expression from a card, is to identify the various characters as operators or operands. The operators are

$$- + * / ( )$$

The operands are the letter variables. Then for each operator we must assign a number that gives its "rank" or "strength." This will determine when the operator enters the final Polish expression. This is the way we implement the convention that multiplications and divisions are executed before additions and subtractions, in the absence of parentheses, and it is the way we take parentheses into account. The hierarchy numbers are

(	1
)	2
+, −	3
*, /	4

A hierarchy number of zero will identify an operand.

These rankings become the entries in another array, this one having 80 integer elements. The input string is called SOURCE and the associated hierarchy array SHIER (for Source HIERarchy).

The basic scheme of the translation is as follows.* Operands are always transferred to the output string (POLISH) as soon as they are encountered. Operators other than a right parenthesis are always transferred to another stack (OPSTCK, for OPerator STaCK) to await transfer to the output string. As operators are transferred to the operator stack OPSTCK, their hierarchies go to the corresponding elements of an array called OHIER (for Operator HIERarchy).

After the transfer of an operand to the output string a check is made to see if the last entry in the operator stack has a higher hierarchy than the next operator in the input, or the same hierarchy; in either case, the operator from operator stack is transferred to the output. Whenever a right parenthesis is found in the input, it is ignored, and the matching left parenthesis, which will always be the last entry in the operator stack at this point, is also ignored.

The reader will want to study the translation system in examples. This can best be done by following the definition given in the flowcharts of Figures 7.16 and 7.17. Figure 7.16 diagrams a straightforward examination of each character of the input string, on the basis of which a hierarchy number is

---

* This translation scheme is based on a publication of the Burroughs Corporation called a "Compilogram," a "game" that graphically illustrates concepts like those involved here.

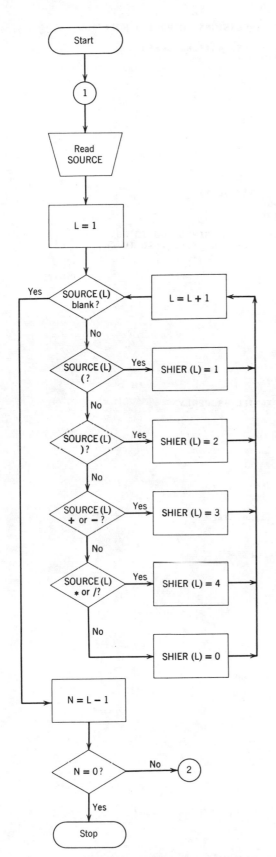

Figure 7.16. Flowchart of the preliminary operations in converting an expression from algebraic to Polish notation. (Case Study 15.)

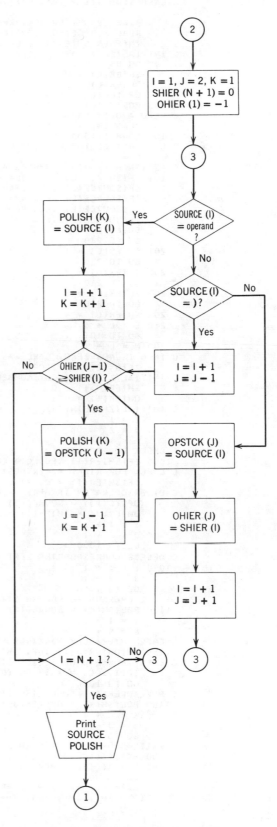

Figure 7.17. Flowchart of the procedure for converting an expression from algebraic to Polish notation. (Case Study 15.)

```
C CASE STUDY 15 - TRANSLATING ALGEBRAIC EXPRESSIONS TO POLISH NOTATION
C
      REAL BLANK, LPAREN, RPAREN, PLUS, MINUS, ASTRSK, SLASH
      REAL SOURCE(80), OPSTCK(80), POLISH(80)
      INTEGER SHIER(80), OHIER(80)
C INITIALIZE ARRAYS TO ZERO OR BLANK
   90 DO 85 L = 1, 80
      SHIER(L) = 0
      OHIER(L) = 0
      OPSTCK(L) = BLANK
   85 POLISH(L) = BLANK
C READ A DATA CARD
      READ (5, 100) SOURCE
  100 FORMAT (80A1)
C L POINTS TO THE CURRENT CARD COLUMN
      L = 1
C ASSIGN HIERARCHY NUMBERS AND TEST FOR FIRST BLANK
  101 IF(SOURCE(L) .EQ. BLANK) GO TO 200
      IF(SOURCE(L) .EQ. LPAREN) GO TO 201
      IF(SOURCE(L) .EQ. RPAREN) GO TO 202
      IF(SOURCE(L) .EQ. PLUS .OR. SOURCE(L) .EQ. MINUS) GO TO 203
      IF(SOURCE(L) .EQ. ASTRSK .OR. SOURCE(L) .EQ. SLASH) GO TO 204
      SHIER(L) = 0
      GO TO 210
  201 SHIER(L) = 1
      GO TO 210
  202 SHIER(L) = 2
      GO TO 210
  203 SHIER(L) = 3
      GO TO 210
  204 SHIER(L) = 4
  210 L = L + 1
      GO TO 101
  200 N = L - 1
C IF N IS NOW ZERO, CARD WAS BLANK
      IF(N .EQ. 0) STOP
C INITIALIZE HIERARCHY NUMBERS TO GET STARTED PROPERLY
      SHIER(N+1) = 0
      OHIER(1) = - 1
C INITIALIZE POINTERS
      I = 1
      J = 2
      K = 1
C CHECK FOR OPERAND
 1000 IF(SHIER(I) .EQ. 0 ) GO TO 1100
C CHECK FOR RIGHT PARENTHESIS
      IF(SHIER(I) .EQ. 2) GO TO 1050
C OTHER OPERATOR IF HERE -- MOVE TO OPERATOR STACK
      OPSTCK(J) = SOURCE(I)
      OHIER(J) = SHIER(I)
      I = I + 1
      J = J + 1
      GO TO 1000
C DELETE CORRESPONDING LEFT PARENTHESIS
 1050 I = I + 1
      J = J - 1
      GO TO 1150
C MOVE OPERAND TO POLISH STRING
 1100 POLISH(K) = SOURCE(I)
      I = I + 1
      K = K + 1
C CHECK HIERARCHY RANKINGS
 1150 IF(OHIER(J-1) .GE. SHIER(I)) GO TO 1160
C CHECK FOR END OF SOURCE STRING
      IF(I .EQ. N + 1) GO TO 1200
      GO TO 1000
C MOVE OPERATOR TO POLISH STRING
 1160 POLISH(K) = OPSTCK(J-1)
      K = K + 1
      J = J - 1
      GO TO 1150
C WRITE SOURCE AND POLISH STRINGS
 1200 WRITE (6, 1300) SOURCE, POLISH
 1300 FORMAT (1H0, 80A1/1H , 80A1)
      GO TO 90
      DATA BLANK, LPAREN, RPAREN, PLUS, MINUS, ASTRSK, SLASH/
     1    1H , 1H(, 1H), 1H+, 1H-, 1H*, 1H//
      END
```

Figure 7.18. The program for converting an expression from algebraic to Polish notation. (Case Study 15.)

```
A*(B+C)
ABC+*

(A+B)*C
AB+C*

A+B*C+D
ABC**D+

(A+B)*(C+D)
AB+CD+*

A-B/C
ABC/-

(A-B)/C
AB-C/

A/B/C
AB/C/

(A/B)/C
AB/C/

A*B/C*D/E
AB*C/D*E/

A*B-C+D
AB*C-D+

A*B-(C+D)
AB*CD+-

A*(B-C)+D
ABC-*D+

A*(B-C+D)
ABC-D+*

A
A

(((A)))
A

((A)+((B)))
AB+

A+B+C+D
AB+C+D+

(A+B)+(C+D)
AB+CD++

A+B/C+D/(E+F+G-H/I)*J
ABC/+DEF+G+HI/-/J*+

(((A+B)*C+D)*E+F)*G
AB+C*D+E*F+G*

A+B*(C+D*(E+F*(G+H)))
ABCDEFGH+*+*+*+

A+(B/C)/(D+(E+F)/(G*H-I/(J/K+L)))-M*N
ABC/DEF+GH*IJK/L+/-/+/+MN*-
```

Figure 7.19. Output of the program of Figure 7.18, showing pairs of expressions, first in ordinary algebraic notation and then the equivalent Polish expression.

placed in the corresponding element of SHIER. The variable N is the count of characters in the SOURCE string up to the first blank column on the card, since we assume no embedded blanks in the input expression. N will be used later to stop the translation process. The program is to be applied to a series of cards, one expression per card; a blank card will signal the end of the deck.

In Figure 7.17 we have what amounts to a definition of the translation algorithm (procedure) as it was outlined above. The reader who wishes to understand the details of this case study will want to follow through the steps of Figure 7.17 with several examples.

The program of Figure 7.18 follows the logic of the flowcharts quite closely. The logic would be virtually impossible to decode given only the program, but with the flowchart for comparison the program has little that is new. The only feature not already illustrated in earlier case studies is the DATA statement, with which we enter the alphameric values BLANK, LPAREN, RPAREN, PLUS, MINUS, ASTRSK, and SLASH.

LPAREN and MINUS had to be identified as REAL in order to avoid diagnostics, which say, in effect, "you can't compare SOURCE(L) and LPAREN—they are not the same type." We know that they are both alphameric, but there is no separate alphameric type. We can put alphameric values into *any* type variable as long as *we* know what we are doing. The logical IF statement will compare two alphameric values just as though they contained ordinary numerical values; if they are equal, they are equal—and it matters not that symbols are involved rather than numbers.

Figure 7.19 displays several pairs of input expressions and translated Polish equivalents, produced when the program was run on a Burroughs B5500.

EXERCISES

*1. Define a statement function to compute

$$\text{DENOM}(X) = X^2 + \sqrt{1 + 2X + 3X^2}$$

Then use the function to compute

$$\text{ALPHA} = \frac{6.9 + Y}{Y^2 + \sqrt{1 + 2Y + 3Y^2}}$$

$$\text{BETA} = \frac{2.1Z + Z^4}{Z^2 + \sqrt{1 + 2Z + 3Z^2}}$$

$$\text{GAMMA} = \frac{\sin Y}{Y^4 + \sqrt{1 + 2Y^2 + 3Y^4}}$$

$$DELTA = \frac{1}{\sin^2 Y + \sqrt{1 + 2\sin Y + 3\sin^2 Y}}$$

2. Define a statement function to compute

$$SLG(A) = 2.549 \log\left(A + A^2 + \frac{1}{A}\right)$$

Then use the function to compute

$$R = X + \log X + 2.549 \log\left(A + A^2 + \frac{1}{A}\right)$$

$$S = \cos X + 2.549 \log\left(1 + X + (1 + X)^2 + \frac{1}{1 + X}\right)$$

$$T = 2.549 \log\left[(A - B)^3 + (A - B)^6 + \frac{1}{(A - B)^3}\right]$$

$$U = [B(I) + 6]^2 + 2.549 \log\left[\frac{1}{B(I)} + \frac{1}{B(I)^2} + B(I)\right]$$

*3. Define a logical statement function to compute the "exclusive or" of two logical variables. The exclusive or is true when exactly one of the inputs is true; it is false when both inputs are false and when both inputs are true. Then write the statements that would be needed to test whether the exclusive or is associative, that is, whether

$$(A \circ B) \circ C = A \circ (B \circ C)$$

in which a circle has been used to indicate the exclusive or.

4. Given three logical variables, A, B, and C, a full binary adder accepts three inputs and provides two outputs, the sum and the carry. The sum is true if any one of the three inputs is true and the others are false or if all three inputs are true. The carry is true if any two or more of the inputs is true. Write logical statement functions to compute these two functions.

*5. Given two one-dimensional arrays of N logical elements each, named A and B, that are to be viewed as the digits of two binary numbers. The two numbers are to be added in binary to produce the $N + 1$ elements of an array named C. Use the functions developed in Exercise 4 in a loop.

*6. Write a FUNCTION subprogram to compute

$$Y(X) = \begin{cases} 1 + \sqrt{1 + X^2} & \text{if } X < 0 \\ 0 & \text{if } X = 0 \\ 1 - \sqrt{1 + X^2} & \text{if } X > 0 \end{cases}$$

Then write statements to evaluate the following expressions.

$$F = 2 + Y(A + Z)$$

$$G = \frac{Y[X(K)] + Y[X(K + 1)]}{2}$$

$$H = Y[\cos(2\pi X)] + \sqrt{1 + Y(2\pi X)}$$

7. Write a FUNCTION subprogram to compute

$$RHO(A, B, N) = \frac{A}{2\pi} \sum_{i=1}^{N} B_i$$

in which B is a one-dimensional array of 50 elements ($N \leq 50$).

Then use it to compute $1/2\pi$ times the sum of the first 18 elements of an array named A; call this SOME.

8. Rewrite the program for Exercise 7 so that N represents the number of elements in the array, which may then have adjustable dimensions.

9. A is any 20 x 20 array. Write a FUNCTION subprogram to compute

$$PD(A, I, J) =$$

$$\frac{A(I - 1, J) + A(I + 1, J) + A(I, J - 1) + A(I, J + 1)}{4}$$

Then use it to compute

$$B_{ij} = (1 - \alpha)B_{ij} + \alpha \frac{B_{i-1,j} + B_{i+1,j} + B_{i,j-1} + B_{i,j+1}}{4}$$

(Could a statement function be used here? Why not?)

*10. Write a FUNCTION subprogram for which the argument list contains A, M, and N, where A is an array name, and M and N are the numbers of rows and columns. The function value is to be the sum of the absolute values of all the elements. The dimensions are to be adjustable.

11. Devise a FUNCTION subprogram which could be called in either of the forms

$$AVER(ROW, L, ARRAY, M, N)$$

$$AVER(COLUMN, L, ARRAY, M, N)$$

The intent is to be able to ask for the algebraic sum of the elements in *row or column* L of an M x N adjustable array.

*12. A is a one-dimensional array with 50 elements. Write a SUBROUTINE subprogram to compute the average of the first N elements and a count of the number of these elements that are zero. Call the subprogram AVERNZ(A, N, AVER, NZ).

Then use the subprogram to get the average of the first 20 elements of an array named ZETA and place the average in ZMEAN and the count of zero elements in NZCNT.

*13. Write a SUBROUTINE subprogram that uses the FUNCTION of Exercise 11 to find the row of an M x N array that has the largest sum; the outputs are the row number and the sum.

Then use the subprogram to operate on an array named OMEGA which has 15 rows and 29 columns; place the largest sum in OMEGAL and the row number in NROW.

This combination of subprograms involves passing adjustable dimensions through a subprogram.

14. Given single variables A, B, X, and L, write a SUBROUTINE subprogram to compute R, S, and T from

$$R = \sqrt{A + BX + X^L}$$

$$S = \cos(2\pi X + A) \cdot e^{BX}$$

$$T = \left(\frac{A + BX}{2}\right)^{L+1} - \left(\frac{A - BX}{2}\right)^{L-1}$$

15. Identify the errors in the following:

a. COMMON A, B(2, 19), R(40),
b. COMMON //R, S, T/LABEL,/U, V, W
c. COMMON G, H, P, Q, Y, Z
EQUIVALENCE (A, P, R), (B, H, S, Z)
d. COMMON A(12), B, C(14)
DIMENSION D(9)
EQUIVALENCE (A(2), D(8), G)
e. EQUIVALENCE (A(3), B(2), C(4)), (A(4), B(6), D(9))

16. Sketch the storage layout that would result from the following:

*a. DIMENSION A(3), B(4)
EQUIVALENCE (A(2), B(1))
*b. DIMENSION C(2, 3), D(3, 2)
EQUIVALENCE (C(1), D(3))
c. DIMENSION E(2, 2, 2), F(4)
EQUIVALENCE (E(5), F(2))

17. Assume a computer in which an integer number and a real number take the same amount of storage space and in which a complex number and a double precision number each take twice as much storage space as a real or integer number. Further, when a complex or double precision number or array element is referenced in an EQUIVALENCE statement, it is always the first of the two storage locations that is meant. Sketch the storage layout that would result from the following:

*a. DIMENSION I(2), R(4), C(3)
INTEGER I
REAL R
COMPLEX C
EQUIVALENCE (I(1), C(1)), (R(1), C(2))
*b. DIMENSION D(4), I(5)
DOUBLE PRECISION D
REAL R1, R2
INTEGER I
EQUIVALENCE (D(1), R1), (D(2), R2), (D(3), I(2))

c. DIMENSION C(5), D(3), S(1), T(1)
COMPLEX C
DOUBLE PRECISION D
EQUIVALENCE (C(1), S(1)), (C(2), T(2)), (C(2), D(1))
d. DIMENSION C(3, 3), D(2, 2, 2), R(20)
COMPLEX C
DOUBLE PRECISION D
REAL R
EQUIVALENCE (C(4), D(7), R(12))

18. Consider the following plan. We wish to make the diagonal elements of a 4 x 4 array A the same as the four elements of a one-dimensional array DIAG. It is proposed to do this with the statement

EQUIVALENCE (A(1), DIAG(1)), (A(6), DIAG(2)),

(A(11), DIAG(3)), (A(16), DIAG (4))

This is quite impossible. Formulate a rule of which this would be a violation and explain why the rule is necessary.

19. Write DATA statements to do the following.

*a. Initialize A to contain 21.9; initialize the complex variable C to contain $1 + 2i$; initialize all 23 elements of STRING to contain 2.0.
*b. Put the words ONE, TWO, THREE, and FOUR in the four elements of NUMBER.
c. Replace the example near the end of Section 7.9 with a statement in which the Hollerith *blank* field appears only once.
d. Place in each location of an integer array named K the element number of the element. The array has 10 elements.

20. Modify the program of Figure 7.18 so that it accepts a dollar sign as signifying exponentiation. The new operator should be assigned hierarchy number 5.

APPENDIX 1. ACTUAL FORTRAN IV IMPLEMENTATIONS

The presentation in the text has been based in large part on the FORTRAN language proposed as a standard by the American Standards Association, a draft of which was published in the October 1964 issue of the *Communications* of the Association for Computing Machinery. Actual compilers accept source programs that differ from the proposed standard in at least three ways.

In the least significant aspect there are variations in permissible numbers sizes about which the proposed standard is necessarily silent.

Second, there are some features of the language of the standard that are not present in all implementations; some, for example, omit double precision and complex operations or do not permit a logical IF.

Third, some implementations go beyond the standard. Some compilers accept arithmetic expressions of mixed mode (real and integer) or permit a subscript expression to be *any* expression rather than limiting it to the forms described in the text.

The accompanying table is intended to indicate the general outlines of all the implementations that were known at the time of writing. The basic idea was to include major items in which the various FORTRANs were known to differ. Items not listed may be assumed to be more or less constant.

This table, however, is not intended to be a complete list of differences. It will not, therefore, be complete enough for the person looking for *all* differences to determine compatibility or to isolate all the program changes necessary for conversion.

The table contains the characteristics of the proposed American Standards Association FORTRAN and Basic FORTRAN. ASA FORTRAN has been the basis of the presentation in this book. ASA Basic FORTRAN is a "subset": a program written in Basic FORTRAN will be accepted by a full FORTRAN compiler, but Basic FORTRAN does not provide all of the features of full ASA FORTRAN. An asterisk indicates that the feature is present.

The table then summarizes the characteristics of the languages accepted by the following manufacturers' machines:

Advanced Scientific Instruments AD-VANCE 6000, 6020, 6040, 6050, 6070, 6080.

Burroughs Corporation B5500

Computer Control Company DDP-24, DDP-116, DDP-124, DDP-224

Control Data Corporation 1604, 3600, 3800, 6400, 6600, 6800

Digital Equipment Corporation PDP-6

Electronic Associates, Inc. 8400

General Electric Company 205, 210, 215, 225, 235, 412, 415, 425, 625, 635

Honeywell, Inc. 200, 800, 1800

International Business Machines Corporation 360, 1401, 1410, 1460, 7010, 7040, 7044, 7090, 7094

National Cash Register Company 315

Philco Corporation 2000

Radio Corporation of America 3301, Spectra 70

Scientific Data Systems 9300

Univac III, 1107

	ASA Basic	ASA	ASI 6000 Series	Burroughs B5500	Computer Control DDP-24, 116, 124, 224	CDC 1604 3600 3800	CDC 6000 Series	PDP-6	EAI 8400	GE 200 Series	GE 400 Series	GE 600 Series
Maximum statement number	9999	99999	99999	99999	99999	99999	99999	99999	99999	32767	32767	99999
Maximum continuation cards	5	19	No limit	9	No limit	No limit	No limit	19	19	No limit	No limit	19
Specification statements must precede first executable statement	*	*	*		*	*	*	*		*		*
INTEGER constant, maximum digits			7	11	7	14	18	11	5	6	7	11
INTEGER maximum magnitude			$2^{23}-1$	$2^{39}-1$	$2^{23}-1$	$2^{47}-1$	$2^{59}-1$	$2^{35}-1$	$2^{16}-1$	$2^{19}-1$	$2^{23}-1$	$2^{35}-1$
REAL constant, maximum digits			11	11	7	11	15	8	7	9	8	9
DOUBLE PRECISION constant, digits					14	25	29	16	14	18		19
REAL, DOUBLE PRECISION magnitude			10^{76}	10^{69}	10^{76}	10^{308}	10^{308}	10^{38}	10^{76}	10^{76}	10^{127}	10^{38}
Variable name maximum characters	5	6	6	6	6	8	8	No limit	6	12	6	6
Mixed mode arithmetic permitted			*			*	*	*	*	*		
Assigned GO TO		*	*	*	*	*	*	*	*	*	*	*
Logical IF, relations		*	*	*	*	*	*	*	*	*		*
DOUBLE PRECISION operations		*			*	*	*	*	*			*
COMPLEX operations		*			*	*	*	*	*	*		*
LOGICAL operations		*	*	*	*	*	*	*	*	*		*
Dimension data in type statements		*		*	*			*	*	*	*	*
Labeled COMMON		*		*	*	*	*	*	*			*
Maximum array dimensions	2	3	3	3	3	3	3	3	7	63	3	7
Adjustable dimensions		*	*	*	*	*	*	*	*	*		*
Zero and negative subscripts								*	*			
Subscripts may be any expression, with subscripted variables permitted				*		*	*			*		
Subroutine multiple entries and/or nonstandard returns							*					*
DATA statement		*	*	*	*	*	*	*	*	*	*	*
Object time FORMAT		*	*		*	*	*	*	*	*	*	*

Honeywell 200	Honeywell 800 1800	IBM 1401 1440 1460	IBM 1410 7010	IBM 7040 7044 (8K)	IBM 7040 7044 (16-32K)	IBM 7090 7094	IBM 360 D level E level	IBM 360 H level	NCR 315	Philco 2000 Series	RCA 3301	RCA Spectra 70 Size A	RCA Spectra 70 Size B	SDS 9300	Univac III	Univac 1107
99999	32767	99999	99999	99999	99999	32767	99999	99999	99999	32767	99999	99999	99999	99999	32767	32767
9	19	9	9	4	9	19	19	19	19	19	No limit	19	19	No limit	9	19
*	*		*				*		*			*				
20	13	20	20	11	11	11	10	10	11	12	7	10	10	7	6	11
$2^{119}-1$	$2^{44}-1$	$10^{20}-1$	$10^{20}-1$	$2^{35}-1$	$2^{35}-1$	$2^{35}-1$	$2^{31}-1$	$2^{31}-1$	$10^{11}-1$	$2^{39}-1$	$10^{7}-1$	$2^{31}-1$	$2^{31}-1$	$2^{23}-1$	$10^{6}-1$	$2^{35}-1$
20	12	20	18	9	9	9	7	7	12	11	8	7	7	12	10	9
	20				16	16	16	16	21	21		16	16	19		17
10^{99}	10^{76}	10^{99}	10^{99}	10^{38}	10^{38}	10^{38}	10^{75}	10^{75}	10^{150}	10^{616}	10^{99}	10^{75}	10^{75}	10^{77}	10^{50}	10^{38}
6	6	6	6	6	6	6	6	6	No limit	6	6	6	6	No limit	6	6
							*	*	*			*	*	*		*
*	*				*	*	*	*	*	*	*		*	*	*	*
*	*	*	*	*	*	*		*	*	*	*	*	*	*	*	*
	*					*	*	*	*	*		*	*	*		*
	*					*		*	*	*			*	*		*
*	*	*				*		*	*	*	*		*	*	*	*
*	*			*	*	*		*	*	*		*	*	*	*	*
*	*				*	*		*	*	*	*		*	*	*	*
3	3	3	3	3	3	7	3	7	No limit	3	3	3	7	No limit	3	7
	*	*			*	*		*	*	*	*		*	*	*	*
									*					*		
									*					*		*
						*		*	*					*	*	*
*	*	*			*	*		*	*	*	*		*	*	*	*
*	*	*		*	*	*		*	*	*	*		*	*	*	*

APPENDIX 2. STATEMENT PUNCTUATION; OPERATOR FORMATION RULES

The page number given for each statement refers to the location in which a discussion of the statement may be found.

Statement	Samples	Page
a = b (arithmetic or logical	A = B + C*D	9
assignment statement)	L = X .GT. 12.0 .OR. M .AND. N	49
GO TO n (Unconditional GO TO)	GO TO 12	20
GO TO n, $(n_1, n_2, \ldots, n_m)$	GO TO N, (1, 123, 12, 4321)	
(Assigned GO TO)		
ASSIGN i TO n	ASSIGN 4321 TO N	
GO TO $(n_1, n_2, \ldots, n_m)$, i	GO TO (1, 123, 12, 4321), N	21
(Computed GO TO)		
IF (e) n_1, n_2, n_3	IF (X − 12.0) 34, 54, 21	20
(Arithmetic IF)		
IF (e) s (Logical IF)	IF (X .GE. 12.0) Y = 23.6 + R	22
STOP	STOP	15
PAUSE	PAUSE	15
END	END	15
DO n i = m_1, m_2	DO 69 I = 1, LAST	66
or		
DO n i = m_1, m_2, m_3	DO 54321 INDEX = INIT, LAST, 5	66
CONTINUE	CONTINUE	69
CALL Name $(a_1, a_2, \ldots, a_n)$	CALL MATMPY (A, B, C, 4, 6, 10)	
SUBROUTINE Name $(a_1, a_2, \ldots, a_n)$	SUBROUTINE MATMPY (A, B, C, I, J, K)	111
FUNCTION Name $(a_1, a_2, \ldots, a_n)$	FUNCTION BESSEL (X, N)	109
RETURN	RETURN	109
READ f, list	READ 819, X, Y, Z	90
READ (u) list	READ (3) A, B, N	89
READ (u, f) list	READ (5, 69) FIRST, LAST	13
WRITE (u) list	WRITE (4) (A(I), I = 1, N)	89
WRITE (u, f) list	WRITE (6, FMT) A(1), A(2), R	13
PRINT f, list	PRINT 26, (A(I), I = 1, 5)	90
PUNCH f, list	PUNCH 900, DELT, EPS	90
FORMAT (specifications)	12 FORMAT (1H0, F10.0/1PE16.7, I6)	13
REWIND u	REWIND 8	90
BACKSPACE u	BACKSPACE 3	90
ENDFILE u	ENDFILE 7	90

Statement	Samples	Page
DIMENSION v ,v, v, . . .	DIMENSION A(10), B(2, 5), C(3, 3, 4)	
COMMON /x_1/a_1/ . . . /x_n/a_n	COMMON /BLOCK1/A, I/BLOCK2/B, C, K	116
	COMMON A, B, C, M, N	115
EQUIVALENCE (k_1), (k_2), . . . , (k_n)	EQUIVALENCE (A, B, C), (I, J)	113
EXTERNAL v_1, v_2, . . . , v_n	EXTERNAL SIN, SQRT, OTHER	118
INTEGER v_1, v_2, . . . , v_n	INTEGER X	39
REAL v_1, v_2, . . . , v_n	REAL A, B, M, LAST, ARRAY(23)	39
DOUBLE PRECISION v_1, v_2, . . . , v_n	DOUBLE PRECISION A, B(2), CUBERT	39
COMPLEX v_1, v_2, . . . , v_n	COMPLEX OMEGA, TRANS	39
LOGICAL v_1, v_2, . . . , v_n	LOGICAL A1, B1, RESULT(100)	39
DATA k_1/d_1/, k_2/d_2/, . . . , k_n/d_n/	DATA A/12.0/, I, J, K, L/2, 3*19/	117

Table A2.1 indicates the types of operands that may be combined by the four arithmetic operators other than exponentiation to form valid arithmetic expressions. Table A2.2 gives the same information for exponentiation. Table A2.3 indicates how logical operands may be combined by the six relational operands to form valid logical expressions.

In all three tables the entries show the type of the resulting expression if valid; an X indicates an invalid combination.

TABLE A2.1
Type of Right Operand

Type of Left Operand →	+ − * /	Integer	Real	Double	Complex	Logical
	Integer	Integer	X	X	X	X
	Real	X	Real	Double	Complex	X
	Double	X	Double	Double	X	X
	Complex	X	Complex	X	Complex	X
	Logical	X	X	X	X	X

TABLE A2.2
Type of Exponent

Type of Left Operand →	**	Integer	Real	Double	Complex	Logical
	Integer	Integer	X	X	X	X
	Real	Real	Real	Double	X	X
	Double	Double	Double	Double	X	X
	Complex	Complex	X	X	X	X
	Logical	X	X	X	X	X

TABLE A2.3
Type of Right Operand

Type of Left Operand →	.EQ. .NE. .GT. .GE. .LT. .LE.	Integer	Real	Double	Complex	Logical
	Integer	Logical	X	X	X	X
	Real	X	Logical	Logical	X	X
	Double	X	Logical	Logical	X	X
	Complex	X	X	X	X	X
	Logical	X	X	X	X	X

APPENDIX 3. BASIC SUPPLIED FUNCTIONS

Table A3.1 lists the characteristics of the external functions that may be expected to be supplied with every FORTRAN IV compiler; Table A3.2 does the same for intrinsic functions. The difference is that between closed and open subroutines (see page 107), plus the fact that the external functions may be named in an EXTERNAL statement, whereas the intrinsic functions may not.

TABLE A3.1   EXTERNAL FUNCTIONS

External Function	Definition	Number of Arguments	Symbolic Name	Type of Argument	Type of Function
Exponential	e^a	1	EXP	Real	Real
		1	DEXP	Double	Double
		1	CEXP	Complex	Complex
Natural Logarithm	$\log_e (a)$	1	ALOG	Real	Real
		1	DLOG	Double	Double
		1	CLOG	Complex	Complex
Common Logarithm	$\log_{10} (a)$	1	ALOG10	Real	Real
			DLOG10	Double	Double
Trigonometric Sine	$\sin (a)$	1	SIN	Real	Real
		1	DSIN	Double	Double
		1	CSIN	Complex	Complex
Trigonometric Cosine	$\cos (a)$	1	COS	Real	Real
		1	DCOS	Double	Double
		1	CCOS	Complex	Complex
Hyperbolic Tangent	$\tanh (a)$	1	TANH	Real	Real
Square Root	$(a)^{1/2}$	1	SQRT	Real	Real
		1	DSQRT	Double	Double
		1	CSQRT	Complex	Complex
Arctangent	$\arctan (a)$	1	ATAN	Real	Real
		1	DATAN	Double	Double
	$\arctan (a_1/a_2)$	2	ATAN2	Real	Real
		2	DATAN2	Double	Double
Remaindering*	$a_1 \pmod{a_2}$	2	DMOD	Double	Double
Modulus		1	CABS	Complex	Real

* The function DMOD (a_1, a_2) is defined as $a_1 - [a_1/a_2]a_2$, where $[x]$ is the integer whose magnitude does not exceed the magnitude of x and whose sign is the same as the sign of x.

TABLE A3.2   INTRINSIC FUNCTIONS

Intrinsic Function	Definition	Number of Arguments	Symbolic Name	Type of	
				Argument	Function
Absolute Value	$\lvert a \rvert$	1	ABS	Real	Real
			IABS	Integer	Integer
			DABS	Double	Double
Truncation	Sign of a times largest integer $\leq \lvert a \rvert$	1	AINT	Real	Real
			INT	Real	Integer
			IDINT	Double	Integer
Remaindering*	$a_1 \pmod{a_2}$	2	AMOD	Real	Real
			MOD	Integer	Integer
Choosing Largest Value	$\text{Max}(a_1, a_2, \ldots)$	$\geqq 2$	AMAX0	Integer	Real
			AMAX1	Real	Real
			MAX0	Integer	Integer
			MAX1	Real	Integer
			DMAX1	Double	Double
Choosing Smallest Value	$\text{Min}(a_1, a_2, \ldots)$	$\geqq 2$	AMIN0	Integer	Real
			AMIN1	Real	Real
			MIN0	Integer	Integer
			MIN1	Real	Integer
			DMIN1	Double	Double
Float	Conversion from integer to real	1	FLOAT	Integer	Real
Fix	Conversion from real to integer	1	IFIX	Real	Integer
Transfer of Sign	Sign of a_2 times $\lvert a_1 \rvert$	2	SIGN	Real	Real
			ISIGN	Integer	Integer
			DSIGN	Double	Double
Positive Difference	$a_1 - \text{Min}(a_1, a_2)$	2	DIM	Real	Real
			IDIM	Integer	Integer
Obtain Most Significant Part of Double Precision Argument		1	SNGL	Double	Real
Obtain Real Part of Complex Argument		1	REAL	Complex	Real
Obtain Imaginary Part of Complex Argument		1	AIMAG	Complex	Real
Express Single Precision Argument in Double Precision Form		1	DBLE	Real	Double
Express Two Real Arguments in Complex Form	$a_1 + a_2\sqrt{-1}$	2	CMPLX	Real	Complex
Obtain Conjugate of a Complex Argument		1	CONJG	Complex	Complex

* The function MOD or AMOD (a_1, a_2) is defined as $a_1 - [a_1/a_2]a_2$, where $[x]$ is the integer whose magnitude does not exceed the magnitude of x and whose sign is the same as x.

ANSWERS TO SELECTED EXERCISES

There are several acceptable answers to many of the exercises. The one shown here is sometimes "better" than other possibilities, but only occasionally is the criterion of "goodness" stated. In other cases there are several equally "good" answers; for instance, it makes no difference whether one writes $A = B + C$ or $A = C + B$. In short, the answers given here are correct but not ordinarily *uniquely* correct. If another answer can be shown to be equivalent, it must be accepted unless other criteria have been stated.

CHAPTER 1

Section 1.4 (page 4)

1. 256.   2.56   −43000.   1.0E + 12   4.92E − 7   −10.0   − 1.E − 16

3. 87,654.3 (comma not permitted); +987 (no decimal point); 9.2E + 87 (too large in most versions); 7E − 9 (no decimal point).

5. Yes.

6. −234. (decimal point not permitted); 23,400 (comma not permitted); 1E12 (E not permitted); +1000000000000 (too large in most versions).

Section 1.5 (page 5)

1. Integer: I, IJK, LARGE, KAPPA.
Real: G, GAMMA, BTO7TH, ZCUBED, CDC160, DELTA, A1P4, ALGOL.
Unacceptable: GAMMA 421 (too many characters); IJK* (* not permitted); J79–12 (− not permitted); R(2)19 (parentheses not permitted); ZSQUARED (too many characters); 12AT7 (does not begin with a letter); 2N173 (does not begin with a letter); EPSILON (too many characters); A1.4 (decimal point not permitted); FORTRAN (too many characters).

Section 1.6 (page 8)

1. a. X + Y**3
    d. A + B/C
    f. A + B/(C + D)
    h. ((A + B)/(C + D))**2 + X**2
    j. 1.0 + X + X**2/2.0 + X**3/6.0
    k. (X/Y)**(G − 1.0)

2. b. $(X + 2.0)/(Y + 4.0)$. Constants may be written in any other equivalent form, such as $(X + 2.)/(Y + 4.)$.
    e. ((X + A + 3.1415927)/(2.0*Z))**2
    g. (X/Y)**(R − 1.0)
    j. A + X*(B + X*(C + D*X))

Section 1.8 (page 11)

1. a. 13.0, real.
b. zero, real.
e.. 4, integer.
f. 4.0, real.
k. 1.33333332, real.
n. 8.0, real (could be 7.9999999 or 8.0000001).
o. 5, integer.

3. a. DELTA = BETA + 2.0
c. C = SQRT(A**2 + B**2) or
C = SQRT(A*A + B*B)
d. R = 1.41421356
g. Y = COS(2.0*X)*SQRT(X/2.0)
h. G = G + 2.0

4. a. AREA = 2.0*P*R*SIN(3.14159265/P)
c. ARC = 2.0*SQRT(Y**2 + 1.3333333*X**2)
e. S= − COS(X)**(P + 1.0)/(P + 1.0)
f. G = 0.5*ALOG((1.0 + SIN(X))/1.0 − SIN(X)))
Preferably written as two statements to avoid computing the sine twice:
S = SIN(X)
G = 0.5*ALOG((1.0 + S)/(1.0 − S))
i. E = X*ATAN(X/A) − A/2.0*ALOG(A**2 + X**2)
l. Q = (2./(3.1415927*X))**0.5*SIN(X)
Since $(2/\pi)^{1/2} (1/X)^{1/2} = \sqrt{2/\pi}/\sqrt{X} = 0.7978846/\sqrt{X}$, this can be written more compactly and thus requires less time in the object program:
Q = 0.7978846/SQRT(X)*SIN(X)
n. Y = 2.5066283*X**(X + 1.0)*EXP(−X)

Section 1.9 (page 14)

1.   READ (5, 94) A, B, C
      94 FORMAT (3F10.0)
          F = (1.0 + A)/(1.0 + B/(C + 6.0))
          WRITE (6, 93) A, B, C, F
      93 FORMAT (4E20.8)

4.   READ (5, 172) A, B, C
     172 FORMAT (3F10.0)
          RADICL = SQRT(B**2 − 4.0*A*C)
          X1 = (−B + RADICL)/(2.0*A)
          X2 = (−B − RADICL)/(2.0*A)
          WRITE (6, 2314) A, B, C, X1, X2
    2314 FORMAT (5E20.8)

6.   READ (5, 300) A, E, H, P
     300 FORMAT (4F10.0)
          X = E*H*P/(SIN(A)*(H**4/16. + H**2*P**2))
          WRITE (6, 50) A, E, H, P, X
      50 FORMAT (5E20.8)

8.   READ (5, 97) A, X, S
      97 FORMAT (3F10.0)
          Y = SQRT(X**2 − A**2)
          Z = X*S/2. − A**2/2.*ALOG(ABS(X + S))
          WRITE (6, 98) A, X, S, Y, Z
      98 FORMAT (5E20.8)

CHAPTER 2

1. a.   Using arithmetic IF:

        IF (A — B) 69, 69, 96

  69 X = 56.9
       GO TO 70
  96 X = 16.9
  70

       Using logical IF:

       IF (A .GT. B) GO TO 77
       X = 56.9
       GO TO 76
  77 X = 16.9
  76

   c.   Using arithmetic IF:

       IF (RHO + THETA — 1.0E-6) 156, 762, 762

       Using logical IF:

       IF (RHO + THETA .LT. 1.0E-6) GO TO 156
       GO TO 762

   d.   Using arithmetic IF:

       IF (X — Y) 11, 11, 12
  11 BIG = Y
       GO TO 13´
  12 BIG = X
  13

       Using logical IF:

       IF (X .LT. Y) BIG = Y
       IF (X .GE. Y) BIG = X

  g. 400 IF (THETA — 6.2831853) 402, 401, 401
     401 THETA = THETA — 6.2831853
        GO TO 400
     402

  h.   IF (G.LT.0.0 .AND. H.LT. 0.0) SIGNS = —1
       IF (G.GT.0.0 .AND. H.GT.0.0) SIGNS = +1
       IF (G * H .LT. 0.0) SIGNS = 0

   j.   IF (A .LT. 0.0 .AND. B .GT. 0.0 .OR. C .EQ. 0.0) OMEGA = COS(X + 1.2)

   l.   GO TO (250, 250, 251, 252, 252, 252, 251, 250), N

  n.   IF (0.999 .LE. X .AND. X .LE. 1.001) STOP
       GO TO 639
       IF (ABS(X — 1.000) .LE. 0.001) STOP
       GO TO 639

  o.   IF (ABS(XREAL) .LT. 1.0 .AND. ABS(XIMAG) .LT. 1.0) SQUARE = 1

2. a.   READ (5, 20) ANNERN
    20 FORMAT (F10.0)
       IF (ANNERN − 2000.00) 40, 40, 50
    40 TAX = 0.0
       GO TO 100
    50 IF (ANNERN − 5000.00) 60, 60, 70
    60 TAX = 0.02*(ANNERN − 2000.00)
       GO TO 100
    70 TAX = 60.00 + 0.05*(ANNERN − 5000.00)
  100 WRITE (6, 30) ANNERN, TAX
    30 FORMAT (1P2E20.7)
       STOP
       END

    c.   X = 1.0
    61 Y = 16.7*X + 9.2*X**2 − 1.02*X**3
       WRITE (6, 62) X, Y
    62 FORMAT (1P2E20.7)
       IF (X .GE. 9.9) STOP
       X = + 0.1
       GO TO 61
       END

    d.   I = 10
    61 X = I
       X = X/10.0
       Y = 16.7*X + 9.2*X**2 − 1.02*X**3
       WRITE (6, 62) X, Y
    62 FORMAT (1P2E20.7)
       IF (I .EQ. 99) STOP
       I = I + 1
       GO TO 61
       END

CHAPTER 3

1. a. (2.0, 4.0)
   d. (5.0, 16.0)
   g. 24.0

2. a. Yes
   c. Yes
   e. Yes
   f. Yes

3. a. Yes
   d. Yes
   f. No
   h. No
   j. Yes
   l. Yes
   n. Yes
   p. Yes
   s. Yes

CHAPTER 4

1.   DIMENSION X(3)
       DIST = SQRT(X(1)**2 + X(2)**2 + X(3)**2)

3.   DIMENSION A(2,2), C(2,2), B(2,2)
       C(1,1) = A(1,1)*B(1,1) + A(1,2)*B(2,1)
       C(1,2) = A(1,1)*B(1,2) + A(1,2)*B(2,2)
       C(2,1) = A(2,1)*B(1,1) + A(2,2)*B(2,1)
       C(2,2) = A(2,1)*B(1,2) + A(2,2)*B(2,2)

5.
```
        DIMENSION A(30), B(30)
        I = 1
        D = 0.0
   456  D = D + (A(I) − B(I))**2
        IF (I .EQ. 30) GO TO 455
        I = I + 1
        GO TO 456
   455  D = SQRT(D)
```

6.
```
        DIMENSION X(50), DX(49)
        I = 1
     9  DX(I) = X(I + 1) − X(I)
        IF (I .EQ. 49) GO TO 7
        I = I + 1
        GO TO 9
     7
```

9.
```
        DIMENSION Y(50)
        S = Y(I) + U*(Y(I + 1) − Y(I − 1))/2.0 +
            U**2/2.0*(Y(I + 1) − 2.0*Y(I) + Y(I − 1))
```

11.
```
        DIMENSION A(7), B(7)
    21  FORMAT (7F10.0)
        READ (5, 21) A
        READ (5, 21) B
        I = 1
        SUM = 0.0
     4  SUM = SUM + A(I)*B(I)
        I = I + 1
        IF (I .LE. 7) GO TO 4
        ANORM = SQRT(SUM)
        WRITE (6, 22) ANORM
    22  FORMAT (1PE20.7)
```

13. Either add the statement
DOUBLE PRECISION A, B
or replace the DIMENSION statement with
DOUBLE PRECISION A(30), B(30)

15.
```
        COMPLEX COMPLX(30)
        I = 1
        SUMABS = 0.0
    81  SUMABS = CABS(COMPLX(I)) + SUMABS
        I = I + 1
        IF (I .LE. 30) GO TO 81
```

17.
```
        LOGICAL TRUTH (40)
        INTEGER TRUE, FALSE
        I = 1
        TRUE = 0
        FALSE = 0
    66  IF(TRUTH(I)) GO TO 29
        FALSE = FALSE + 1
        GO TO 36
    29  TRUE = TRUE + 1
    36  I = I + 1
        IF (I .NE. 41) GO TO 66
```

CHAPTER 5

1.
```
      DIMENSION A(30), B(30)
      D = 0.0
      DO 23 I = 1, 30
   23 D = D + (A(I) − B(I))**2
      D = SQRT(D)
```

4.
```
      DIMENSION M(20)
      DO 92 I = 1, 20
   92 M(I) =I * M(I)
```

5.
```
      DIMENSION R(40), S(40), T(40)
      DO 3 I = 1, M
    3 T(I) = R(I) + S(I)
```

7.
```
      DIMENSION F(50)
      MM1 = M − 1
      DO 692 I = 2, MM1
  692 F(I) = (F(I−1) + F(I) + F(I+1))/3.0
```

8.
```
      DIMENSION B(50)
      BIGB = B(1)
      NBIGB = 1
      DO 42 I = 2, 50
      IF (BIGB .GE. B(I)) GO TO 42
      BIGB = B(I)
      NBIGB = I
   42 CONTINUE
```

10.
```
      DIMENSION A(15, 15), X(15), B(15)
      DO 61 I = 1, 15
      B(I) = 0.0
      DO 61 J = 1, 15
   61 B(I) = B(I) + A(I, J)*X(J)
```

12.
```
      DIMENSION RST(20, 20)
      DPROD = RST(1, 1)
      DO 1 I = 2, 20
    1 DPROD = DPROD*RST(I, I)
```

13.
```
      DO 67 I = 100, 300
      X = I
      X = X/100.0
      Y= 41.298*SQRT(1.0 + X**2) + X**0.33333333*EXP(X)
   67 WRITE (6, 68) X, Y
   68 FORMAT (1P2E20.7)
```

18. a. I = I1 − 1
   6 J = J1 − 1
   7 IF (I .EQ. I1 .AND. J .EQ. J1) GO TO 9
    IF (I .LT.1 .OR. I.GT.8 .OR. J.LT.1 .OR. J.GT.8) GO TO 9
    IF (BOARD(I, J) .EQ. 0) WRITE (6, 8) I, J
   8 FORMAT (2I5)
   9 J = J + 1
    IF (J .LE. J1 + 1) GO TO 7
    I = I + 1
    IF (I .LE. I1 + 1) GO TO 6

  c. IF (I1 .EQ. I2) GO TO 16
    IF (J1 .EQ. J2) GO TO 17
    LEGAL = .FALSE.
    GO TO 15
   16 J = MIN0(J1, J2) + 1
    LIMIT = MAX0(J1, J2)
    IF (LIMIT .EQ. J + 1) GO TO 18
   20 IF (BOARD(I1, J) .NE. 0) GO TO 19
    IF (J + 1 .EQ. LIMIT) GO TO 18
    J = J + 1
    GO TO 20
   17 I = MIN0(I1, I2) + 1
    LIMIT = MAX0(I1, I2)
    IF (LIMIT .EQ. I + 1) GO TO 18
   21 IF (BOARD(I, J1) .NE. 0) GO TO 19
    IF (I + 1 .EQ. LIMIT) GO TO 18
    I = I + 1
    GO TO 21
   18 MOVE = .TRUE.
    GO TO 15
   19 MOVE = .FALSE.
   15

  e. INTEGER WPIECE, PIECE, VALUE(6)
    VALUE(1) = 1
    VALUE(2) = 3
    VALUE(3) = 3
    VALUE(4) = 5
    VALUE(5) = 10
    VALUE(6) = 0
    WPIECE = 0
    DO 67 I = 1, 8
    DO 67 J = 1, 8
    PIECE = BOARD(I, J)
   67 IF (PIECE .GT. 0) WPIECE = WPIECE + VALUE(PIECE)

CHAPTER 6

2. a. M = bb12X = bb407.8Y = bb − 32.8
3. READ (5, 238) BOS, EWR, PHL, DCA
  238 FORMAT (4F8.0)
6. READ (5, 233) LGA, JFK, BAL, TPA
  233 FORMAT (2I3, 2E14.7)
7. a. FORMAT (2I7, 2F8.2)
 b. FORMAT (2I7, 2F6.0)
 c. FORMAT (I6, I8, 2E13.5)
 d. FORMAT (I6, I8, 1P2E12.4)
 e. FORMAT (3HbI =, I6, 4HbbJ =, I6, 4HbbR =, F6.1, 4HbbS =, F6.1)
 f. FORMAT (3HbI =, I6/3HbJ =, I6/3HbR =, F6.1/3HbS =, F6.1)
9. READ (5, 99) N, (DATA(I), I = 1, N)
  99 FORMAT (I2, 10F7.0)

11. a. One data card will be read. It should have seven
numbers punched in it, with four columns for each number;
if decimal points are not punched, the numbers will be taken
to be integers and converted to real form. The first of
the numbers should begin in column 1.

b. One data card will be read. It should have a two-
digit integer punched in columns 1–2, and a maximum of 10
four-digit numbers punched in the columns following.
There should be as many numbers as the value of the integer in
columns 1–2.

c. Two cards will be read. The first should
contain an integer in columns 1–2. The second should contain
as many four-digit numbers as the value of the integer in the
first card.

d. $N + 1$ cards will be read. The first should contain an integer
in columns 1–2. There should be as many cards following
as the value of this integer, each containing a four-digit number
in columns 1–4.

13.   WRITE (6, 49) A, B, X, Z
    49 FORMAT (2F12.4, 2E20.8)

15.   WRITE (6, 58) ((ABC(I, J), J = 1, 4), I = 1, 10)
    58 FORMAT (11H1MATRIX ABC///(1P4E20.7))

17.   FORMAT (2I2, 1PE20.7)
         DO 14 I = 1, M
         DO 14 J = 1, N
    14 PUNCH 13, I, J, STL(I, J)

18.   READ (5, 29) (MONTH(I), I = 1, 12)
    29 FORMAT (12A3)

         WRITE (6, 30) MONTH(I)
    30 FORMAT (1Hb, A3)

20. a.   (10F10.2)
      b.   (1P5E20.6) or (1P5E20.6/1P5E20.6)
      c.   (F10.2//(1P3E20.6))

24.   DIMENSION G(48, 80)
         INTEGER A
         DATA BLANK, DOT, XPRINT/1H ,
         1H., 1HX/
         DO 42 I = 1, 48
         DO 42 J = 1, 80
    42 G(I, 40) = BLANK
         DO 64 I = 1, 48
    64 G(I, 40) = DOT
         DO 65 J = 1, 80
    65 G(24, J) = DOT
         DO 69 A = 9, 360, 9
         T = A
         T = T/(180.0/3.14159265)
         X = COS(T)
         Y = SIN(T)
         I = 6.0*(Y + 4.0) + 0.5
         J = 10.0*(X + 4.0) + 0.5
    69 G(I, J) = XPRINT
         I = 48
    71 WRITE (6, 70) (G(I, J), J = 1, 80)
    70 FORMAT (80A1)
         I = I − 1
         IF (I .NE. 0) GO TO 71
         STOP

CHAPTER 7

1.
```
DENOM(X) = X**2 + SQRT(1.0 + 2.0*X + 3.0*X**2)
ALPHA = (6.9 + Y)/DENOM(Y)
BETA = (2.1*Z + Z**4)/DENOM(Z)
GAMMA = SIN(Y)/DENOM(Y**2)
DELTA = 1.0/DENOM(SIN(Y))
```

3.
```
LOGICAL EXOR, A, B, ANS1, ANS2
EXOR(A, B) = A .AND. .NOT. B .OR. .NOT. A .AND. B
ANS1 = EXOR(EXOR(A, B), C)
ANS2 = EXOR(A, EXOR(B, C))
```

5.
```
      LOGICAL A(40), B(40), C(41), K, SUM, CARRY
      C(1) = SUM(A(1), B(1), .FALSE.)
      K = CARRY(A(1), (B1), .FALSE.)
      DO 28 I = 2, N
      C(I) = SUM(A(I), B(I), K)
   28 K = CARRY(A(I), B(I), K)
      C(N + 1) = K
```

6.
```
      FUNCTION Y(X)
      IF (X) 10, 11, 12
   10 Y = 1.0 + SQRT(1.0 + X*X)
      RETURN
   11 Y = 0.0
      RETURN
   12 Y = 1.0 − SQRT(1.0 + X*X)
      RETURN
      END

      F = 2.0 + Y(A + Z)
      G = (Y(X(K)) + Y(X(K+1)))/2.0
      H = Y(COS(6.2831853*X)) + SQRT(1.0 + Y(6.2831853*X))
```

10.
```
      FUNCTION SUMABS(A, M, N)
      DIMENSION A(M, N)
      SUMABS = 0.0
      DO 27 I = 1, M
      DO 27 J = 1, N
   27 SUMABS = SUMABS + A(I, J)
      RETURN
      END
```

12.
```
      SUBROUTINE AVERNZ(A, N, AVER, NZ)
      DIMENSION A(50)
      AVER = 0.0
      NZ = 0
      DO 19 I = 1, N
      AVER = AVER + A(I)
      IF (A(I) .EQ. 0.0) NZ = NZ + 1
   19 CONTINUE
      AN = N
      AVER = AVER/AN
      RETURN
      END

      CALL AVERNZ(ZETA, 20, ZMEAN, NZCNT)
```

13.   SUBROUTINE LARGE(A, M, N, SUM, ROWN)
         DIMENSION A(M, N)
         SUM = AVER(ROW, 1, A, M, N)
         ROWN = 1
         DO 39 I = 2, M
         BIG = AVER(ROW, I, A, M, N)
         IF (BIG .LE. SUM) GO TO 39
         SUM = BIG
         ROWN = I
      39 CONTINUE
         RETURN
         END

         CALL LARGE(OMEGA, 15, 29, OMEGAL, NROW)

16. a. A(1) A(2) A(3)
            B(1) B(2) B(3) B(4)
     b.   C(1,1) C(2,1) C(1,2) C(2,2) C(1,3) C(2,3)
            D(1,1) D(2,1) D(3,1) D(1,2) D(2,2) D(3,2)

17. a.   C(1) C(1) C(2) C(2) C(3) C(3)
            I(1) I(2) R(1) R(2) R(3) R(4)
     b.   D(1) D(1) D(2) D(2) D(3) D(3) D(4) D(4)
            R1   R2   I(1) I(2) I(3) I(4) I(5)

19. a.   DATA A, C, (STRING(I), I = 1, 23)/21.9, (1.0, 2.0), 23*2.0/
     b.   DATA (NUMBER(I), I = 1, 4)/3HONE, 3HTWO, 5HTHREE, 4HFOUR/

INDEX